THE TEACH YOURSELF BOOKS
EDITED BY LEONARD CUTTS

PHYSICAL GEOGRAPHY

in the
GEOGRAPHY
Section

Prepared under the special
direction and scientific
Editorship of

PROFESSOR FRANK DEBENHAM
Cambridge University

TEACH YOURSELF GEOGRAPHY

THE USE OF GEOGRAPHY
by F. Debenham

ECONOMIC GEOGRAPHY
by W. S. Thatcher

GEOGRAPHY OF LIVING THINGS
by M. S. Anderson

HISTORICAL GEOGRAPHY
by J. B. Mitchell

PHYSICAL GEOGRAPHY

By

R. F. PEEL, M.B.E., M.A.

Professor of Geography, University of Bristol
(*formerly Lecturer at Cambridge*)

With sixty-five figures drawn by the author

THE ENGLISH UNIVERSITIES PRESS LTD
102 NEWGATE STREET
LONDON, E.C.1

First edition 1952
Second edition (revised) 1958
Second impression 1960
Third impression 1962

*Made and Printed in Great Britain for the English Universities Press, Ltd., London
by C. Tinling & Co., Ltd., Liverpool, London and Prescot.*

A GENERAL INTRODUCTION TO THE SERIES

IN planning a series of volumes to be called *Teach Yourself Geography*, it was necessary for me, as Editor, to choose between alternatives, and I want you to understand why I made the decision I did and what we have set out to do.

It would have been possible to adopt the delightful, and very successful, method used by the English Universities Press historians, who present each volume in their series as the story of a period based upon the life of a great man. Our geography series might well have had the pattern of a Place and its People for each book until the world was covered. The result would have been a new series of Regional Geographies which, though useful, would have been mainly descriptive in character and not fundamental to the subject. They would have been a loose pile of stones rather than a masonry structure keyed together to make a building.

Now, geography was described by one of its greatest recent exponents as not so much a subject as a point of view. With that in mind, I decided it was better to take the other alternative : to lead readers to the top of the mountain whence they could get that view, rather than just give them a series of peeps at individual parts of the landscape.

In my key volume, I set out to provide the incentive for that climb, outlining the route and giving a general idea of the prospect at the summit. The title of the book is *The Use of Geography*, and if interest, contentment and an increased power of judgment are sufficient rewards, then geography is useful indeed. You will find I have dealt mainly with the structure of the subject and its aims, with hints as to the ways and means of achieving some part of it : an understanding of Place in all its bearings. My chief object was to show that geography is for everyone, and that it is full of interest at every stage, and that it is a practical subject.

The four companion volumes concern themselves more closely with technique—if such a formidable word can be used to describe the approach to each of the divisions into which geography can be conveniently separated for the purpose of study.

Thus Professor Peel's book deals with the physical background; those aspects of air, land and water which, quite independently of man, affect the environment in which we live, and which are almost, but not quite, beyond our control. He points the way towards learning about the inanimate world around us, and his treatment of this branch of the subject is as thorough as the length of the book will permit.

Mrs. Anderson in her *The Geography of Living Things* deals with the animate side of environment, culminating in the highest of the animals, Man himself. In some ways she is opening up a new development of Geography, or at least a new focusing point, for you will find that she emphasises the biological influences which constantly affect man for good or ill and which have in large measure determined where and how he lives ; why he varies so much in appearance, and even in character. Her vivid style is well suited to such a fresh viewpoint. If this book is a study of man as an animal living under essentially the same biological controls as other animals, then Mr. Thatcher leads us to consider man as a highly organised social being with trade between places and peoples as a dominating control.

He calls his book *Economic Geography*, an experiment. Each of these volumes is an experiment—and certainly if it is an experiment to take an apparently intricate subject like this and reduce it to a lively simplicity by talking to his reader as he might at his own fireside, then we could do with many more such experiments. Even such a forbidding subject as the Mechanism of Exchange can become absorbing when chatted about by a kindly tutor possessed of a cheerful pessimism and an infinite understanding. The case for Economic Geography rests very safely in his hands.

Finally, the geographer must look back as well as forward if he is to study fully the interaction between Place and Man. The geographies of the past are in some respects the most powerful influences which mould the geography of the present. Miss Mitchell deals in a scholarly way with these in her *Historical Geography*. Because it is a new line of approach she has to spend some time in explaining what it is and is not. The rewards are great, for when rightly understood there is something peculiarly fascinating in tracing the Past and the Present, in viewing Place, whether on parish- or country-scale as determined very largely by what has happened before. This volume should put Historical Geography very firmly on its feet as an integral part of the subject as a whole and one which any reader can share in and profit by.

Lastly, I should like to explain that this series is a combined effort. One of the reasons for selecting the authors from my own staff was so that we could work together as a team. Yet even frequent consultation is not in itself sufficient to achieve agreement and a common point of view, and it is as much the personality of my authors as their knowledge that is responsible for the unity we hope will appear in the separate volumes of this series. I am, in fact, proud to introduce to the general reader these members of a staff who have made my duty easy not only as Editor, but in the more arduous capacity of running the large department of which they form a part.

FRANK DEBENHAM

The Department of Geography,
  The University,
    Cambridge.

CONTENTS

INTRODUCTION

DEFINED literally Geography is " writing about the earth ", but the modern subject aims far beyond mere description. The facts about the earth's surface are nowadays to a large extent common property, recorded in great detail in volumes of statistics and on official maps. Geographers today seek the causes and connections underlying those facts. They try to interpret the vast and complex diversity of the earth's surface, and to trace the relationships between its natural conditions and the distribution, activities, and problems of mankind. As some Historians interpret particular epochs of time, so some Geographers concentrate on the interpretation of particular regions or countries ; but others specialize on different aspects of the earth as a whole, or on particular phases of the relations between man and the earth. Geography has thus many branches, and some illustration of its wide range of interests will be found in the various volumes making up this series. But all Geography, even when it concentrates upon human issues, must rest upon a thorough understanding of the physical earth, for the earth provides the settings in which all human problems exist. Physical Geography, the branch which studies the physical earth, is thus the **foundation** of the whole subject.

The contents of this book can, however, be viewed from another standpoint as well. While it affords the essential background to the proper understanding of any country, or to the geographical aspects of any human problem, Physical Geography can also be studied with great interest and profit for its own sake ; for the new meaning it gives to the scenery and weather that make up the constant background of our lives. In this second guise it stands beside the field sciences like Geology, and indeed Geology, like many another subject now regarded as quite a separate science, originally grew out of the older Physical Geography. With the great increase in knowledge about the earth, sub-division of the traditional all-embracing subject long ago became inevitable ; but we do well to remember that this trend has in no way altered the realities of nature. Although today Meteorology has taken over the study of the atmosphere, and Geology, Geophysics, and Geomorphology that of the solid earth, while Oceanography and Hydrology with their numerous sub-divisions concentrate upon the natural waters, nature does not recognise these arbitrary divisions. On the earth itself land, water, and air all exist together, and the physical reality of any place is compounded of all three. Nor are the three by any means independent, or really separate. Matter continuously passes from one to the other, and they are knit together by a host of interacting processes. The total complex of features and conditions that we call the physical environment varies continuously over the earth, but everywhere it reflects a sort of dynamic balance. The distinctive feature of Physical Geography, and its great value, is that it takes all the important components of this physical complex within its orbit, concentrates its attention particularly upon the connections between them, and seeks to interpret the physical environment as a dynamic entity.

In a small introductory book like this it is not easy to treat so wide a subject from both the standpoints from which it may be approached, and to combine a reasonable selection of its more basic findings with some discussion of their relationships and wider implications. Many topics have had to be omitted, and many others are treated very sketchily, while an unjustified impression of certainty and knowledge may well be created by the brief and simple way in which various difficult matters have been discussed. For instance, the problems of river-erosion and river-valley evolution are by no means so well understood as perusal of Chapters VI and VII might suggest, and cogent attacks have recently been made upon the theories outlined. But any attempt to include all the qualifications desirable would have made this book five times its present length, and to the layman quite unreadable. Of necessity also the various strands which make up the physical environment have had to be in large measure treated separately, but some attempt has been made to show how they are in reality knit together. To achieve this, much factual detail has had to be sacrificed, but a short Bibliography is given at the end to guide those who may wish to follow up particular topics in greater detail. As many illustrations have been included as space would permit, but the impossibility of reproducing detailed world maps of relief, climatic elements, soils, and other matters in a book of this size renders it necessary for the serious reader to consult such maps in one of the standard atlases at the appropriate points. This inconvenience is regretted, but this is, after all, no textbook. Its purpose is to convey broad ideas rather than detailed facts, and its main aim is to show that the earth we live on can be viewed as a single vast, highly-complex, but often surprisingly delicately balanced machine. Aristotle once wrote :

"The principal object of natural philosophy is not the form of the material elements, but the composite thing, and the totality of the form, independently of which those elements have no existence."

It is in the hope of conveying some useful ideas about that "composite thing", the earth we live on, that the following chapters have been written. My thanks are due to my former colleagues, Professor F. Debenham, Professor J. A. Steers, Mr. W. V. Lewis, and Mr. A. A. L. Caesar, for their helpful criticisms of certain portions. To my wife I would express both my apologies for inflicting this book so much upon her, and my gratitude for her unwearied interest and assistance.

CHAPTER I

GENERAL CHARACTERISTICS OF THE EARTH

WE may conveniently start by taking an imaginary external view of the earth, and noting briefly its more outstanding characteristics. Viewed in its entirety it is a globular body some 8,000 miles in diameter which turns steadily each day on an axis whose ends mark the North and South Poles, and at the same time advances at an average rate of some 67,000 miles an hour on a gigantic annual circuit of the sun. The curvature of the earth's surface, though normally inappreciable to us at ground level, is of fundamental importance. It underlies all the diversity of climate over the earth, and has to be taken carefully into account in planning routes for long-distance air or sea navigation. Moreover this curvature makes it impossible to construct a flat map of any large area that is wholly free from distortion. Conventional maps of hemispheres, or worse of the whole world, inevitably present grossly misleading ideas of the true shapes and relationships of the earth's features. Only a model globe can show these correctly, and the reader is urged to study such globes whenever he gets a chance. One good result of air travel is that it has forced us to remember that the earth really is round, and that the shortest distance between eastern Canada and the U.S.S.R., for instance, is over Greenland. Actually the earth is not quite spherical, being a little flattened around the two Poles (a result of its constant rotation), but this flattening is of little practical importance.

After shape and size, the next thing we must note about the earth is its constitution. Fundamentally it is built of combinations of the various chemical elements, but in the more general sense we can distinguish three major divisions of its matter, solid, liquid, and gaseous. The solid globe is enclosed within the outer layer of mixed gases we call the Atmosphere, which not only provides the air we breathe, but acts as a cushion round the earth, modifying the impact on it of the sun's rays, and using the energy they provide to carry out all sorts of work. Stimulated by that energy, the gases of the atmosphere interact continuously with the solid and liquid materials of the earth, while those react on one another, in a most complex chain of processes which lie at the very heart of Physical Geography. We shall be meeting these interactions between the earth's materials all through this book.

Within the atmosphere lies the solid globe, its outer crust built of the great range of mineral aggregates we call rocks, its interior composed of materials about which we have as yet little knowledge. Between solid earth and atmosphere, however, is interposed a somewhat variable layer of water sometimes called the Hydrosphere. This completely covers about 71% of the solid globe, only 29% being exposed as " dry " land, but even on the latter there is always *some* water present. Land life would be impossible if this were not the case. The emergent 29% of the crust is divided up into a number of large patches (the continents) and a host of islands, large and small, and the pattern these form is the most fundamental pattern in the earth's geography. It affects conditions on the surface in all sorts of ways, and has had inestimable effects upon the course of human history. It would be pointless, however to attempt to describe this pattern, for study of a model globe reveals it better than could any verbal description. A few points about it perhaps deserve comment. There is a peculiar tendency for the continents, despite their quite irregular shapes, to taper southwards. The two Americas, Africa, and the Indian peninsula show this best. Then most of the land is crowded into the northern hemisphere, the southern being mainly ocean. Much speculation has been devoted to the origin and meaning of these peculiarities, but we have as yet no very satisfactory explanations. They are clearly bound up with the evolution of the earth itself, a matter we can touch on only very briefly in this book.

It is worth emphasising, however, that land only exists on the earth at all because its surface is by no means smooth. Certain patches of it stand out as flattish bulges, others as ridges and peaks, and between there are wide tracts relatively depressed. Fortunately there is not enough water to cover the whole of this irregular surface. The oceanic waters are confined by gravity to the lower areas, and the tops of the bulges and smaller protuberances stand out as dry land. Yet although of such immense importance—for without them there would be no land, and mankind could never have come into existence—these differences of level in the surface are but trifling in relation to the size of the earth. Only some 12 miles difference in height separates the summit of Mt. Everest from the deepest point on the ocean floor, no great matter in comparison with the earth's circumference of 25,000 miles. Reduce the earth to the size of a football, and the ocean basins would be imperceptible depressions etched in its surface, the oceans themselves a mere surface dampness.

The major differences in level that decide the pattern of land and sea are not alone, however, in diversifying the earth's surface. It reveals a vast variety of other irregularities. The most outstanding are the great mountain chains like the Alps, Himalayas and Andes. These for the most part run in lines or belts of sinuous shape, and trace out distinctive patterns over the earth. A great ring of them encompasses the Pacific Ocean, some elements traversing the ocean floor with only the mountain tops emerging, while a second great system runs through southern Europe and across southern Asia to branch out and mingle with the first in Indonesia. Wider patches of elevated land occur here and there, as in central Asia and East Africa, while other extensive tracts of the continents are low and flat. Broad depressions, deep narrow trenches, and isolated peaks further diversify the exposed surface, while superimposed on the major features is an infinite wealth of smaller hills and valleys. Even the ocean floors, little as we yet know of them, reveal a great diversity of features. The whole of this variety of external form we call the earth's surface relief. As we shall be dealing with the solid earth and its features in the first part of this book, we may conveniently here ask the obvious question, what is the significance of this irregularity in the earth's surface, and how did it come into existence?

In earlier days these features were regarded as fixed and eternal, and while the Biblical account of creation was accepted

literally, and the age of the earth thought to be little greater than
recorded human history, it seemed indeed impious to question
this view. Right up to the 19th century the earth's mountains
and valleys were thus attributed to specific past " cataclysms of
nature," if not to the original creation. The very different way in
which we now view them derives from the penetrating genius of
the great pioneer geologists, especially James Hutton (1726-1797),
who observed that so far from being changeless, landscape
features undergo *small* changes all the time. This in itself was
perhaps no new discovery; the significance came with a growing
realisation of the total inadequacy of earlier ideas about the age
of the earth, and the implications of small persistent changes
carried on over almost unimaginable periods of time. Despite
many proverbs, it is a matter of common observation that stone
is not, in literal fact, indestructible. Examination of any old
stone wall shows that it does slowly decay. Then all rivers
carry mud down to the sea off the lands, and that mud must have
been worn off the land, and must in fact represent the products of
decay of its rocks. Such mud, washed into puddles by rain, is
left as a thin film when the puddles dry out. All these things are
common knowledge; but the early geologists found that our
British countryside is built mainly of great formations of solid
rock themselves in many cases made up of innumerable overlying
layers of just the same sort of mud; mud which, though now
hardened and compressed, must have been originally laid down
film upon film in standing water. At a minimum estimate periods
of hundreds of thousands of years must have been needed for the
building of such rocks, and as geological investigation proceeded
it became apparent that most of England was built of a great
range of such formations lying on top of one another " like slices
of bread and butter on a plate." As the lower rocks must have
been formed before the upper were laid upon them, the geological
time-scale had to be ever expanded backward as investigation
proceeded, and geologists began to conceive of an age for the
earth in terms of hundreds of millions of years rather than the
5,000 years of Biblical creation. Today it is generally believed
that the earth is between 4,000 and 6,000 million years old, and
with a time-scale of this magnitude even the most trivial changes

that we can see going on in the earth's hills and valleys take on an entirely new significance. An illustration will help to underline this point.

Since it was re-built three centuries ago, St. Paul's Cathedral is estimated to have lost on average half an inch of stonework over its exposed surfaces through natural decay. If we apply this figure to the open countryside, making due allowance for the many differences in conditions, it becomes apparent that over even a few hundred years quite measurable changes must take place in the scenery. It has been calculated, indeed, that on average a whole foot of material is removed from the entire face of Britain every 3 or 4,000 years. But the rocks exposed in the Scottish Highlands are believed to be hundreds of millions of years old, and most of Britain has been land for at least ten million years. Clearly during these immense spans of time thicknesses of rock to be measured in hundreds or even thousands of feet must have been worn away, and all the detailed landscape features must have come slowly into being during, and as a result of, this gradual wearing away of the surface. So far from being the product of specific " cataclysms of nature ", we must therefore conclude that our hills and valleys have slowly evolved as a by-product of continuous land-destruction; the valleys having been carved out, and the hills representing for the most part merely fragments of earlier higher-level land surfaces left outstanding between the excavated valleys. The investigations of geology and physical geography over the last hundred years have made it abundantly clear that virtually all the smaller relief features of the earth have originated in this way, and that a universal process or differential sculpture, technically called *Denudation*, has profoundly modified the shapes of even the largest features. Much of this book will be concerned with the processes and results of denudation, but we may here say a word about its general nature.

It results from the constant attack upon the solid earth of its atmosphere and surface waters, an attack in part chemical, in part mechanical, and inspired principally by the force of gravity and the energy of the sun's rays. When exposed, the earth's rocks are not really in harmony with the external conditions, and a constant attack goes on upon them in nature's effort to achieve an equilibrium. The first phase of the attack is static, consisting of decomposition and disintegration of the rocks by atmospheric agencies. This is called *Weathering*. But were this all, the rocks would get slowly buried under the products of their own destruction, and the attack would slow down and stop. On land it is mainly slopes and differences of level that prevent this happening, for the rock wastes tend to slide away downhill, their movement being greatly assisted by rainwater. Ultimately much of the material gets washed into streams and rivers, which like gigantic conveyor-belts carry it away to dump it into the seas. Wind, and occasionally moving ice, also help to remove the products of weathering, but these moving agencies affect the surface in other ways as well. During their progress they scour away and dig into the land, while around exposed coasts the waves of the sea also cut into the land and carry away the proceeds to drop them in deep water. This destruction by moving agencies is called *Erosion*, and it constitutes the second phase of the external attack. The whole compound process, save the operations of the sea, proceeds most rapidly on the higher ground and steeper slopes, and so works to *reduce* the earth's relief, carving away the high spots, and dumping the wastes in the hollows. So far as we can judge it has been in continuous operation since the earliest days of the earth, working fast on steep rugged ground, slowing down as the relief is reduced, and certainly the bulk of our present landscape features have come into being through its operations. But if this is so, and the earth is really as old as the geologists claim, clearly we are faced immediately with the problem of explaining how any marked upstanding relief can still exist at all. Why have not all the great mountains long ago been worn down flat, and how did they get elevated in the first place to allow denudation to work on them and carve them up?

To answer these questions we have to take account of a second group of forces and agencies that work on the earth's surface. These reside within the earth itself. Study of the build of continents, and of the internal structure of mountain chains, reveals that over the aeons of its history the earth has continuously reacted against the smoothing out of its surface. As land areas have been worn down, so they have been uplifted again. The present continents themselves, we find, have in a manner grown during geological time, with many changes in their shapes and sizes, and possibly with changes in their very locations. More spectacular still have been the periodic phases of upthrust of great mountain chains, which seem to have occurred in occasional " earth-storms " of great internal activity. For the mountains we see today are by no means original features of the earth. Most of them are in fact quite young by geological standards, and it is to their very youth that they owe their eminence, for denudation has not yet had time to carve them away. Scattered over the earth we find many traces of earlier mountain-systems once as great as the Alps now worn away quite flat. In the fullness of time the present Alps and Himalayas will also be reduced to low hills and dust, only no doubt to be replaced by new mountains that the earth is even now beginning to prepare. By means slow and continuous, or spasmodic and violent, the " solid " earth has thus continuously parried the attacks of denudation, re-created the irregularities of its surface, and so perpetuated the external attack upon them.

In approaching the study of the earth's external form and features, it will thus be clear that we must be very chary of using the word " permanent ". In the long-term view the only thing truly permanent about the earth's surface is change. Some of the major features such as the great ocean basins do certainly appear to be very old, and to date back perhaps to the earliest days of the earth. Presumably also there have always been continents, though we know that they have markedly changed their shapes and sizes through geological time. The smaller features, however, are all in varying degree ephemeral, and to obtain a true understanding of them we must learn how they have evolved, what is happening to them now, and what is likely to happen in the future. Every feature on the earth has its own history, and each undergoes constant change in response to the processes acting on it. In most cases the rates of change are indeed so slow as to be virtually immeasurable and of no practical significance to mankind, but this is not true in every case, and

slow alteration of physiographic features or conditions thought
to be quite fixed and constant has given mankind some nasty
shocks over the centuries. In principle, indeed, we can conceive
of all the earth's surface features as being the creation of opposed
agencies working on the stony materials of its crust: one set
external and based in the atmosphere and surface waters, which
work to smooth out the surface; the other based on forces inside
the earth which distort the surface again and recreate its relief.
In any particular region the existing landscape can be viewed as
the current stage reached in the battle, with the character of the
materials worked on, the local rocks, exercising an important
effect upon its progress; but the vast time-scale in which
the struggle is carried on must always be borne in mind. We
will approach the earth's relief features from this standpoint,
starting with the internal forces responsible for creating the
dislevelments and contortions out of which denudation has
carved the features we now see.

CHAPTER II

THE OUTER CRUST AND THE INTERIOR

IT will be clear from the discussion in the last chapter that to understand the face of the earth as we now see it we must look into the past, and for the major and more enduring features of the earth's architecture this means going a long way back indeed. We cannot in this short book outline the whole of the earth's history, but some idea of its presumed mode of origin and earlier evolution is useful background to an understanding of its later history and present character.

We have no certain knowledge of how the earth originated, and in consequence there has been a whole series of theories on this subject, none of them capable of final proof or disproof. A recent one derives the earth, like the other planets that circle round the sun, from the explosion and disintegration of a second and even larger star which used to move round the present sun in close association. This event is presumed to have occurred between 4,000 and 6,000 million years ago. This theory is too new for all its implications to be clear, and it is not universally accepted; but however created, it seems inherently likely that the earth started life as a whirling mass of incandescent gaseous material which as it cooled gradually shrank and condensed to a liquid state, and with further cooling developed a solid outer crust while still liquid inside.[1] Continued cooling through the eras of geological time would presumably lead to a gradual thickening of this solid crust inwards, and from external observation we might deduce that the earth today is solid all through. It is certainly quite cool, rigid and hard externally, and reacts to astronomical forces almost like a solid body; but various lines of evidence indicate that parts of its interior have probably been liquid at relatively recent periods in the past and may be so even today.

There is first the matter of the earth's internal temperature.

[1] Cosmogonical ideas change rapidly. Some recent theories suggest a very different genesis and early history for the earth. (1959).

Observations in deep mines the world over show that everywhere the temperature rises inwards from the surface. The rate of increase is somewhat variable, but averages about 55°F. per mile of depth. We do not know how far downwards this rate of increase is maintained, but if it persists unaltered, at depths of 25 to 30 miles the temperatures must be above the (surface) melting-points of all known rocks, and we might conclude that below this depth the earth's materials must still be liquid. But the melting-points of rocks are raised by increase of pressure, and the pressure also increases inwards. It is thus difficult to be certain about the physical state of the material at great depths within the earth, and indeed words like solid and liquid begin to lose their ordinary lay meanings in this context, for we have little information on how materials behave under such enormous pressures and temperatures continued over long periods of time. By all normal physical standards the earth's outer shell 25 to 30 miles thick seems to be entirely solid, and geophysical evidence shows that it is, for the most part at least, as rigid as steel. But at greater depths many geologists conceive the material to be in a stiff but glassy state, conceivably capable of " flowing " under great and long-continued stresses, and so hot that it readily becomes fluid if the pressure on it is locally reduced. It is probable that volcanic activity of some types reflects such a release of pressure on this hot deep-seated material by the penetration of deep fissures through the rigid crust which permit the "magma" (as the deep-seated material is called) to liquefy, rise up through the cracks, and pour out on the surface (*see* Chap. IV).

The origin of the earth's internal heat, however, raises some problems. Traditionally it was thought to be residual, the surviving heat remaining from the original incandescent condition. If this were so, it must have been gradually leaking away since the earliest times by conduction through the crust and dissipation to outer space through the atmosphere, and the interior should have been getting steadily cooler throughout geological time. Heat certainly does leak out to the earth's surface (though it makes an insignificant contribution to our comfort) and the rate is known; but comparison of this rate with estimates of the present and original internal temperatures gives a time interval over which the cooling could have been going on quite out of harmony with other estimates of the earth's age. This apparent contradiction was resolved when it was realised that the earth's internal heat may not be entirely, or even mainly, residual. It is now believed that the fires are, as it were, continually being stoked up, for most of the deep-seated rocks contain small quantities of radio-active minerals which in their spontaneous breakdown liberate heat. With this internal heat-creation, clearly the earth's interior will not have cooled down so fast as was earlier supposed, and indeed it may not be cooling off at all, or at least not consistently. Recognition of this possibility revolutionised ideas about possible sources of the energy that has so manifestly disturbed the earth's surface at many periods of its history, but until we know more about the distribution of radio-active material within the earth it is dangerous to theorise too confidently. Recent arguments suggest that the zone containing radio-active elements may be quite thin and superficial, and that below it the rise in temperature inwards is not maintained. Indeed it has been claimed that the deep interior of the earth may be quite cool; " no hotter than a wood-fire " as Hoyle expressed it in a recent series of radio talks. We really have no certain evidence either way.

Apart from the debatable questions of its temperature and physical state there are, however, a few other things we can infer about the earth's interior. The main mass of the external crust is generally considered to be composed of rocks which are tough, heavy, and crystalline, and which bear in their crystalline structure clear evidence of having solidified from a former molten state. Rocks of this nature, like granite, are called *Igneous* (Latin: *Ignis*—fire). It is true that such rocks do not form the ground-surface over wide areas of the continents, but this is because they are there mostly buried under a layer, thick or thin, of rocks of secondary origin like limestone, shale or sandstone. We will examine the character of these rocks, and the problems posed by their distribution, a little later. Here it is sufficient to remark that they are to be regarded, from the overall earth-structure point of view, as a relatively thin surface skin over the continents whose main foundations are composed of crystalline material. But there is a significant distinction in the distribution of the crystalline material of the crust. Apart from some local exceptions, that which builds the continents is consistently less dense than that which underlies the ocean floors. Granite, with a density of about 2.7 is typical of the continental material, but the ocean floors seem to be built in the main of rocks akin to the dark fine-grained basalt, with a density around 3.0. Here we find an explanation of the higher elevation of the continental " bulges " on which we commented in the last chapter. These stand higher because composed of lighter material, and apparently represent portions of a rather lighter crust that formed on the surface of the earth in its original outer solidification, rather as slag forms on the surface of molten iron in a blast-furnace. The puzzling thing is why, in this event, this crust only occurs in isolated patches. Why did not a thin layer form all over? or if it did, what has happened to the rest of it ? (Actually a thin layer of the lighter material does seem to occur on the floors of the Atlantic and Indian Oceans, but not on that of the open Pacific.) Three theories have been advanced to explain this puzzle. An early one, that the missing lighter crustal material is to be sought in the moon, the latter having been torn away from the earth in earlier days leaving a great scar still marked by the bed of the Pacific Ocean, is not now seriously entertained. Alternative ideas are that prior to the final solidification of the outer layers of the earth convectional currents piled up the lighter crust into patches, just as patches of scum are formed on boiling jam ; or secondly that there was indeed originally a thin shell of lighter crust all over, but that this became broken and folded up into patches by later earth-movements. The problem really remains unsolved, but whatever the correct answer the facts appear beyond dispute, and there is good evidence for the view that the denser basaltic material continues right under the lighter patches of continental material, which can thus be thought of as rafts " floating " in the denser material below. Floating may seem a queer word to use of materials which are stiff and rigid, but as we shall see later there is some justification for it. The two types of crustal material are commonly distinguished as *Sial* (from *si*lica and *al*umina the predominant minerals) and *Sima* (*si*lica and *ma*gnesia), the former being the lighter granite material, the latter the heavier basaltic. Together, these two " shells " are regarded as making up the essential outer crust of the earth.

We can be fairly sure about matters so far from direct geological data, assisted by geophysical observations. About what lies at greater depth we can only draw inferences. The mass of the whole earth can, however, be estimated fairly simply, and since we know its dimensions we can calculate its density as a whole. The figure arrived at, 5.5, is a good deal higher than that of even the densest surface rocks, which implies that the deep interior must be composed of very heavy materials indeed, perhaps with a density around 12.0. A popular view is that it is composed of a core of metallic nickel and iron, possibly surrounded by a zone of fused sulphides. Between this central core and the outer crust lie zones of intermediate density, but there appears to be not a gradual transition, but an arrangement of the materials into concentric shells, the density changing fairly sharply at their junctions. This is deduced from the behaviour of earthquake waves as they travel through the earth. The rate at which such waves travel is largely governed by the density of the medium through which they pass, and any abrupt change of density causes a plane of discontinuity at which the velocities of the waves are altered and their paths bent, and from which certain waves are reflected back to the surface. The details of analysis of earthquake waves are highly technical and need not detain us, but a point of interest is that one type of these waves, called the distortional or S type, will not pass through the central core of the earth, and this suggests that it may be still in some measure liquid.

The problems of the earth's interior are of great scientific interest, but our concern is really with its surface, and it may well be asked how these matters bear on the realm of physical geography. One connection, however, has already been indicated; the apparent physical cause of the differences in level between continental surfaces and ocean floors. But as we shall see in the next two chapters, internal and surface relationships have been often much more dramatic than that. Before proceeding to these topics, however, we may conveniently discuss here a development of the sial-sima distinction which bears closely on the earth's surface patterns through the mechanism of up-and-down movements of areas of the crust. Such movements have been of the greatest importance in the geological growth of the continents and the evolution of the present land and water pattern.

That the level of different parts of the earth's crust has altered appreciably, and often repeatedly, over geological time, cannot be doubted. The most impressive evidence is that afforded by the distribution and character of the " stratified " rocks ; rocks like sandstone, limestone, and shale, that we mentioned earlier as forming a sort of skin over the greater part of the continental surfaces. In Britain such rocks form the surface over virtually the whole of England, much of Wales, and the lower eastern parts of Scotland. From below them, in the hill-country of the north and west, granite and other crystalline rocks break through in local patches, and over the Scottish Highlands a third type of rocks, the hard, contorted, and often largely crystalline varieties like quartzite, slate, schists, and gneisses, appear in profusion. These are rocks called *Metamorphic* or " altered ", in which the original characteristics have been completely changed by tremendous heat and pressure, and we find them, for reasons that will become apparent later, closely associated with regions of ancient mountains. The stratified rocks, in their unaltered state, are quite different from either the metamorphic varieties or the crystalline igneous rocks. They are built-up rocks of secondary origin, formed from the residues created in the destruction of pre-existing rocks, and consisting of small separate particles or fragments more or less firmly bonded together. The particles are coarse in the case of a sandstone, extremely fine in the case of a clay or shale. A sandstone, for instance, is no more than a mass of loose sand grains such as one can see on the sea-shore cemented together by some chemical precipitate like lime, silica, or an iron salt (it is iron salts that give sandstones their common yellow, brown, or reddish colourings); in short, a sort of natural mortar. All these rocks generally occur in the form of super-imposed layers or *strata*, and the majority were built by the accumulation of layer upon layer of sediment settling to the bottom of some body of water. For this reason they are commonly called the *sedimentary* rocks, though the self-explanatory term *derived* rocks will also be encountered.

Rocks of this type, piled up often to thicknesses of over 10,000 feet, cover about three-quarters of the earth's continental surfaces, but most of them were indisputably laid down on former sea-floors. The massive limestones, grits, and shales that build the Pennines originated beneath the sea no less than the clays around London. This is proved not only by their structure, but by the inclusion amongst their mineral grains of remains of long-extinct marine organisms : shells, casts, and skeletons of creatures that lived in the seas on whose floors these rocks accumulated. These remains, called " fossils ", are of the greatest importance to the geologist, for by their aid he can assign particular beds of rock to the geological period in which the organisms lived, and so both date individual beds and correlate formations of similar age in different regions and even in different continents. The physiographic significance of these remains, however, is that they prove conclusively that over the span of geological time most, if not all, of the continental areas must at one time or another have been beneath the sea. Note that we say sea and not ocean. The common sedimentary rocks are built largely of rock wastes washed off lands, which come to rest in the relatively shallow seas around continents and on their submerged margins, and never reach the deep ocean floors. What the distribution of the sedimentary rocks tells us is that to permit seas to flood over great areas of their surfaces, and to lay down on them considerable thicknesses of sediment, the continents must have moved gently up and down over geological time, often by amounts of several thousand feet. Movements of this type, which apparently took place extremely slowly, are often called *Epeirogenic*, or " Continent-building " movements, since it was by their aid that the continents acquired their surface skin of sedimentary rocks. It must not be supposed, however, that the continents and ocean basins ever, as it were, exchanged roles. The degree of submergence of the continental surfaces was relatively slight, and we can find on land no rocks at all like the deposits that accumulate on the really deep ocean floors. Conversely, there is no evidence that the latter have ever been land.

By tracing out the distribution of formations laid down in seas in the same geological periods, it is possible to prepare maps of the changing distribution of land and water over the earth's history, and very strange such maps look, for they bear little resemblance to our present maps of the earth. The resemblance grows stronger as we come nearer to the present day, although even in quite recent times, geologically speaking, wide areas now land were under the sea, and areas now sea-covered were probably land. England was still united to the Continent for long after man had evolved, and at periods little more ancient most of the

Fig. 1. Elevated marine cliffs, west coast of Scotland.

North Sea was dry land. Today new sedimentary rocks are being laid down on its floor, but in the distant future it may quite well become dry land again. We have much evidence of quite recent changes of level recorded in our landscape features, and in some parts of the world movements can be detected going on at measurable rates even today.

One of the most striking types of evidence for such vertical movement is the presence, at various points around our coast, of old sea-beaches and cliffs now standing high above the reach of the waves (*see* Fig. 1). Some, in western Scotland, stand at heights of as much as 100 feet. Features of this type occur in many places along the west and south coasts, and are well marked among the islands of western Scotland. Good examples can also be found on the east coast of Scotland. Conversely, dock excavations have often revealed old land-surfaces bearing tree-stumps and peat now lying buried under sand and mud many feet below low-tide level. Here is clear evidence of both uplift and depression in geologically modern times, and even more recent movement is recorded for instance along the coast of Norway and around the Baltic, where the harbours of some mediaeval fishing villages are now high and dry. At places around the Baltic the land is rising from the sea at a rate of as much as a centimetre a year. Even in Britain we have evidence of movements during historic times. Roman settlements along the Thames estuary and elsewhere are now drowned, while there is some evidence of a slight uplift in north-western Britain.

Changes of level of this type are very difficult to correlate and measure, and even more difficult to interpret. The only fixed mark to which we can refer them is mean sea-level; and apart from the difficulty of establishing a really precise " average " position for the surface of a body of water which is rising and falling all the time with tidal movements, and is subject to irregular changes under the influence of wind and weather, we have always to reckon with the possibility of longer-term progressive changes in the ocean level itself. Any upheaval or depression of parts of the ocean floor would change the level of the surface, and over long time-intervals the accumulation of sediment on the sea-bottom will reduce the capacity of its basins and alter the water-levels. In addition, however, we have to reckon with the possibility of changes in the actual amount of water held in the oceans, and as we shall see later there is good reason to believe that such changes have in fact occurred from time to time. When we speak of " vertical movements " in the earth's crust, and " changes of level ", it will be clear that we run the risk of over-simplifying a very complex matter. Always we have to ask whether it is the land that has moved, or the water, or both. But allowing for all possible variations in the water element, it is quite certain that the solid crust itself has moved up and down to a considerable degree over geological time, and in some areas is still so moving. Many raised beaches are no longer parallel to the ocean surface, but are tilted and warped. Only up-rising of the land could produce such effects, and when we recall the extent and thickness of the marine sedimentary rocks, and the heights to which they have been lifted, it is quite clear that movements of the earth's crust have been responsible. We are thus faced with the problem of explaining how such differential movements can go on in an earth's crust that appears so rigid and stable.

A clue to this puzzle is contained in the idea of *Isostasy*, which implies that the earth's crust is in a state of balance. Earlier we noted that the continental masses, composed of rather lighter rocks than the ocean floors, stand up above them, and we suggested a cause-and-effect connection between these facts, using the dubious word " floating ". Detailed investigation of the structure of the earth's outer crust shows that, in fact, a sort of flotation principle does appear to operate. This was first inferred from reflection upon the curious behaviour of plumb-bobs during survey operations near large mountains. A plumb-bob only hangs down because its " bob " is attracted by gravity towards the centre of gravity of the earth ; but all large masses of material exert gravitational attraction, and suspended near a large mountain a plumb-bob should be pulled a little out of the vertical towards the mountain by the latter's own attraction. If we calculate the mass of such a mountain we can, knowing the mass of the earth, calculate what the deviation of the plumb-line out of the vertical ought to be. Observations of this type carried out around mountains revealed, however, that the latter often attracted the plumb-bob much less than they ought to have done. Indeed in some cases they even repelled it. From this curious fact some deduced that the mountains must be hollow, standing like gigantic blisters on the face of the earth, and fantastic as this idea otherwise is, it had at least the merit of explaining how the enormous weights of mountain-chains can be supported by the earth's crust without its buckling. But a more reasonable and equally effective explanation was soon put forward, which has been supported by gravity observations carried out in many parts of the world. Other things being equal, the strength of the gravitational "pull" at any place depends simply on its distance from the centre of the earth, and if the height of the place is known, its exact position, and the true shape of the earth, it is easy to calculate what the value of gravity there should be. Any difference between this calculated value and that actually observed at the place is called a " gravity anomaly ". Now it has been found that over mountains very often gravity values are a good deal less than they ought to be ; there are persistent " negative gravity anomalies ". Over the ocean basins and other large depressed areas (in the elevational sense) by contrast, gravity anomalies are on the whole consistently positive. These peculiarities, taken in conjunction with the irregular behaviour of plumb-bobs near mountains, led to the idea that the arrangement of the earth's materials of varying density below the two types of feature is different : that there is an excess of lighter material below mountains (which reduces the gravitational pull from what it ought to be) and below ocean basins an excess of denser material (which increases it). Applied to the sial-sima division of the outer crust this would imply that below the continents, and especially below mountains, the lighter sial material projects downwards, while below the oceans it thins out and the denser sima more nearly approaches the surface (*See* Fig. 2). The visible upward-projecting mountains, in short, seem to have below them even larger downward-projecting " roots ", and this being so it seems reasonable to assume that these roots support them by a flotation mechanism analagous to that of an iceberg floating in water. The substratum material, as we noted earlier, is probably quite hot, and while not liquid in the ordinary sense may well be able to react by slow deformation and flowage to great and long-continued stresses. If we imagine a material like pitch or asphalt, with stiffer irregular cakes of stone " floating " in it, we get some approximate idea of this concept. Since the difference in density between the sial rafts and the sima in which they float is not great (2.7 to 3.0) we should expect the continents to float low, with little freeboard, and this seems to agree well with the findings of the gravity surveys. We can thus picture the arrangement of sial crust and sima substratum something as in Fig. 2.

The significance of this flotation idea will be obvious. Here we have at once a mechanism whereby vertical movements can

B

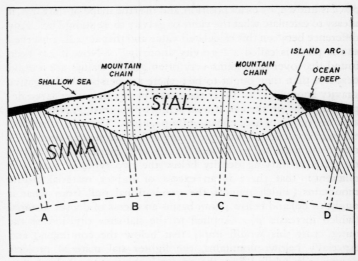

Fig. 2. The Principle of Isostasy, or Balance in the earth's crust. The mass in each of the four columns is the same, so that pressures at A, B, C, and D are equal.

be brought about, for if the crust is floating in balance any disturbance of that balance should result in movement. Piling up of excess weight on an area should result in sinking; removal of material should initiate rising. But by the operations of denudation alone material is always being re-distributed about the earth's surface, and were there no restriction to movement we could accordingly expect a continuous state of slow crustal movement in response. In reality it is clear that no such continuous and immediate system of adjustment can go on, for the outer crust is not composed of a series of loose separate columns free to slide up and down, but is a stiff continuous shell of considerable strength. Only when the stresses overcome that strength should we expect rising and sinking to start; and that is pretty well the situation that we find by analysis of the gravity observations. The larger crustal features appear to be fairly well " compensated ", i.e. to be floating in balance, but many of the smaller ones are not. They are supported by the strength of the outer shell. Nevertheless, given sufficient re-distribution of stresses, movement will apparently start and continue.

Here then we have a possible explanation of how the continental blocks have been able to move up and down, permitting seas to flood great areas of their surfaces in the past and lay down on them sheets of sedimentary rock. Here too we may find the explanation of the movements responsible for elevated marine cliffs and strand-lines. The accumulation of great masses of ice on the crust, such as we know today in Greenland and the Antarctic, might well be expected to exceed the strength of the crust to support and result in a general bowing-down around them ; and as we shall see, there is much evidence to suggest that this does happen. The present rising of Scandinavia is generally attributed to slow recovery after depression of that area under the weight of past ice-sheets. But there is another aspect of isostasy that is of great importance to interpretation of the earth's surface features. The great mountain-chains stand up majestically above the surface, and must have been elevated to that position. We have seen that they are probably supported by deeply-submerged roots, " floating high " because of the local accumulation of lighter material below them. Clearly the creation of those roots has been an essential part of their evolution, and we may surmise that as denudation wears away the surface projections, and so reduces the load, so the buoyancy of those submerged roots will cause continuous rising. To destroy a mountain-chain completely, therefore, may well demand the removal of far more material than is visible in the present mountains themselves, for they may well rise even as they are worn down. Wherever we find denudation or other agencies affecting major transfers of material about the surface, or otherwise interfering with the state of balance, we must therefore expect isostatic adjustments, with some sort of vertical movement, to be eventually initiated. This concept of balance in the earth's crust is bound up in all sorts of ways with the evolution of its surface features, and it introduces us at once, and on a major scale, to the idea of natural balances in the physical earth which is one of the most important lessons that Physical Geography has to teach.

CHAPTER III

EARTH MOVEMENTS AND THEIR SURFACE EFFECTS: HOW MOUNTAINS ARE BUILT

THE stratified rocks which build most of the land surfaces of the earth, such as sandstones, shales, and limestones, mainly originated as we have mentioned on the floors of relatively shallow seas. They grew by the addition from above of film upon film of sediment settling gently down to the sea floor, and by this mode of growth they acquired the distinctive layered or " bedded " structure which is their main characteristic. Forming over wide areas of nearly flat sea-floor their strata as originally laid down would lie almost horizontal, and if uplifted to form land without deformation would retain that horizontal disposition on land today. Over considerable areas of the continents we do find them so disposed. The Chalk of East Anglia, for instance, although having a very slight general inclination or " dip " towards the coast, appears to the eye to lie over great areas quite flat and undisturbed, while in central Russia formations of sedimentary rock cover thousands of square miles without sensible tilt or distortion. In such areas clearly all that has happened, since the rocks were originally laid down, is that gentle vertical movements in the earth's crust have converted areas formerly sea into land. But in other regions the picture is very different.

Anyone who has travelled through the Alps, or in Britain through the Scottish Highlands, North Wales, or the Lake District, can scarcely have missed seeing cliffs or quarry faces in which the exposed strata were tilted up at a sharp angle, and often bent, broken, or even contorted into great loops. Beautiful examples of such deformations are to be seen at every turn in the Jura mountains of eastern France, where the rivers have sawn deep gorges through the parallel ridges and exposed their internal structures. In such regions it looks as though some giant had crumpled up the strata just as you can ruck up a heavy table-cloth by pushing your hand across the table. Clearly distortions

of the strata of this nature could not have come about by simple
uplift. They reveal lateral compression, and can only have been
formed by horizontal movements in the earth's crust very different
from the simple up and down movements we have so far studied.

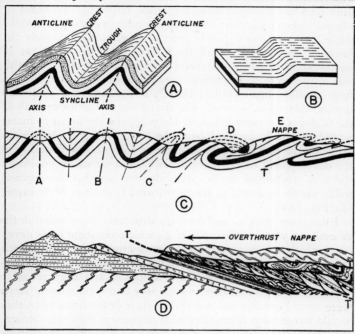

Fig. 3. Types of Folds:
    (A) Parallel inclined folds,   (B) Monoclinal fold
    (C) Gradation from simple open folding (A) into inclined fold (B), overfold
        (C), recumbent fold (D), and overthrust " nappe " (E) (T: Thrust plane).
    (D) Overthrust structure in N.W. Highlands of Scotland.

Structures of this type, in which the strata are bent and contorted,
are called *folds*.

Folded structures are found in great variety in the continental
rocks, and we have every shade of transition from the gentlest of
shallow undulations to structures in which the folds are tightly
packed together or even piled on top of one another (Fig. 3). In

the simpler types of folding we can distinguish the *anticlines*, or up-folds, from the *synclines*, or down-folds, the inclined parts of the strata being called the *limbs* of the folds. Occasionally such simple open folding is quite symmetrical but more often one limb dips more steeply than the other, indicating one-sided or unequal pressure. Folds in which one limb lies nearly horizontal while the other dips sharply are called *monoclinal*. Clearly the intensity and complexity of the buckling reflect the degree of compression to which the strata were subjected, and when this was very severe we may find *overfolds* developed, and these in turn grading into *recumbent* folds. If pressure was continued beyond this stage, generally the stretching of the lower limb of the fold was so severe that it would snap, and the upper elements would then ride forward over the lower along a *thrust-plane*. Some of the best examples of extreme compression resulting in the development of extensive thrust-planes, on which enormous slices of contorted rocks overrode one another for several miles, are to be found in the north-west Highlands of Scotland. (*See* Fig. 3.D.)

Even more extreme and complex structures are revealed in the central and western Alps, where gigantic recumbent folds developed which may have carried sheets of crumpled rock from the south right over the central axis of the mountains. Such far-travelled folded masses are called " nappes ", and they record a tremendous degree of compression, for if the component strata were spread out flat and restored to their original positions they would cover many times the extent of country they now occupy. We will return to the Alps later when we examine the mechanism that produced these extraordinary structures.

Folds, then, indicate lateral compression of the strata, and initially they must have thrown the ground surface into new relief, the anticlines rising as ridges, the synclines forming valleys. Such original, or structural, relief is termed *Tectonic* (Greek : *Tekton*—a builder). It is rather rare, however, that we find such original folded relief substantially unmodified. Folds did not form overnight. They are structures imposed on hard stiff rocks, and although those rocks were no doubt much less resistant when the folding took place, the buckling undoubtedly developed very slowly, and even as the strata were arched up they would be under the continuous attack of denudation, an attack which would intensify as the slopes steepened. Today, after several million years since the last major phase of earth-storm and folding, denudation has so modified the ground-surface that in many folded regions we can no longer trace any simple and direct relationships between individual structures and the surface forms. In any folding, the strata in the synclines tend to get compressed, those on the anticlines stretched, fractured and weakened. This assists the natural concentration of

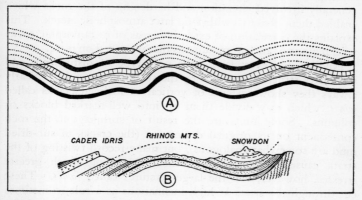

Fig. 4. Inversion of relief :
  (A) Anticlines carved into valleys, synclines standing out as ridges.
  (B) Generalised structure of the Snowdon area.

atmospheric attack on the higher ground, and as a result anticlines tend to get worn away faster than synclines. After long denud-ation, it is thus not uncommon to find the original relationship of anticlines with ridges reversed, the synclines now standing up as ridges, the anticlines having been carved into valleys, to give a sort of " inverted relief ": Snowdon has a structure something of this sort (Fig. 4). More commonly, however, in much denuded regions of complex structure, it is difficult to trace any systematic relations at all between structure and surface. Many such regions in fact have undergone such severe and prolonged denudation that the ground-surface is now low-lying and nearly flat. In such areas it is only by careful study of the pattern of rock-outcrops on the planed-off structures, and measurement of the direction and amount of " dip " in the various beds, that the geologist can deduce the original structures and tell us perhaps that here mighty mountains once stood. Prior to this stage, however, although detailed correlation of individual folds with surface features may be impossible, we generally find an overall relationship of mountainous and hilly country with regions of past folding. In part this is due to the uplift which frequently accompanied folding ; in part to the fact that severe folding generally involved alteration and hardening of the rocks which enabled them better to withstand later atmospheric attack. This explains the correlation of extensive areas of metamorphic rocks with regions of ancient mountains that we noted on p. 14.

Folding, however, is not the only type of disturbance and secondary structure revealed by the sedimentary rocks. Nearly always they show systems of vertical or inclined cracks called *joints*, which may divide them up into well-marked blocks or columns. Some joints are the result of shrinkage in the rock consequent on its original drying-out (the cracks in sun-dried mud are somewhat analogous), but many record twisting of the strata caused by earth-movements. Revealing much greater stresses, however, are the large fractures called *faults*. These cut through the strata at high inclinations as a rule, sometimes vertically, and nearly always the beds on either side of the fracture have been displaced relative to one another. The amount of vertical displacement is called the " throw " of the fault, and in some faults it amounts to thousands of feet. It must not be thought, however, that in such cases the movement occurred all at once ; the sudden snapping of the crust and falling away of the ground on one side of the fracture by a thousand feet is not an occurrence we can visualise happening even on our tormented earth. In such cases the large ultimate displacement was produced by a long sequence of minor slips, for once faults form there is a tendency for movement along them to recur. Study of the type of displacement along a fault often allows us to determine the nature of the stress that caused the fracture (*see* Fig. 5). *Normal* faulting is clearly due to tension, for the rocks now occupy a longer expanse than they did originally; but we also find *reversed* faults in which the movement is the other way round, the strata on one side having ridden up over those on the other, clearly owing to compressive forces. *Tear* faults,

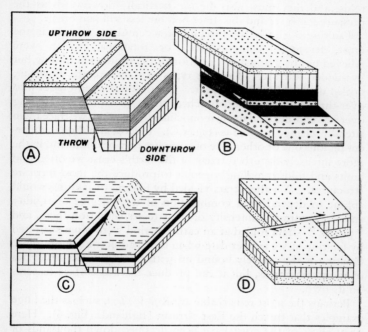

Fig. 5. Types of faults:

(*A*) *Normal fault, produced by tension.*
(*B*) *Reversed fault, produced by compression.*
(*C*) *Normal fault grading into monoclinal fold.*
(*D*) *Tear fault, produced by shearing stresses.*

again, indicate rotational or torsional stresses in the ground.

Faults seldom occur singly. More commonly the strata are broken up into a mosaic by a large number of these fractures of varying throw and lateral extension. Traced on a map, however, they generally form a fairly consistent pattern, lying in systems

running more or less parallel in one, two, or more main directions. There may, too, be great " master-faults " extending
hundreds of miles, linked by systems of minor faults. Traced
out laterally, however, all faults sooner or later die out, as do
folds, and they must also die out vertically downwards as the
pressure increases and the strata become less stiff and brittle.

Faulting is clearly the product of accumulated stresses in the
crust, tensional, compressional, or rotational, which were
relieved not by gradual deformation of the strata as in folding but
by sudden fracture. The two types of structure are, however,
not so distinct as might appear. Overfolding often grades into
over-thrusting, the over-stretched strata breaking and sliding
over one another, and many monoclinal folds, when we trace them
laterally, change into faults (Fig. 5.C). Indeed, although in different regions one or other type of structure may be dominant, in the
more intensely disturbed tracts of the earth's crust we often find
faults and folds mingling together to produce the most intricate
structures. Whether strata yielded by folding or faulting would
appear to depend on a combination of their degree of rigidity
and the nature and intensity of the stresses acting on them, and
" plastic " strata folded at an earlier period were often shattered
by faulting at some later date when they had become more rigid.
Faulting is thus closely bound up with folding in the structures
of mountain-chains, but it can produce marked surface features
on its own.

Perhaps the most remarkable are *Rift Valleys*, such as the huge
examples that trench the East African Highlands (Fig. 6). Here
great slices of the crust have been dropped down thousands of
feet between parallel fault-systems, to create long trough-like
valleys in which occur the major East African lakes. The
elongated shapes of lakes like Rudolf, Edward, Albert, Kivu,
Tanganyika and Nyasa, and their linear arrangement, reveal
clearly the influence of the fault-pattern, which is but part of a
far-flung system of fractures that extends north to include the
Red Sea and the trench of the Dead Sea and Jordan valley. The
magnitude of the " throw " in these faults is underlined when
we note that the floor of the Dead Sea is some 2,600 feet below
the sea-level of the Mediterranean, and that some of the East

African lakes are among the deepest in the world. The whole system extends over more than a sixth of the earth's whole circumference, and is one of the most extraordinary features of our globe. It is not yet clear whether the system as a whole was produced by tension or compression. It seems simplest to regard

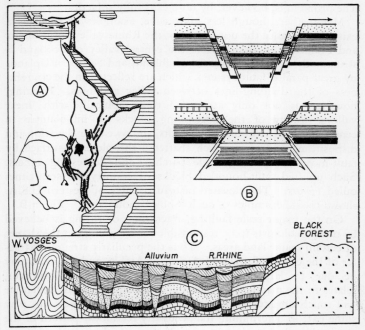

Fig. 6. *Rift Valleys :*
  (*A*) *Rift pattern of East Africa.*
  (*B*) *Alternative theories of rift valley structure—above, tensional ; below, compressional.*
  (*C*) *Cross-section of rift valley of the Rhine, north of Mulhausen, based on borings.*

it as made up of normal faults produced by tension, and the valley-floors as having fallen inwards under the stretching, like slipped keystones in an arch. The zig-zag pattern appears to favour this view. Some geologists however believe that many of the faults are of the reversed type, and the whole structure due to compression, the depressed valley-floors being held down by the overriding on them of the surrounding walls. Gravity surveys have supported this view by revealing belts of negative gravity anomalies, possibly indicating that segments of lighter crustal material have been forced downward. [1] (*See* Fig. 6.B.) The problem is, however, by no means fully solved.

Many other, though less impressive, examples of rift-valleys exist, for instance the upper part of the Rhine valley from Mainz and Frankfurt to Basle, while the central valley of Scotland is structurally separated from the Highlands and Southern Uplands by great parallel fault-systems which are reflected in the straightness of the dividing-lines between valley and hills. Faulting, however, is not only associated topographically with linear valleys. Many of the upstanding blocks of hill-country in central Europe are bounded by faults, and owe their elevation and disposition to stresses which shattered the old land-surface by fault-mosaics, uplifting some patches, and depressing others. Such uplifted fault-bounded blocks of country are sometimes called *Horsts*. The elevated plateau country of western U.S.A. shows classic examples of such " block-mountains." (Fig. 7.B.)

On the major scale faulting, fracturing, or rifting is believed by many geologists to be responsible for roughing out the shapes of certain major land areas. Thus the peculiarly straight character of the coasts of much of Africa, of Arabia, and of India, may be due to large-scale fracturing. This problem, however, relates to the manner in which the continents evolved, which we will touch on later. On a smaller scale, faulting seems to play some part in determining the peculiarly rectilinear pattern of the fiords that dissect the coast of Norway (although their topographic forms owe much to the sculpture of past glaciers), and study of a map will reveal comparable " straight-line " patterns in the valleys and coastal lochs of western Scotland which suggest fault-influence. Inland we sometimes find that faults have guided the development of river-systems by bringing together sets of rocks of varying resistance, while a more direct influence on topography is revealed in some straightish wall-like cliffs, abrupt slopes, and escarpments, such as the great wall-like slope which rises abruptly from the Vale of Eden to form the western

[1]More recent work (1953) has however thrown doubt on these earlier results.

edge of the northern Pennines. In general, wherever we find unusually straight features on the earth's surface, fault-influence is to be suspected; but caution is necessary in attributing too much to faulting, and often we suspect fault-influence without being able to prove it. The effects of denudation must be

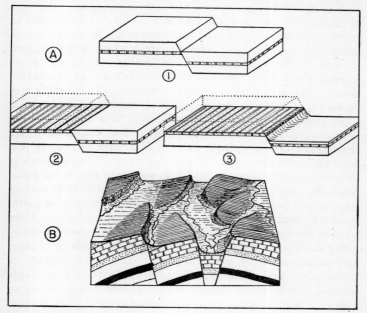

Fig. 7. *Faulted relief:*
(A) *Evolution of a "fault-line" scarp: (1) original fault scarp, (2) scarp removed by denudation, (3) secondary scarp created by resistant bed exposed on upthrow side of fault.*
(B) *Fault-block structure in the Great Basin of the western U.S.A.*

(after W. M. Davis)

remembered also. Unless the "throw" is very great, and the movement fairly rapid, continuous wearing away of the surface may prevent any cliff or scarp from developing over a fault. On the other hand, as denudation proceeds, such a scarp may come into existence long after the fault-movement has ceased, through the exhumation of strata of different resistance brought together by the faulting. (Fig. 7.A.)

Our knowledge of the mechanisms of faulting and folding, and our deductions concerning the forces responsible for them, are naturally based on study of the structures themselves, for we can seldom if ever watch the processes in operation : although of course they may be going on today for all that, too slowly to attract our notice.[1] In faulting, however, the movement is naturally jerky, and we are made painfully aware of it from time to time by the phenomena of earthquakes. Earthquakes are more or less violent tremors in the ground caused by any sudden shock, friction, or relief of stress in the crust. The shaking may be so slight as to be imperceptible to our senses, and in fact slight tremors occur almost continuously, as is revealed by the delicate mechanism of seismographs. But occasionally the shaking is severe and causes widespread damage and loss of life. Such violent shocks may arise in various ways. Some accompany violent volcanic eruptions, and it is suspected that some result from the slumping of large masses of unstable sediment on steep slopes on the sea-floor. But the great majority of earthquakes undoubtedly result from movement along faults. Even a slight settling movement along a big fault will cause a devastating earthquake, for such faults often run for hundreds of miles and penetrate deeply into the earth. The great majority of earthquakes, perhaps 90%, originate by movements at fairly shallow depths in the earth's crust ; mainly within the upper 5 miles. Nearly all the remainder originate in the upper 25 miles of depth ; but a small number seem to originate even below the crust, and some have been traced as deep as 700 km (about 435 miles). These deep-focus earthquakes are of great interest for the evidence they afford about the physical state of the material at great depths within the earth, but as physiographic phenomena earthquakes are not in themselves of great importance save in the damage they sometimes cause to life and property, for they are the results of crustal stresses rather than primary agencies. For this reason, as might be expected, we find that 90% of major earthquakes originate in the zones of the earth's crust most recently disturbed by intensive folding and faulting, and

[1]Evidence has been found in some parts of the world of appreciable movement in folded structures during historic times.

this leads us to examine the distribution of such belts of instability over the earth, and to consider the controversial problems of their origins and the mechanisms that produced them.

Although gentle warping and minor fracturing are found very widely in the continental rocks, the complex and intensive crumpling involving a considerable localised shortening of the strata is confined to certain well-marked zones or belts which coincide with present or past mountain-systems. The great mountain-chains are all essentially folded structures and occur in far-flung patterns of lines and arcs. Geological study of their structures reveals the somewhat astonishing facts that they are largely built of sedimentary rocks laid down on sea-floors, while the highest and most impressive chains, like the Alps, Himalayas and Rocky Mountains, are all relatively young in geological terms. As we mentioned, many much more ancient belts of folding can be traced, but the great mountains that once stood upon them have been planed down by aeons of slow denudation into low hills, and the oldest of all have been reduced to feature-less plains. All, however, reveal the same features of intense crumpling, dislocation, and hardening of their strata that we can see in the Alps, and to obtain some background to the history of our present mountains we may glance briefly at what geology has to tell us of earlier mountain-systems.

The earth's present major folded mountain-chains all belong to the so-called " Alpine " system, and were built during the Tertiary division of geological time; perhaps some 10 to 50 million years ago. Before them there had existed mountains built in the Cretaceous period, nearly 100 million years ago, and much greater ones built during the " Variscan (or " Hercynian ") *orogenic* (mountain-building) phase in late Carboniferous and Per-main times, perhaps 250 million years ago. Earlier still, there had been the " Caledonian " mountain-building epoch in middle Palaeozoic times, some 400 million years ago, in which the original mountains of Scotland and Norway were built, while geologists now recognise at least three earlier phases of mountain-building dating back into the dim three-quarters of the earth's history that is called " Pre-Cambrian " or " Archaean " time, about which we have as yet little knowledge. In all the later and better-known periods of mountain-construction, however, we find that events seem to have followed a very similar course. In each case the intense compression and folding was limited to certain linear belts of the crust, but the disturbance was world-wide in scope. In the active belts there first developed slowly-deepening " sags " in the crust, called geosynclines, in which accumulated great thicknesses of sediment worn off the surrounding land areas. These geosynclines often deepened and extended for millions of years, but in the end a relatively rapid and violent " revolution " occurred, in which great earth activity squeezed up these belts of thick plastic sediment, and crumpled their rocks into the contorted structures we see today. Finally the whole crumpled mass rose up to build new linear systems of mountains. We must not, of course, think of these events as happening overnight. The actual mountain-folding probably took hundreds of thousands of years, but in comparison with the vast spans of time between them these mountain-building phases appear as short and sharp spasms in the earth's history. In them new tectonic relief was relatively quickly created, only to be whittled away again in the long intervening eras of quiescence and denudation. For most of its history the earth has been quiet, its surface relief subdued, and its conditions less diversified than we know them today. The present diversity results from the fact that so little time—relatively speaking—has elapsed since the Alpine mountain-building era. If past form is maintained, the earth's surface will become in due course characterised again by a vast uniformity long before fresh outbreaks of internal activity occur to replace the long-vanished Alps and Himalayas.

But the mountain-building phases not only created new relief on the earth, majestic though in the long run ephemeral. By them the continents appear to have grown. In every continent we can recognise a core or nucleus of very ancient rocks called a " Shield ". So altered, or metamorphosed, are the rocks of these Shields that it is often difficult to determine their original nature, but running through them we can often trace the planed-off roots of Archaean mountain-systems, probably reduced to plains before life appeared on our planet at all. These Shields are thus mainly areas of subdued relief, and appear to have withstood later earth-stresses as resistant blocks against which the later mountain-systems were folded. In part they are covered by younger sedimentary strata lying little disturbed, but where exposed their crystalline rocks frequently contain rich mineral veins and bodies of ore. It is from such areas—the Laurentian Shield of Canada, the crystalline platform of the Congo basin and so on—that are extracted many key minerals, including that lodestone of modern commercial geology, uranium ores. Welded on around these Archaean cores, however, we have in each continent successive belts of structures added by the phases of mountain-building we outlined above. In structural build, Europe thus shows the following elements (*see* Fig. 8).

(1) The core is the Archaean shield of Fenno-Scandia, whose ancient crystalline rocks are exposed over Sweden and Finland. Eastward, over the Russian plains, the shield is buried under little-disturbed sedimentary rocks.

(2) In middle Palaeozoic times was added the Caledonian mountain-belt of the north west. Although much of this chain has since sunk beneath the seas, fragments are exposed in Ireland, N. Wales, the Lake District, Scotland and Norway. In all these areas the S.W.-N.E. " grain " of the rock-structures reveals the alignment of the original folding. It is to be stressed, however, that the *present* hills and mountains are by no means the original mountains, which were worn away millions of years ago. What we see now are but the bevelled-off roots, re-elevated by more recent uplifts and dissected by rivers and glaciers into quite a new pattern of relief ; a pattern in which, however, the influence of the original tectonic " grain " can clearly be seen.

(3) The third element is the wedge-shaped area in western Europe formerly occupied by the Variscan mountains. The folding here ran west-to-east with various loops, but again we see no trace today of the original mountains. The present patchwork of uplands, valleys, and basins was created by fracturing and differential movement of the platform created by the planing away of the original mountains, under stresses from the south incurred when the fourth element, " Alpine " Europe, was added in Tertiary times. It was these relayed Alpine pressures also which thrust up most of our present British hills.

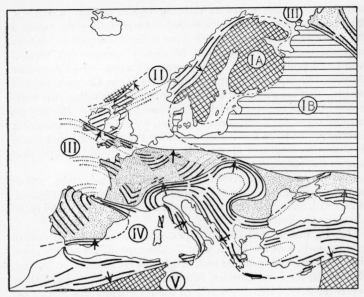

Fig. 8. *Structural divisions of Europe :*

(*IA*) *Baltic shield of exposed Archaean rocks ;*   (*IB*) *Russian platform.*
(*II*) *Caledonian orogenic belt. Mountain stumps today partly covered by later sedimentary rocks.*
(*III*) *Variscan (Hercynian) orogenic belt. Original structures exposed in uplifted blocks ; more recent sedimentary rocks cover the sunken basins between.*
(*IV*) *Alpine, or Alpid, orogenic belt.*
(*V*) *Archaean Shield of Africa.*
Heavy lines indicate the main axes of folding ; arrows the directions of overfolding.

The earlier Variscan structures, however, guided the movements and we can trace them underground in the faults and folds of our coalfields.

(4) In " Alpine " Europe, the fourth and most recently-added component, the sinuous folded chains of mountains and sunken intervening basins are still clearly apparent ; but although the pattern of high and low ground is entirely tectonic, the detailed shapes we now see bear little relation to those originally thrust up. Millions of years of steady denudation have worn more material off the original Alps than is contained in the

present visible mountains, and were it not for induced isostatic rising they would probably already be insignificant hills. While the structural lines and arrangement of rocks have clearly guided the sculpture, the actual forms we now see are thus essentially denudational. One element of the Alpine system, the Atlas Mountains, lies south of the Mediterranean, which itself seems to be a residual remnant of the great geosyncline in which accumulated the sedimentary rocks now built into the various mountain chains. South of the Atlas lies the enormous crystalline block of Africa, a continent almost entirely " shield ", with folded mountains welded on only in the extreme north (the Atlas) and the extreme south (the Cape Ranges). Africa thus presents a marked contrast in structure to Europe, a contrast reflected in their respective types of surface relief. In Europe we have diversity ; in Africa monotony. Who shall say how much this contrast has contributed to the very different history of man in the two continents ? The other continents are mostly intermediate between these two extremes, but all reveal that they have grown in much the same way.

Taking now the Alps as an example, we may glance rather more closely at what seems to have been the chain of events in the growth of a great mountain system. (Fig. 9). For an immense span of time, certainly from later Palaeozoic days, the great " Tethys " geosyncline grew and deepened between the nuclear continents of Europe and Africa. Into this were poured the land-wastes of both continents until the sediments reached great thickness. In due course, the two bounding crustal blocks began to move together and to crush between them the mass of sediments, the movement being mainly that of " Africa " northward. Under the pressure great folds arose in the floor of the geosyncline. Further pressure piled these up on top of one another ; volcanic activity and the transformation of the deeper-seated rocks by heat and pressure into metamorphic varieties accompanied the final compression ; and as its roots were thrust downwards the whole mass rose under isostatic compensation. As the pressure came mainly from the south there was a general overfolding northwards, the mountains being piled up on to the southern edge of the European block. This effect was most

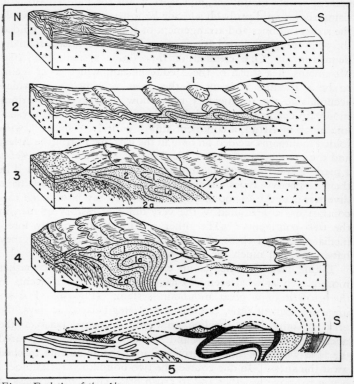

Fig. 9. Evolution of the Alps :

    (1) *Deep sedimentation in the 'Tethys' geosyncline between Variscan Europe and the African block.*

    (2) *Pressure from the south ; folded ridges are thrust up in the floor of the geosyncline.*

    (3-4) *The whole geosyncline is progressively squeezed out, the overfolded structures being piled up on the southern edge of Europe.*

    (5) *Diagrammatic section of the Western Alps today, showing structural relationships (modified after Argand).*

pronounced in the Alps themselves, where sediments originally laid down on the African shores of the geosyncline now build the outer Alps of northern Italy, while parts of those same sediments were carried right over the axis of the chain on great " nappes " and can now be found up in Switzerland (Fig. 9.(5)). Ultimately the movements ceased, and the area was left more or less as we now see it, save for subsequent denudation of the mountains, some later uplifts and depressions, and the foundering of some areas between fracture-lines. Analysis of other great mountain-chains shows that all evolved in somewhat similar fashion, with horizontal compression of a sedimentation-trough and final vertical uplift, though the compression was generally nothing like so severe as in the Alps. In some of the Tertiary chains movement has not yet ceased, and those around the western Pacific in particular remain zones of instability.

From this account there emerge the intriguing problems of how such extensive lateral movements in the earth's crust can have taken place, and what forces produced them apparently at long but fairly regular intervals in the earth's history. These are highly controversial matters upon which we can touch only lightly.

Broadly speaking, two possible sorts of mechanism can be envisaged.[1] The earth as a whole may have progressively decreased in size, its contraction causing its outer crust to wrinkle up after the manner of the skin of a drying apple ; or, if the earth has remained the same size, there must have been periodic relative movement between different portions of its crust. The stiff crustal blocks, in other words, must have altered their geographical positions, and in so doing pinched up the weaker geosynclinal belts between them.

The first of these two ideas was for long accepted as the cause of mountain-building. As we noted, the earth's interior was thought to have cooled steadily, and as it cooled it would shrink, and the crust would become too big for the shrunken interior. Periodically the resultant stresses would become too great for the strength of the crust to resist, and it would collapse inwards, the " slack " being taken up by crumpling of the weakest belts to build new mountains.

This idea is still strongly championed by some geologists, but there are various difficulties inherent in it, and recognition of the creation of new heat inside the earth by radio-activity

[1] *At least* two. New possible mechanisms for mountain-building continue to be suggested, but adequate discussion of them is beyond the scope of this book.

offered possibilities of alternative mechanisms. For many years geologists and other students of the earth's past had been puzzled to account for the presence, in widely separated areas, of fossils of species of life that only survived a short time before dying out. It is inherent in orthodox views of evolution that the same form of life is most unlikely to have evolved twice, in different areas, so when such geographically-distinct occurrences were found it had to be assumed that they were connected, and that the species had migrated from one place to the other. But as often great oceans lay between, just how land species could have done so was a mystery. The explanation first favoured was that at the periods in question land-connections existed spanning the oceans between the critical areas, and that the species migrated along these " land-bridges," which later foundered. This idea, however, contradicts the generally-accepted view that the deep oceans have never been land, and it is difficult to think of a mechanism for sinking land-bridges of this magnitude. An alternative explanation, ridiculed when it first appeared but now championed by many biologists, is that the continents themselves moved about the face of the earth in the remote past, and that the various areas where the puzzling species occur were, at the periods when the latter lived, united together into one compact land-mass. This theory, known as that of " Continental Drift ", was championed by the German climatologist A. Wegener, who marshalled an impressive array of evidence in its favour. Not only is there the evidence from the distributions—otherwise still inexplicable—of some past animal and plant species, but there is much geological evidence, and the intriguing matter of the " jigsaw " fit of the continents. There is a fairly close parallelism for instance between the opposed coasts of Africa and S. America. If S. America is brought across the Atlantic it fits tolerably well against Africa, the great projection of Brazil being accommodated in the Gulf of Guinea. By closing the rifted Red Sea, swinging India round, and bringing Australia across, a compact land-mass can be formed of all these elements, and we bring into plausible proximity the scattered traces of land glaciers dating from the Carboniferous period which are found in all these far-flung land-masses. Many features of strong geological simil-

arity are also to be found down the African and American coasts
which fit neatly together on this reconstruction (Fig. 10). Wegener went so far as to suggest that originally *all* the continental sial
crust was in one piece, but that through the operation of astro-

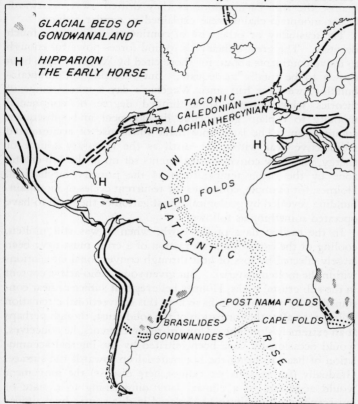

GLACIAL BEDS OF
GONDWANALAND

H *HIPPARION
THE EARLY HORSE*

TACONIC
CALEDONIAN
APPALACHIAN HERCYNIAN

H

MID
ALPID FOLDS
ATLANTIC

H

POST NAMA FOLDS
CAPE FOLDS
BRASILIDES
GONDWANIDES
RISE

Fig. 10. Geological similarities on the two coasts of the Atlantic (after Du Toit).

nomical forces this mass split up and its parts gradually drifted
away to their present positions. Wegener explained the folded
mountain-chains as a result of this continental movement. He
conceived that Europe drifted away north, but that in later times
Africa, also drifting north, overtook it and crushed up the

Alpine chains from the downwarped basin between. The great western " wall " of mountains down the entire length of the two American continents he viewed as resulting from the crumpling of the advance edge of these two continental masses against the stiff Pacific floor as they drifted away westward. Other mountain-chains were explained in similar fashion.

The feasibility or otherwise of continental drift is still much debated. The great difficulty is to find forces powerful enough to move continents about, for those cited by Wegener have been shown to be totally inadequate. But reverting to mountain-building, we have had since Wegener's day a whole range of theories which invoke some limited degree of continental mobility to explain geosyncline development and subsequent compression. The later ones make much use of accumulated radio-active heat within the earth as the necessary source of energy, and slow convectional currents set up in the sub-crustal zone by the rising temperatures as the primary mechanism. Holmes, for example, conceives the recurrent cycles of mountain-building revealed by geological investigation of the earth to have operated something as follows.

In the earliest days of the earth, when it was still molten, cooling of the exterior and formation of a crust must have been largely effected by loss of heat through convectional circulations within the molten material. But given some radio-active content in the sub-crustal rocks, Holmes believes that sufficient heat continued to be generated to have kept this convectional circulation going even after the formation of the solid crust, though perhaps at an extremely slow rate. Upward-rising currents, he conceives, would occasionally have been initiated by the internal accumulation of heat, to bring the hot material up towards the surface. Gradually (for reasons we cannot here discuss) the movement would accelerate to a climax, later diminishing to a state of quiescence again, only to be replaced in due course by a similar circulation elsewhere. Where the rising currents came up under the crust they would have to diverge and move apart laterally ; and the considerable frictional drag exerted on the base of the continental platforms Holmes believes may have been sufficient to move them about, and in places to stretch and fracture them to produce the great " fracture belts " we can trace on the surface. Where two currents met, however, material would be forced downwards, and would tend to drag down the crust with it ; and this, Holmes believes, is how geosynclinal " sags " originated, to deepen not because of the weight of sediment accumulating in them, but because of further down-drag on their floors. Eventually, however, as the currents quickened to their climax, the crustal slabs bounding such sags would get drawn together, and the whole mass of sediments in the geosyncline would be compressed. This compression would force its lower parts down as " roots ", whereupon isostatic balance would cause a general rising of the crumpled mass to elevate its upper parts into a new chain of mountains. The whole cycle, it must be emphasised, would take tens of millions of years to complete, and there are many complications that space will not·permit us to mention ; but the theory, though clearly still speculative, does offer a feasible and consistent explanation of the earth's perplexing habit of periodically rumpling its skin into new mountain-chains. We should be grateful for this habit ; for although we live soon after one of the greatest earth-storms of its history, and in consequence large tracts of its surface are still too rugged for our use, the earth would be a dull place indeed if we had come on it in its more normal habit of somnolent uniformity.

CHAPTER IV

VOLCANOES AND VOLCANIC SCENERY

THE types of earth-disturbance we have so far considered are not phenomena we can watch in action today. No little imagination, and considerable faith in the truth of geological principles, are necessary for us really to credit the earth with the instability we have described. When we turn to volcanic activity, however, things become a little easier, for here we have obvious evidence of the power locked up in the earth. Volcanoes are active in many parts of the earth today, and when they erupt things happen quickly. Entirely different in character as volcanoes appear from the inert structures of mountains, we find nevertheless that there are certain strong connections between them.

There are about 500 volcanoes on earth today that are either still active or are known to have been active in historic times, but there are several thousand more which although now quiet were clearly in action in the recent geological past. When the distribution of all the " recent " volcanoes is studied, certain significant relationships become at once apparent. Two-thirds of them are strung out along the great belt of folded mountains of recent origin that encircles the Pacific Ocean—the Pacific's " Girdle of Fire " as they have been called—and many of the remainder lie along the Eur-Asian stem of the Alpine mountain system from the Mediterranean to S.E. Asia. Other groups occur mainly in regions of other types of recent crustal disturbance, such as the fractured regions of the Middle East and East Africa, and the shattered and part-foundered " province " centred on Iceland, while the remainder are for the most part scattered over the basins of the great oceans. Clearly there is some general connection between volcanic activity and crustal disturbance, whether by the building of folded mountains or deep faulting, and this connection is underlined when we expand our view to cover more ancient volcanoes. For vulcanism is

44

no new phenomenon. It has existed since the earth's earliest days, and we find groupings of ancient and long-extinct volcanoes, now heavily denuded, associated with the tracts of older folded mountains like the Variscan and Caledonian. Even the rigid " shield " areas were not, in their earlier days, immune, for we find ancient rocks of volcanic origin mingled with their other highly-altered and worn-down materials. Only occasionally and sporadically, however, have these rigid continental blocks been troubled by more recent volcanic outbreak. Vulcanism is clearly associated with crustal dislocation and disturbance.

The reason for this broad correlation becomes apparent when the nature of volcanic activity is considered. To the layman the word volcano generally suggests a " smoking " conical mountain like Vesuvius, which periodically bursts into violent eruption to pour out molten rock, or lava. The ancients indeed conceived volcanoes to be " burning mountains ". In reality there is no true combustion. The " smoke " is mainly steam and fine dust, and the glow reflected in it at night comes from the incandescent molten lava welling up from below, which derives its heat from the earth's interior. Volcanic activity, in all its forms, is indeed caused simply by penetration of hot " magma " from the interior into the earth's outer crust, and its escape at the surface. The outer crust, as we noted, is built mainly of crystalline rocks, themselves believed to have originated in the main from an original molten state, but now cool and stiff for 20 or more miles down. At deeper levels, however, the material is still very hot, and liable to become liquid if the tremendous pressure on it is reduced. Such relief of pressure can occur if the crust is locally stretched and fractured, or thinned and crumpled, by the stresses involved in mountain-building, and in such regions it appears that the deep-seated magma is able to expand, liquefy, and force itself upward into the cavities and fissures resulting from the crustal dislocations. Its upward ascent may be assisted by its own heat which, it is believed, may in some cases melt out passages, but a further important mechanism assists the rising. Deep-seated magmas all contain steam and other gases held in solution, just as carbon dioxide is held dissolved in soda-water in a flask. On the relief of pressure these

gases bubble out, froth out the magma, and in their expansion
help a good deal to force it upwards. The violence of the uprush seems to depend largely on the amount of included gases,
but the nature of the passage also affects this matter. If open
passages exist right to the surface, and the ascending lava is
of gentle habit, it may flow out quietly ; but if the passage is
constricted or ends below the surface, and especially if the magma
contains much gas, pressure may build up until the obstruction
is blown away in violent explosions. Volcanoes which erupt
in periodic phases of explosive violence do so very often because
the magma coming up is viscous and readily solidifies and chokes
the outlet. Gas pressure then builds up below the seal until it
can blow out a new passage.

All types of volcanic activity which result in the effusion of
magma and other products at the surface are called " Extrusive ",
but there is a great deal of penetration of the crustal rocks which
does not break right through. This is called " Intrusive ", and
many intrusive bodies of cooled and solidified volcanic rock
generally surround and underlie surface volcanoes. We only
get to know about such intrusions either in mining operations,
or when later denudation has worn down the surface rocks
sufficiently deeply to expose them, but when they are revealed
they may affect the development of landscape features a good
deal. We will examine later the variety and surface effects of
volcanic intrusions, reviewing first the various types of surface
activity.

It will be clear from the foregoing account that the essential
feature of a volcano is the fissure, or pipe, through which the
deep-seated magma reaches the surface. The traditional conical
hills are incidentals, built by the volcano of the materials it throws
out, and many volcanoes do not build them at all. The type of
surface features that a volcano creates, and the general nature of
its activity, seem to depend upon the nature of its vent-hole, the
depth of the magma-reservoir, and the character of the magmatic
products that come up. We can classify volcanoes in these
terms.

The most obvious division is between " fissure " and
" central-vent " types. The former are rare among the earth's

present active volcanoes, though they occurred on a vast scale in the past, and some examples can be seen working today in Iceland. Here the passage is an extensive fracture or group of fractures. Lava may pour out all along such fractures, or may be confined to a string of points along them. Volcanoes of this type generally have little explosive activity, and their main product is a very fluid type of lava. Welling gently up, this often flows away for great distances and in solidifying covers large areas with superimposed thin sheets of rock. Successive flows thus tend to build up flattish plateaux, with a pseudo-stratified structure. The lava-plains of Iceland are of this nature, while examples can be seen in Skye and Mull ; but much more extensive ones occur in the western United States, in South America and in peninsular India. In the last-named an area of some 200,000 square miles of the Deccan is covered by vast lava-flows piled up to a thickness of 4,000 to 6,000 feet. Fissure-eruption of this type is thus associated with regions of extensive and deep-seated fracturing, and the type of structure that gives rise to " block-mountains " and " horsts ".

The " central-vent " type of volcano by contrast taps its magma reservoir through a single pipe or hole, and the products of its activity are spread out around this hole. It is this sort of volcano that builds conical mountains, and the majority of the earth's present active volcanoes are of this type. Some occur apparently at random, but the majority are arranged in lines, like those strung along the Japanese and East Indian island arcs, and appear to overlie deep-seated linear fractures or magma reservoirs of long and narrow shape incorporated into the roots of the mountains. Central-vent volcanoes, however, vary a great deal in surface form and mode of activity. A single explosive eruption may leave just a clean-punched hole ringed round with a little debris and the upturned edges of the local rock. The " Maare " of the Eifel region of north-west Germany are of this type. (Fig. 11 C.) Repeated or continued eruption, however, can build up large surface forms. Such mountains as Etna and Fuji-yama are built entirely of the materials thrown out of their central vents. In this type of activity a large proportion of the ejected material consists of finely-pulverised solid frag-

ments called "pyroclasts"—dust, so-called volcanic ash, and
larger solid fragments of lava.   This fragmental material, thrown
high into the air, falls back to ground to accumulate as an "ash-
cone".   If such cones grow large, however, they generally

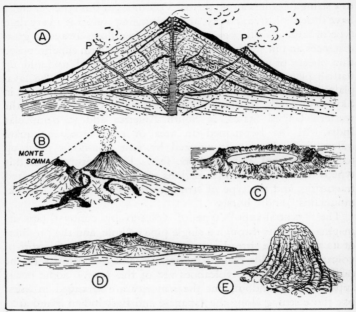

Fig. 11. *Types of Volcanoes:*
    (*A*) *Structure of a composite cone (after A. Geikie).*
    (*B*) *Caldera and inner cone of Vesuvius (dotted line shows the original profile).*
    (*C*) " *Maar* ", *or explosion ring.*
    (*D*) *Low-angle basalt cone, or* " *shield* ".
    (*E*) *Steep-sided dome of acid lava (Reunion).*
    (*In sketch* (*A*), *letter* P *indicates parasitic cone*).

become of composite structure due to outpouring of liquid lava
between the more explosive eruptions. (Fig. 11 A). Quite
frequently in such volcanoes, between the main phases of eruption
the liquid lava solidifies in the central pipe, and in the next phase
of activity a path is forced out sideways.   In this way "para-

sitic " craters and cones may grow on the sides of the main construction. Sometimes the pressure beneath the choked vent builds up to such a point that the whole top of the original structure is blown off in a tremendous explosive episode, leaving a wide basin rimmed with the shattered flanks of the original cone. Such a great cavity is called a " caldera ". Vesuvius blew its head off in this way in the great eruption that overwhelmed Pompeii and Herculaneum in A.D. 79, leaving the outer ridge called Monte Somma (Fig. 11 B.). The present active cone has grown since that date inside the caldera. Most great calderas, however, seem to be due only in part to this blowing to bits of the original head. Crater Lake, Oregon, occupies a huge caldera about 6 miles across which must originally have been surmounted by a cone some 12,000 feet high which nourished glaciers (the grooves cut by these glaciers can be seen scoring the outer flanks of the caldera). It is thought that this cone sank in and was engulfed by a great uprising of fluid magma. A mighty explosive cataclysm was experienced in 1883 when the volcanic island of Krakatoa (Dutch E. Indies) virtually disappeared. The historic island was composed of pieces of an earlier caldera, added to by newer cones. It had shown no signs of activity for two centuries until in August 1883 preliminary eruptions culminated in two days of stupendous explosions during which most of the island disappeared. Glowing particles were thrown up to a height of 50 miles, and the greatest explosion was heard in Australia, 3,000 miles away. Although most of the island seems to have been engulfed, vast quantities of pulverised material were thrown into the air, and some of the dust travelled several times round the earth before coming to rest, causing spectacular sunset effects. Such volcanic dust thrown out by explosive eruptions contributes a good deal to the normal dust content of the earth's atmosphere, and is a main constituent of the material that settles to the floors of the deep oceans, far beyond the limits reached by land derived mud.

But all central-vent volcanoes do not erupt explosively. Some behave quietly like the fissure volcanoes, pouring out very fluid lavas which flow long distances. Since the emission is from a central point these lavas build up wide and gently-sloping lava domes, and the volcanoes are accordingly called "shield" volcanoes (Fig. 11 D). The best-known examples are in the Hawaiian Islands. The giant Mauna Loa, which rises from the ocean depths, is 300 miles across at its base, and rises all of 30,000 feet from the ocean floor. Its summit comprises the main island of Hawaii, rising 13,670 feet above sea-level. At the top is a great crater 1½ miles across, but this shows no current activity. Kilauea, a subsidiary centre, has however an open crater in the floor of its summit caldera full of incandescent lava which surges about, moves up and down in the pipe, and sometimes throws up lava fountains. The lavas, when they spill over, run like water for long distances, sometimes cascading into the sea. In some central-vent volcanoes, however, the lava is stiff and pasty. As they do not flow freely, such lavas tend to build up narrower and steeper-sided domes (Fig. 11 E). Good examples are to be seen among the extinct volcanoes of the Auvergne in central France. While there is a general difference between fissure and central-vent types of volcanoes in behaviour, it is thus clear that the central-vent type are very variable. The causes of variation in their habits seem to relate to the depth of their magma-supply and its chemical nature.

The liquid magma that is brought up by volcanoes solidifies on cooling to become one or other of the igneous rocks. Many hundreds of different varieties of igneous rocks are recognised by geologists, differentiated by variation in their mineral and chemical composition, and in their crystalline texture. Lavas, cooling rapidly on the surface, generally develop only very small crystals. In basalt, the most abundant type, the crystals are hardly visible, and in obsidian the whole rock solidifies as a sort of natural glass. The material solidifying in the deeper necks of volcanic pipes, and in underground intrusions, cools more slowly and generally shows a better-developed crystalline structure, while the largest crystals generally occur in the deepest "plutonic" varieties, rocks like granite[1] and gabbro. Crystal-texture is thus a useful guide to the original habitat of any igneous rock,

[1] Granite has been generally accepted as the typical plutonic igneous rock, but recent studies have shown that many granites are probably of metamorphic origin.

and helps in its classification; but the important differences are those of mineral and chemical composition. Nearly all igneous rocks contain some percentage of free quartz (silica), and according to the percentage are classed as Acid, Intermediate, Basic, and Ultra-Basic. The acid varieties, rich in silica, are lighter than the basic, which are richer in heavy metallic minerals, and are generally darker in colour. Now we saw that the continental blocks are built mainly of the lighter Sial type of rocks. So far as these are igneous, they are of the Acid, silica-rich group. The Sima under the oceans, and below the continents, is Basic, and seems to approximate to the composition of Basalt—the commonest basic lava. Examining the lavas emitted by volcanoes, we find that those situated in the great ocean basins almost all emit only basic lavas. Continental volcanoes emit all types; but it is possible that those which emit basaltic lavas are deep-seated, and draw their material from the deep Sima layer. They therefore behave like the oceanic volcanoes. The central-vent types of explosive habit emit intermediate and acid lavas, which are generally viscous, and contain much water and other gases. It seems reasonable to suppose that they tap magma reservoirs located within the Sial blocks, into which much of the silica-rich continental material has been melted. Other factors may influence the behaviour of volcanoes, but the magma-nature seems to be the most important.

Whatever the pattern of its activity, every volcano only persists in full vigour for a finite period, and eventually goes through stages of decadence to become extinct. But after violent activity has ceased much heat may still be given off from the cooling magma below, and various minor phenomena based on this heat are to be found in declining volcanic areas. " Fumaroles ", " Solfataras " and " Mofettes " are names given to vents which emit volatile gases of sulphur, borax, and other elements, carbon dioxide, and steam. Ground water coming in contact with the heated rocks may emerge as hot springs. So-called " mud-volcanoes " occur where such water mingles with the decayed soft tuffs and ash deposits, to well up as hot liquid mud. The most spectacular of such phenomena are, however, " Geysers ", from which water heated to high tem-

C

peratures is periodically thrown high into the air. The operating mechanism is generally slow accumulation of super-heated steam in enclosed cavities which periodically reaches a critical pressure. Some geysers erupt with great regularity, like " Old Faithful " in Yellowstone Park, U.S.A., while in the Great Geyser of Iceland the water rises 200 feet. As geyser and hot spring water is generally rich in dissolved silica, beautiful terraces are often built by deposition of this silica as the water evaporates. The famous white terraces of Rotomahana in New Zealand were unfortunately destroyed by volcanic eruption in 1886, but many fine examples remain in New Zealand and Yellowstone Park.

We must now turn from the mechanism of volcanoes to their effects on scenery. These are two-fold. There are first the direct surface effects produced by the volcanic activity itself, and secondly the later effects due to denudation acting on the extruded and intruded igneous rocks. Most striking in the former category are the great ash and lava cones built up around some central vents, which include some of the earth's largest isolated mountain peaks. Etna is the largest of such structures in Europe ; Kilimanjaro, Mt. Kenya, and Mts. Elgon and Meru are outstanding examples in Africa. In the Middle East Mt. Ararat is a volcanic peak, as is Mt. Elbruz which dominates the Caucasus. Around the Pacific great volcanic peaks are too numerous to list, including giants like Chimborazo and Cotapaxi in the Andes, and Popocatapetl in Mexico. Most of the peaks in the mountainous island arcs of the western Pacific are volcanoes, as are all the " high " islands in the open Pacific (as distinct from the " low " coral islands). Isolated island groups in the Atlantic and Indian Oceans are also mostly of volcanic origin, such as Ascension, St. Helena, and Reunion. Modern oceanographical research has also revealed an unsuspected wealth of volcanic constructions on the ocean floors, for it must be remembered that a great deal of volcanic activity occurs underwater.

Calderas and craters produce distinctive ring-shaped hollows, and when the activity ceases these commonly fill with water to produce crater-lakes. Much more important, however, are the great basaltic plateaux mentioned earlier. They have completely masked the pre-existing topography in the areas they over-whelmed.   Built up of flattish sheets, they tend to produce rather monotonous landscapes, but often broken by distinctive stepped edges.   The internal contraction set up by cooling frequently

Fig. 12. *Volcanic scenery after denudation:*
    (A) Stepped outlines of plateau-basalt country (McLeod's Tables, Skye).
    (B) Columnar jointing in basalt (Fingal's Cave, Staffa).
    (C) Columnar structure in an eroded volcanic neck (The Devil's Tower, Wyoming,
       U.S.A.).
    (D) Volcanic necks and stumps in the town of Le Puy, France.

produces in such lava-flows a distinctive structure of vertical joints, which occasionally divide up the whole mass into stacked hexagonal columns.   This structure is beautifully displayed in the great basalt-flows that cover Antrim as in the Giant's Cause-way, and in the related Fingal's Cave on Staffa (Fig. 12 B.)

This vertical jointing helps to produce the tabular stepped outlines
so characteristic of plateaux-basalt scenery. It can be seen to
advantage in both Antrim and the Inner Hebrides, as for instance
in northern Skye (Fig. 12 A).

We are now turning from the original constructional effects of
vulcanism to compound effects produced by weathering and
erosion acting on the volcanic rocks. The bulk of the earth's
" volcanic landscapes " come under this heading, for denudation
sets to work to modify volcanic structures even as they are
building, and when vulcanism ceases, it takes over all stages of
their further evolution. The forms that emerge eventually lose
all resemblance to the original structures, for the factors governing their shapes become the disposition and relative degrees of
resistance of the different bodies of igneous rock. Some
volcanic products, like the less consolidated ash deposits, are soft
and rapidly erode away, but the majority of lavas and injected
rocks are hard and tough, withstanding well mechanical wear and
tear, though more susceptible to chemical decay. As erosion
proceeds, the more resistant rocks therefore tend to be left
standing out in bold relief. The effects can be seen well displayed in Skye, or Mull, for the Inner Hebrides were the centre
of great volcanic activity in Tertiary times. In southern Skye
the Red Hills are carved out of granite which, although resistant,
crumbles under weathering, and produces rounded forms. The
Cuillins, by contrast, are carved out of gabbro, a dark, very
tough, and coarsely-crystalline plutonic rock, the basic equivalent
of the acid granite. Less easily decayed, it produces a much
more craggy and jagged type of scenery. Another well-known
example of volcanic landforms developed by differential denudation is afforded by the peculiar domes and necks of rock around
which is built the town of Le Puy, in central France (Fig. 12 D).

Scotland, however, can again show features of this type quite
as fine. The curious isolated dome-like hills of Ailsa Craig, the
Bass Rock, North Berwick Law, Traprain Law, Dumbarton Rock,
Largo Law and many others are all the " necks " of ancient
volcanoes, in which the solidified lava has resisted denudation
better than the surrounding country rock and so stands out as a
distinctive mound (Fig. 13). Other distinctive hills in central

Scotland that owe their existence in part to past vulcanism are the Ochils and Sidlaws, the Campsie Fells, the Eildon Hills near Melrose, and, most familiar of all, Arthur's Seat and the Castle Rock at Edinburgh. The volcanic activity responsible for all these

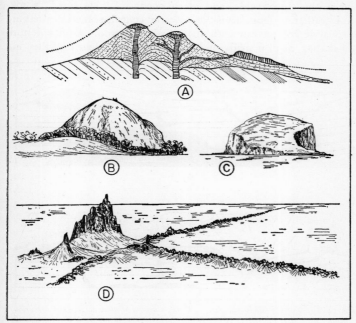

Fig. 13. Volcanic scenery after denudation :
(A) Largo Law, Fifeshire, the denuded stump of a volcano
(B) North Berwick Law, and,
(C) the Bass Rock, both volcanic necks.
(D) Ship Rock, New Mexico, a heavily eroded volcanic neck in arid country, with several radiating dykes.

features was, however, much earlier than that of the Hebrides. It dates back to Carboniferous times, when our coalfields were being formed.

We have by no means exhausted the variety of volcanic scenery. There remain the features resulting from the exposure by denudation of intrusive structures originally buried (Fig. 14). Among the principal types of igneous intrusions to be noted are *dykes*, which are wall-like structures formed by lava consolidating in vertical cracks. They generally cut indiscriminately across the countryside, and often occur in " swarms ", sometimes radiating from a visible volcanic centre, sometimes having no visible connection with an exposed volcano. Under denudation they may, if made of rock less resistant than that they cut

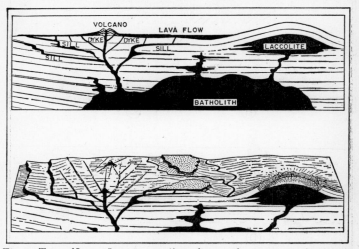

Fig. 14. *Types of Igneous Intrusions.* *Above, diagram of main varieties of intrusions ;* *below, their possible effects on the landscape after long denudation.*

through, be carved down into wide gullies ; or if more resistant they may stand out as " walls ". A famous example of upstanding dykes radiating from a weathered volcanic neck is that of Ship Rock in New Mexico (Fig. 13 D.)

Sills are sheets of igneous rock injected between the bedding-planes of sedimentary strata, which often lie nearly horizontal or at gentle inclinations. Where they outcrop they frequently produce marked topographic effects, if more resistant than the rocks around them. The great Whin Sill of northern England, a thick sheet of dolerite injected between the sandstones, lime-

stones, and shales of the northern Pennines, is exposed in places
from upper Teesdale to the Farne Islands.   North of the Tyne
its tilted edge outcrops to form the magnificent cliffs along the
top of which the Romans shrewdly sited Hadrian's Wall.   In

*Fig. 15. Outcrops of the Whin Sill.   Above, scarp north of the Tyne (the Roman
Wall runs along the crest) ; below, High Cup Nick, upper Teesdale.*

upper Teesdale it forms the cliff around the head of High Cup
Nick, and the great ledges over which the Tees tumbles at High
Force and Cauldron Snout.   Its tough resistant character is
emphasised by the extensive use made of it for road-metal (Fig. 15).

Dykes and sills are offshoots of the upper and middle levels of vulcanism. Associated with them are sometimes found larger bodies of consolidated rock called *Laccolites* and *Lopoliths* which, when exposed, give more extensive patches of igneous rock in the landscape. Deeper still, in the original activity, there were the great reservoirs of magma occupying vast chasms perhaps in part melted out by the magmatic heat. The magma solidifying in such great reservoirs formed large bodies called *Batholiths*, and in the older deeply-denuded regions of folded mountains we frequently find the upper portions of such batholiths now exposed among the worn-down mountain roots. Typically built of granite, they are often of immense dimensions and unknown depth. Most of the extensive patches of granite we find in the older hilly regions of Britain are probably the exposed tops of batholiths ; Dartmoor and Bodmin Moor ; the Criffel, Cairnsmore of Fleet, and Loch Doon in S.W. Scotland ; and many large tracts in the Highlands such as that of the Cairngorms. Similar extensive and often elongated exposures of granite batholiths are to be found in the tracts of worn-down Variscan mountains of western Europe (for instance in Brittany), in the ancient mountains of Norway, and equally in the heart of the Alps, Rocky Mts., and other branches of the Tertiary mountain-systems. The topographic features associated with these enormous deep-seated intrusions vary with the nature of their rock and the balance of denudational processes working on them. At lower altitudes large exposures of granite such as Dartmoor typically give rounded hill-forms, because though hard the rock is somewhat readily rotted by chemical attack—a subject we shall pursue in the next chapter. At high altitudes, however, where frost action is powerful, granite may be cut into sharp jagged ridges and peaks, although even here it seldom gives the really sharp " needles " and crests characteristic of some of the tougher and finer-grained igneous rocks.

Although there are still some doubts about the origins and significance of batholiths, their distribution clearly suggests a further point of correlation between the subjects of this chapter and the last. Presumably many of the present active volcanoes are grouped along linear magma-reservoirs in the roots of the folded mountains along which they are strung.   In due course, these will consolidate, and after aeons of future denudation, their tops may become exposed as future granite patches in the stumps of the mountain-chains.   Conversely, the exposed batholiths in the Scottish Highlands may perhaps have fed ancient volcanoes that existed soon after the Caledonian mountains were raised, but of which every trace has long since been swept away together with the mountains themselves.   This verges on to controversial ground, and indeed the simplified account given in this chapter must not lead the reader to imagine that we know all about volcanoes.   Many points about them are still unsolved mysteries.

CHAPTER V

THE AGENCIES OF LANDSCAPE SCULPTURE

IN the opening chapter the reader was invited to imagine the earth's surface as a sort of battlefield upon which two opposed sets of processes have worked through the long ages of geological time to produce the features we see today. One set of those processes, those based on forces within the earth, we have now reviewed. Whether by uplift and depression, by crumpling, by fracture, or by volcanic disturbance, these have worked in somewhat spasmodic fashion to dislevel the surface, and to create new relief. Their operations, however, have only served to stimulate to more vigorous action the external processes of denudation which strive ceaselessly to smooth out the surface by wearing away the higher areas and spreading the residues in the hollows. Viewing the whole history of the earth's surface we can thus conceive each major phase of earth-activity as re-setting the stage and thereby starting off with maximum vigour a new cycle of denudational attack. In its earlier phases, as we shall see, this carves up the tectonic relief into a myriad new forms, ·hereby vastly increasing the surface diversity ; but later on, by its concentrated attack upon the higher ground, it begins to reduce the whole surface to a more uniform and subdued condition. We live in a geological era but little after the climax of an outstanding period of earth-activity. Tectonic relief, in the form of linear chains of folded mountains, faulted troughs, and volcanic constructions, is still prominent over the earth, and for that very reason denudation is extremely active. Already it has bitten deeply into the Alpine mountain chains, and has set its seal upon the landscape patterns over the whole earth. We turn now, therefore, to study the operations of this world-wide process of external sculpture in some detail. The distinctive part played in it by the sea we can leave aside for examination later, treating here the overall attack of the atmosphere and the land-waters it feeds. This " sub-aerial " phase of denudation is, however, itself a compound process, made up of the combined operations of many different agencies. To study it we have to separate out the various strands, but it must be stressed that this division is quite artificial. In nature all the processes go on together, in varying proportions under different controlling circumstances, and all are in some degree inter-dependent.

In principle, we can divide up the work of sub-aerial denud-ation into four phases, some of which we mentioned earlier. *Weathering* is the static attack of the atmosphere upon rocks which decomposes them and breaks them up. *Transport* covers the removal of the resultant debris. *Erosion* is the active wearing away of land-surfaces by moving agencies like rivers, wind, and waves ; while *Deposition* (sometimes considered a distinct process from denudation) covers the dumping of the residues of land-destruction in sheltered locations to build new rocks. All phases may well be going on together in a given locality, but on land deposition is, on the whole, a subordinate process and often only temporary. On the higher areas, in particular, destruction is the dominant theme. Many conditions govern the nature of denudation, control its rate, and guide its results, the most important being the nature of the local climate, the nature of the relief being worked on, and the character and disposition of the rocks that build the relief. We will note the effects of these " variables " as we go along.

Weathering. The processes that cause the disintegration and decay of rocks can be divided in principle into mechanical and chemical, although in practice both go on together and react on one another. Taking the mechanical aspect first, temperature changes demand close attention. Simple changes of temperature, as between day and night, set up in rocks stresses which can con-tribute much to their weakening and crumbling. In a rock like granite, for instance, the component mineral crystals are of several different types which expand and contract by different amounts under changes of temperature. The stresses set up, in time, may be sufficient to break the firm bond between the crystals. On a larger scale, such stresses may split fragments, or even large masses, off the parent rock. The effects are seen best in regions like the great deserts, where much bare rock is exposed, and extreme changes of temperature occur. The ground is there often littered with shattered rock fragments. In the tropics, exposed blocks of rock, especially the coarsely-crystalline igneous rocks

Fig. 16. *Weathering* :
  (*A*) *Enormous boulders produced by exfoliation-weathering of granite, J. Uweinat, Libyan Desert (after photo by W. B. K. Shaw).*
  (*B*) *The screes, Wastwater, a product mainly of frost-weathering.*

like granite, often develop into rounded boulders by the peeling off of thin curved surface sheets, a process called " exfoliation " (Fig. 16 A). A distinct " onion-structure " may develop by this process, which has been widely attributed to temperature-changes rending away the heated and expanded surface layers from the cooler interior (for rocks are poor conductors of heat.) Other explanations are, however, possible. Cold rain falling on heated rocks may also cause splitting and cracking.

Much more potent than direct temperature-change shattering are, however, the indirect effects through the medium of freezing water. All rocks contain cracks, pore-spaces, and fissures, in particular the systems of cracks we noted earlier called " joints ". Rain-water penetrates into such cracks and, if it freezes, expands by one-ninth of its volume. The bursting stresses set up are tremendous, as we all know from the way they burst our water-pipes. On exposed rock-faces in nature, great slabs and blocks may be prised off by this means. Successive freezings will lever such blocks away from a cliff-face until they fall to accumu-late as the " scree " which lines the foot of almost all steep cliffs. The Great Screes of Wastwater in the Lake District were mainly built in this way (Fig. 16 B). Even after the blocks have fallen the action continues, breaking them up into smaller and smaller fragments. In the garden frost action is valuable in breaking up hard clods to produce fine loose soil, which it does by prising the soil particles apart through expansion of the water-films between them. In nature, frost is a primary agency of rock-destruction over much of the earth. In high mountains particularly it is the main factor producing steep cliffs, knife-edge ridges, and sharp pinnacles, by progressive levering away of rock-fragments from exposed faces. (*See* Chap. x).

The chemical processes involved in weathering are more complex, and although less obvious, are in total of much greater importance. To be effective, they nearly all require the presence of water, and act most vigorously at high temperatures. All rainwater contains small quantities of dissolved atmospheric gases, particularly oxygen and carbon dioxide. The latter, dissolved in water, forms a weak acid, and occasionally traces of other acids such as nitric are present (nitric acid is formed in small quantity during thunderstorms). Once on the ground, rainwater may also pick up humic acids formed by decaying vegetation, and penetrating into the rocks this acidulated water sets up slow chemical decay of the rock minerals. The processes are well illustrated by considering what happens to granite, apparently so strong and durable. Granite is composed in the main of mixed crystals of quartz, pinkish or grey felspars, and specks of black mica. The quartz crystals are little affected, but the felspars and micas are readily attacked, and break down through a sequence of chemical changes to yield soluble salts like lime, potash, and soda (which are washed out in solution by rain), and an insoluble residue of hydrated aluminium silicates—which are simply particles of clay. Left without support, the quartz crystals fall away to become sand, while the soft clay particles are washed out into streams and rivers. This chemical " rotting " and destruction of granite can be seen at work on Dartmoor or any other granite area. The tors on Dartmoor are surrounded with loose coarse sand, while the streams are choked with the clays. In the Tropics, where the process goes on at its fastest, granite surfaces can be found so deeply rotted that a spade can be pushed into the rock without resistance. Apart from decomposing the rock, these chemical changes alter the volume of its minerals, so that secondary mechanical stresses are also set up. " Exfoliation " of rocks, which we earlier mentioned, is attributed by some authorities to volumetric expansion of the rocks affected under slow chemical decay.

The other igneous rocks are attacked in much the same way as granite, the metallic minerals of the basic varieties being hydrated and oxidised. Exposed basalt, for instance, nearly always has a dark-brown weathered skin stained by the rusting of its iron minerals. The sedimentary rocks are mostly less liable to chemical attack, for they are built in the main of the inert residues left by the destruction of earlier rocks. But in a sandstone the bonding cement of lime or an iron salt may be dissolved out again leaving the sand grains loose to roll and blow away, while limestones, because of their chemical nature, are susceptible to a special kind of chemical attack. Limestones are composed largely of lime, either chemically precipitated or in the form of shells and skeletons of marine organisms which accumulated on the floors of the seas in which they grew. Water containing carbon dioxide reacts with this calcium carbonate, slowly transforming it to calcium bicarbonate which is removed in solution. It is this solvent reaction which is responsible for the topographic pecularities of limestone country (*see* Chap. VIII). The insoluble clay particles in such limestones are left on the surface during the gradual solution of the rock, and accumulate as a variety of clay deposits, like the " Terra Rossa " so common on limestone country round the Mediterranean.

The balance and rates of weathering processes in any area are governed mainly by the nature of the rocks, and the external conditions of climate. In hot wet regions chemical processes are most active. In the deserts lack of water slows them down, as do the low temperatures of the Polar regions. In both the latter types of climate, however, mechanical weathering proceeds vigorously. The products of weathering are generally continuously and almost completely removed from high steep ground, so that nothing impedes further attack on the bedrock ; but on gentler relief the rate of removal may be equalled or even exceeded by the rate of formation. On such country therefore the bedrock is generally covered by a surface " skin " of weathered material. Geologically such formations are termed " residual ", and they are the raw materials of soils, those vitally important compound mineral and organic substances upon which we, in company with all forms of land life, depend for our food supplies. We cannot treat soils effectively within the small compass of this book, but we will touch on them again later. Here it is appropriate to stress that although the form of vegetation cover, and the multiple forms of organic life that exists within them, contribute greatly to the variety of soils, their basic material is derived by weathering from the rocks below them, and the balance of weathering processes, itself largely controlled by climatic conditions, determines to large degree their overall character. Thus in the Tropics, where deep weathering is the rule, and where wet seasons alternate with dry seasons, a common residual deposit is *laterite*. Evaporation in the dry season draws ground water upwards and dissolved minerals are deposited near the surface and oxidised; but the heavy summer rains wash out the soluble salts and in time much of the silica so that there accumulates a surface layer of insoluble aluminous hydroxides and oxidised iron compounds. These tend to cake into impervious crusts, and the whole formation becomes infertile and useless for agriculture. *Bauxite,* sometimes an important source of aluminium ore, is another variety of surface residual deposit developed from different types of parent rock under rather different climatic conditions. But we must return to weathering itself. Mention of soils reminds us that organic agencies also contribute to the breakup of rocks. Tree-roots work down into crevices and open up new cracks ; rodents burrow into soft formations and loosen their particles for the wind to blow them away ; while many small plants like lichens and fungi abstract mineral salts from rocks, and by their decay contribute acids to ground-waters. On the other hand vegetation also exercises an important stabilising and binding influence on the mantle of weathered material, helping to hold it in place against the agencies of transport (*see* Chap. XVI). We can conveniently treat the movement of weathered material, and the erosion carried out by the agencies responsible for that movement, together.

Transport and Erosion. The main agencies which remove the residues of weathering, and in their movements also cut into and wear away the ground surface, are gravity alone; wind; and water, snow and ice moving under gravity. Direct gravitational movements operate most obviously on steep slopes and cliffs, from which loosened fragments fall, roll, or slide to accumulate where the gradient lessens. But mass-movements of material under gravity, both sudden and gradual, also frequently occur. Avalanches of unstable rock-fragments, somewhat akin to snow-avalanches, sometimes occur in mountainous areas like the Himalayas, and have been known to block river-valleys, ponding back the water until it bursts through the barrier to cause disastrous floods. Material apparently quite stable, but bounded by steep slopes or cliffs, will occasionally slip or slump downwards as a landslide. Small movements of this sort are responsible for the little parallel steps or terraces that are often to be seen on the steep grassy slopes of moorland valleys, which can easily be mistaken for sheep-tracks. Larger-scale movements may shift thousands of tons of material, whether through the undercutting of a sea-cliff, the over-deepening of a valley, or by lubrication of water along favourable underground structures. *Slumping* occurs when the ground slides in a series of slices separated by curved fracture-planes, the movement being rotational, while larger *landslides* are generally caused by water-lubrication in unstable structures, as when a mass of limestone overlies slippery shales with the bedding-planes dipping towards a cliff or steep slope (Fig. 17).

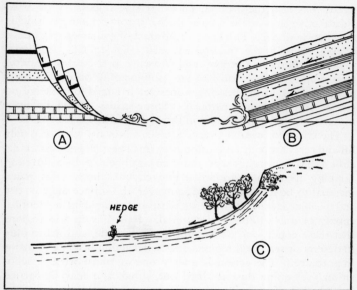

Fig. 17. *Gravity-movements :*
   (*A*) *Slumping in a sea-cliff.*
   (*B*) *Structure conducive to landslides.*
   (*C*) *Soil-creep on a slope, shown by bending of trees and piling up of soil against hedges.*

Less spectacular than such large-scale sudden movements, but in total much more important, is however the slow *creep* of soils and loose surface materials downhill, which takes place even on the gentlest slopes.   Any disturbance of the loose particles, by rain-beat, soil-wash, ploughing, or the feet of men and animals causes a slight downhill movement which, over centuries of time produces marked effects on the landscape.   It is this movement that is largely responsible for the smooth flowing curves so characteristic of our hill and valley scenery, the weathered material creeping slowly down from the hills and tailing out into the valleys. The reality of this movement can be gauged from the silent evidence of tilted fences, and the outward curve of tree-trunks near the ground, on valley side slopes. Very often a distinctive step can be seen at the hedgerow dividing two fields on a gentle slope. This is also a product of soil-creep, the hedge having held up the moving material (Fig. 17 C). In Arctic regions, alternate freezing and thawing assists this gravity-movement. Actual soil-flowage (solifluction) occurs in thaw periods, and by frost-heaving stones get arranged into intriguing stripes and polygonal patterns. Stone-stripes caused by frost movement can even be seen on the higher Lake District Hills.

The effects of *wind* are very variable. Normal winds can only lift and carry away in suspension very small particles of dust grade, although they can shift sand and even small pebbles by rolling and hopping movements in favourable circumstances. For much material to be moved by wind, however, the surface must be dry and friable, lacking in obstructions, and providing a plentiful supply of finely pulverised material. It is only in arid regions that these conditions are found on a large scale, and hence only in deserts or semi-arid regions does wind action become of major importance. The action is mainly one of transport and deposition. The fine dust is sifted out, lifted, and may be carried long distances before it settles again in regions of damper climate, calmer air, and vegetation which retards the wind-speed near the ground. Such dust is " exported " in vast quantities from the great desert regions. Much eventually drops into the seas and oceans, but in some regions like north China there has been consistent deposition of it on land to build distinctive fine-grained deposits called *loess*. Very porous, but exceedingly fertile (because the valuable plant-food salts have not been removed by water-solution, as is often the case in water-deposited formations), this loess generally forms first-class agricultural land. A belt of it runs across central Europe, built by winds sifting out dust from material washed out of the residues dumped from melting ice at the time when great ice-sheets covered

northern Europe (*See* Chap. X).   Wind, however, can only move
the coarser sand-grades of rock waste limited distances, for damp
ground and vegetation hold them up.   The bulk of the sand
in deserts thus stays within their confines, to be blown about
and built into dunes.   In damper regions, sand-blowing is
mainly confined to the sea-shores where wide expanses of sand
are exposed and dry out at low tide.   Behind such tracts, where
onshore winds prevail, we generally find coastal sand-dunes,
prevented by ground-relief and vegetation from migrating
inland.   The *erosive* action of wind is, in most areas, of minor
importance, for wind alone is incapable of wearing away hard
rock.   Only when it drives considerable quantities of sand against
protruding rocks can it effect much wear and tear, and such
action is mainly confined to the great deserts.   Wind has, however, one quality as an agent of landscape sculpture which is
almost unique.   It can carry material uphill, and so can hollow
out enclosed depressions.   We will examine more fully the
effects of wind in shaping the landscape when we turn to review
desert regions in Chapter ix.

Dismissing wind rather briefly then, we may also defer for later
consideration the agencies of snow and ice, for they operate
effectively over even more restricted areas of the earth than does
wind—the Polar regions, and the higher mountain tracts where
snow lies all the year, and considerable bodies of ice thus get a
chance to form.   We may just note in passing, however, that at
several periods in the geological past permanent snow and ice
have covered much greater areas of the earth than they do today,
one such major phase of " glaciation " having occurred quite
recently by physiographic standards.   Over wide areas now
enjoying genial climate the imprint of ice-denudation is still very
apparent, so that its study has a wider importance than might at
first appear.   Over most of the earth today, however, *running
water* is by far the most important agency engaged in moving
the residues of weathering and sculpturing the land-surfaces, and
we will be concerned for the next two chapters almost entirely
with its operations.   The source of supply of water on the land-
surface is everywhere ultimately precipitation from the atmosphere, whether by rain, or snow, and transporting and erosional

work is done at every stage from the original falling to earth to the time the water runs out of river-estuaries into the sea.

The direct beating of *rainfall* on the ground has effects we are inclined to overlook.   Gardeners will know that it can compact the soil-surface quite effectively, but in favourable conditions it can carve up the ground into distinctive forms.   In regions normally rather dry, but subject to sudden heavy rainstorms—like some of the lands round the Mediterranean—peculiar " gash-erosion " often occurs in patches of soft friable rocks in hilly country.   A maze of deep, V-sectioned gullies develops, these gullies growing to dissect the ground into isolated pinnacles and knife-edge ridges.   This type of surface may become almost impassable.   In the western United States, where it is strongly developed in some areas, it is expressively called " badlands ".   Cutting into a soft clay containing scattered large boulders (such as the " boulder-clay " left by past glaciers (*See* Chap. X), this rain-erosion may create curious earth-pillars on top of which large boulders are perched.   The boulders preserve the columns of soft earthy material below from destruction until they topple off, when the columns rapidly crumble away (Fig. 18 A).

Fig. 18.

   (*A*) *Rain-cut gullies and earth pillars* ("*demoiselles* "), *Durance valley, Dauphiné, S. France.*

   (B) *Pot-holes cut in a rocky stream-bed.*

Once on the ground, rainwater, or that released from melting snow, begins to move under gravity. We shall study later how different factors govern the percentage of rainfall that is free so to move, but assuming that there is some surface " runoff ", it will greatly assist the movement of weathered residues down the slopes. Soluble salts will be taken away in solution, solid particles washed out, and larger fragments eased downhill by the lubricating effect of water-films seeping below them. Moving in quite thin films, or twisting surface rills, " rain-wash " thus enormously assists the downward movement of the mantle of rock-wastes ; but no natural slopes are entirely even, and as the surface water flows on it tends to become concentrated into definite channels. The greater scour in such channels cuts out small " gashes ", which deepen and become permanent. Down-hill these run together, permanent streams are formed, and the junction of many such streams creates large rivers. The trunk river thus becomes like a main artery carrying off the surface waters from a large area, and with them their transported rock-wastes. As streams and rivers play the leading role in landscape-sculpture over most of the earth, we must examine in some detail how they carry out their work.

The material streams carry is in part brought into them by surface rainwash, in part excavated by their own erosive action. An important, though invisible, part of it is carried in solution. This may make up a third or more of the whole. The visible part of the " load " (as the material carried by rivers is called) consists of rock particles ranging in size from those needing a microscope to see them up to large boulders. Under normal flow conditions the finer particles of mud grade are carried in suspension, turbulence in the water checking their tendency to settle. Grains of sand move along mostly near the bottom in hopping and rolling movements. Pebbles are rolled along, and their movement may be intermittent, while the larger cobbles may only be moved during occasional floods, remaining for most of the time stationary on the river-bed. The ability of a river to move all these various grades of material depends on the one hand upon the shape, size, and weight of the various fragments ; on the other upon the volume and speed of flow of the water.

Of these factors, speed of flow, or velocity, is by far the most important—although, of course, other things being equal a large river will transport more material than a small one. As the rate of flow increases, however, the transporting power is increased in far more than simple proportion. By doubling its velocity, a river's power to transport mixed debris is multiplied between 8 and 16 times, while the volume of the largest stone it can move is multiplied as much as 50 or 60 times.[1] This explains a problem that often puzzles holiday-makers visiting hilly districts; namely how the huge boulders that cumber the beds of tiny moor-land streams got there. Improbable as it looks, the stream itself brought them down from higher up, where they probably rolled into its bed under gravity. It can only move them, however, on perhaps one or two occasions in a period of years, when in abnormal spate—for in floods, not only does the volume of streams vastly increase, but the rate of flow is also much greater, because friction with the banks and ground below does not increase in proportion. All rivers that experience a seasonal variation in flow are thus much more active in their work of landscape sculpture at some periods of the year than at others. Indeed, the bulk of the year's work of any stream is done during the few weeks of flood conditions, and during the low-water months very little work is done at all. However, if we take the long-term view, it is clear that all the materials we see cumbering river-beds can be thought of as in process of movement, though that movement may be intermittent. Not only is the movement intermittent, however; it is also differential, for smaller particles travel both faster and further than large ones. The sorting out of the transported material is helped by differential deposition. In all normal rivers the gradient, or slope of the bed, flattens out down-stream, and accordingly the current slackens off progressively towards the mouth. At any point the water can only carry as much as its rate of flow will permit, and as the flow slackens, trans-ported material must continuously be dropped. Naturally the

[1] These figures are illustrative only. Experiments have shown that with a load of mixed debris a river's transporting-power is proportional to between the 3rd and 4th powers of its velocity, while for fragments of the same shape the radius of the largest that can just be moved is proportional to about the square of the bottom velocity.

largest fragments are dropped first, and so a continuous sorting-out of the debris occurs as they work downstream. Scarcely noticeable if you visit just one reach of a river, this grading-out of transported materials become quite obvious if you follow a stream from headwaters to mouth. In the steep hill sections, large boulders and cobbles line the stream-bed. Lower down these become rare, and give place to shingle-banks. These in turn die out to give place to beds of sand, and down near the mouth little is to be seen but fine mud. Further, although in principle all the waste that a river brings down is " in transit ", there is generally a limit to which fragments of any given size can travel, and there they stay until worn down smaller. For this, and various other reasons, at every stage down from the hill gathering-grounds a good deal of material is liable to get either temporarily or permanently abandoned. In its evolution a river thus builds boulder-spreads, shingle-banks, and beds of sand and mud. Such river-deposited formations are called " Alluvial deposits " and they are, in embryonic form, one of the groups of the sedimentary rocks.

Erosion goes on concurrently with transport in a river, but itself is made up of several distinct processes. By direct *hydraulic action* the water picks up loose fragments from its bed and banks, and carries them away. Water alone can carve effectively by this means into soft formations. Solution aids the process in the case of partly-soluble rocks, this process being called *corrosion*. It is of major importance in limestone regions. In areas of resistant non-soluble rocks, however, most of the work of erosion is done by the solid fragments that the river carries with it, this process, a mechanical grinding and scouring, being called *corrasion*. The larger fragments, pebbles, cobbles and boulders, are mainly responsible, for they are rolled, dragged and bounced along the river-bed and hurled against all projections. By their continued impact and grinding in time even the hardest rocks are worn away and the river-bed deepened and enlarged. This process can be seen at work best in the steep upper portions of rivers where sections of bare rock are exposed (lower down most rivers flow over beds of alluvial material they have deposited). In such rocky sections you can often see

" pot-holes " in the river-bed, circular cavities drilled into the solid rock (Fig. 18 B).   At low water periods these may be dry, and in the bottom you will often see several rounded stones. In high water periods you can hear these stones grinding round, and it is they that have drilled out the hole under the impetus of swirling eddies.   By enlargement such pot-holes join up, and in time a small gorge is cut through the rock-platform.   By the widening and deepening of clefts started in this way have evolved many well-known and beautiful river-gorges in this country. Gorges of this type often contain alternating waterfalls and deep " plunge-pools ".   The latter are simply enlarged potholes, drilled deep and wide by boulders swirled round by the plunging waters.   Beautiful illustrations of all these features are to be seen in Swilla Glen of the Kingsdale Beck above Ingleton, which terminates in Thornton Force.   In the long run, of course, the broken profile of such gorges becomes smoothed out, because the waterfalls are continually undercut by the swirling boulders and spray.   Blocks fall away from their lips, and the falls retreat and diminish in height, ultimately to disappear.   But such an end-result will have entailed a considerable lowering of the whole river-bed, and the creation of a deep gorge-like valley.

Pot-hole cutting is the most rapid type of river-corrasion, but it can only operate effectively in the steep upper reaches where swift currents combine with bare rock and a plentiful supply of coarse debris in the river-bed.   A slower and less spectacular grinding away of the bed and banks by transported material persists downstream, but as the current slackens direct corrasion diminishes, and solution and hydraulic action become relatively more important.   In the middle and lower courses of well-developed rivers, however, with the slackening current all erosional processes work more slowly, and much counter-deposition goes on, to become more pronounced towards the mouth.   This changing balance of processes is closely related to the character of the valley at different points, and to the various types of landforms that evolve during the course of river-development.   We will treat these matters in the next chapter, but there is one other process going on in rivers that we must not overlook. The wear and tear is not confined to the river-bed.   The boulders, pebbles and sand themselves get steadily worn away. This process, called *attrition*, gradually reduces the size of all stones as they move downstream, and gives them the characteristic " water-worn " rounded shapes that we associate with river-pebbles. The material ground off goes to swell the volume of fine sand and mud carried seaward.

The various processes of denudation that we have discussed in this chapter co-operate over the earth in varying proportions according to the controlling circumstances, which are mainly those of climate. It is seldom possible to separate out their effects entirely, and even more difficult to measure their respective rates of action. Both by its scope and effectiveness, and because it affects the greater part of the earth's lands, there is, however, no doubt that running water in its various forms is by far the most important agency of land denudation. Thus the Mississippi River, which drains over half of the whole United States, carries down into the Gulf of Mexico about two million tons of rock-wastes every day. Averaged out, this represents a lowering of the whole drainage-basin by about 1 foot every 3,500 years. Estimates based on similar measurements for the other great rivers of the earth indicate that together they remove some 8,000 million tons of material from the earth's lands every year, about a third of this material being in solution. Again averaged out, this indicates a lowering of their drainage-basins of 1 foot every 9,000 years or so ; but the rates are of course locally very variable. The Irrawaddy basin, for instance, is being lowered on average 1 foot every 400 years, but the areas drained by the sluggish Siberian rivers lose material at scarce a hundredth of that rate. Within each river-basin also the rate of reduction is much faster over the higher and steeper ground that it is lower down, and in the lower river-valleys the ground may actually be made up. This brings us to variation in landscape-sculpture within river-basins and the variety of forms that evolve as river work proceeds.

CHAPTER VI

THE FORMS AND FEATURES OF
RIVER VALLEYS

IT will be clear from our examination of the way in which rivers
work that the balance of processes going on in them shows a
progressive change as they flow from hills to sea. When we
turn to study their valleys, the significance of this change is very
apparent.

In a normal well-developed river, at least three different sections or types of valley can be distinguished between source and
mouth. Most rivers start with a converging group of small
streamlets on high moorland or hill country, which combine to
form the main stream. Up in the hills, the valley in which this
flows is quite small, but often deeply-cleft, narrow, and in cross-
section like the letter 'V'. This deeply-cut trench shows that
the stream is engaged in rapid downward erosion. Although
the volume of water is still small, slopes are steep, and the current
is in consequence swift. Abundant rock-waste slides into the
stream from the rapid weathering of steep surrounding slopes,
and conditions are thus favourable for active stream-cutting.
Pot-hole formation plays a large part in this cutting, and the
stream-profile is generally markedly irregular, with many rocky
ledges, sections of rapids, and small waterfalls. The narrow
cross-section reveals that lowering of the stream-bed is proceeding
more rapidly than weathering, rainwash, and the like can wear
back the valley-sides. These therefore often approach the
limits of stability, and slumping and gravity-rolling of larger
fragments occur frequently to add new erosion-tools to assist the
stream in its work. In plan, such upland valleys are generally
somewhat sinuous, and viewed from down-stream the deeply
incised trench swings about with the water hidden behind over-
lapping spurs (*see* Fig. 19 A). Higher up the hillsides the slopes
commonly flatten out into the rolling moorland tops, giving
curves upwardly-convex in profile, but in regions of high jagged

mountains steep straightish slopes commonly lead right up the heights. This upper, active, and irregular portion of the river valley is often called its " torrent course ", and such valleys are styled " youthful " or " immature ".

As one proceeds downstream the river grows in volume and its valley deepens, but at the same time the gradient of its bed slackens off and the current in consequence becomes less swift.

Fig. 19. Youthful stream-valleys in mountain country ; above, on British moorlands, below, a torrent-gorge with alluvial fan in the Alps.

Sometimes the transition is abrupt, especially in the case of mountain streams entering a main river, and at such points the sudden check of current may cause dumping of much of the material being carried to build " alluvial fans " (Fig. 19 B). These can be observed at many places in mountainous areas like the Alps, while examples on the grand scale can be seen along the western foot of the Andes in Peru, and along the edges of mountain-girt basins in central Asia. In the normal British river, however, the transition is gradual, and the "torrent" course grades into the "valley" course. With reduced velocity the river is unable to erode its bed so fast, so that the rate of wearing-back of the valley-sides becomes, by comparison, more rapid. The cross-profile thus gradually changes to a wider U-shape, with a rounding-off of the sharp "nick" at the bottom by soil-creep and wash down the valley-sides. In addition, however, the valley generally widens out, and we now begin to find narrow strips and patches of flat ground fringing the river, first on one side, then on the other. These are *constructed* by the river. Flowing more slowly, it is unable to carry onwards all the material brought down by the swift upper waters and a proportion is dumped to form "alluvial flats". If you study one of these you will find that it has a foundation of coarse cobbles and pebbles, generally with finer silt on top. In upland valleys such flats are of great value to man for a variety of purposes. They offer, for example, often the only flat ground for football pitches, but recreation must compete with agriculture, for the alluvial silt is often very fertile. The higher patches are commonly under arable crops, but the lower, still subject to inundation in time of flood, are more generally used for hay. Flooding is responsible for the layer of fine silt on these flats, but the coarser material below was spread abroad by the twisting migrations of the stream itself, a factor of major importance in the widening-out of the valley-floor.

Water flowing under gravity will seldom hold a straight course for long. Slight irregularities in the ground set up kinks and bends, and once formed these tend to enlarge themselves into loops. This development is due to the momentum of the flowing water (Fig. 20). Entering a bend the main flow of the water (A-B) tries to go straight on, and so the current impinges on the outer bank at B. This piles up the water on the outer side of the curve, and to remedy this bottom currents are set up directed back towards the centre of the river and the inner bank, so that in passing round such bends the water takes on a corkscrew motion. To get round the bend, however, the water has to flow faster round the outer side, while on the inner edge its motion is checked. The net result is a concentration of erosion along the outer bank, which gets continually undercut and worn away, while along the inner curve material is deposited in spreads of shingle and sand. The channel thus grows asymmetric in cross-section, and as time goes on it progressively migrates outwards, enlarging the size of the loop and leaving a built-up shelving bank of stony alluvium in the "core" of the loop. But owing to the momentum of the water, the erosion continues

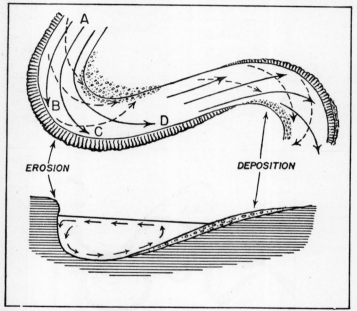

Fig. 20. Development of a meander, in plan and section.   In upper sketch solid lines denote surface flow, broken lines bottom flow.

round the corner of the bend, i.e. at C. and D. in Fig. 20, so that even as the loop enlarges it tends to move slowly downstream. When such loops become pronounced they are called "meanders", and in course of time meander-development contributes much to the evolving valley-form. As the meanders grow they sap into the base of earlier spurs, undercut them, and carve them away, while as the meanders slowly migrate downstream, so the

points of outward cutting also move on, and the valley-spurs are
everywhere in turn planed back. A flattish-floored trench is
left over which the " sweep " of the meandering river spreads
alluvial materials, thus building the flats earlier noted. The
downstream migration of the meanders is, of course, very slow,

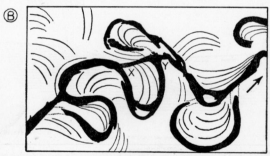

Fig. 21:
   (A) River-terraces (diagrammatic).
   *(B) Meanders in the flood-plain tract of a river (Mississippi flood-plain, near
        Greensville, Mississippi. The ' cuts ' at X and Y are artificial.)*

and as the river is at the same time lowering its bed, patches of
gravel and alluvium tend to be abandoned along the valley-sides
at levels above that of the more recent alluvium. These are
called " meander terraces ". Generally their inner edges are
cut into cusps marking the former positions of the stream at

stages subsequent to their own deposition. In the long-term view, of course these features tend to get destroyed again during the lowering of the whole valley-floor, but they persist a long time by human standards (Fig. 21 A.).

Downstream again the " valley " tract gently merges into the third section, the " flood-plain " tract of the river's course. The valley-sides retreat further apart, their slopes diminish, and the divides between the valley and its neighbours dwindle to low swells in the ground. The river itself is now sluggish and flows entirely on a built-up bed of its own creation. The separate riverside flats have merged into a widening tract of flat alluvial plain, and unless artificially straightened the river winds across this in an intricate meandering course. Often the meanders have doubled right back on themselves, and cases can be seen where the river in time of flood has taken a short-cut across the narrow neck of a meander and cut off the loop entirely (Fig. 21 B). In such " cut-offs " arcuate " oxbow lakes " are left, but they soon fill up with silt and marsh vegetation (Fig 22 A). Such short-circuiting of meanders seems to limit the size to which they can grow, and there are apparently relationships between the volume and current of a river and the radius of the meanders that develop in it. But movements in the river are not confined to the growth and downstream sweep of individual meanders. The whole stream and its " meander-belt " tend to migrate about across the flood-plain, although such migration takes place very slowly and in most lower river-valleys is now checked by human action.

In the flood-plain tract the river is working very slowly, and emphasis has shifted from erosion to deposition. Sea-level fixes a lower limit to erosion (since the river only flows under gravity), and as it is approached the gradient becomes slight and the water-flow gentle. Often, indeed, the river's problem is to keep open a channel at all, since mud is always being dropped from the sluggish stream and building up the channel floor. In its early youth, the river was much shorter and swifter, the checking of its current on approaching the sea was more sudden, and the material it dumped in the estuary was coarse. As the river-valley evolved, however, and lengthened (for rivers ' grow ' by extending their headwaters backwards), the gradient in the lower reaches became progressively gentler and finer material was laid down. The topmost material on the flood-plain is thus entirely fine silt, (the only grade now brought down by the river right to the sea), spread over the growing plain of deposits partly by the slow migrations of the river, partly by the spreading abroad of its waters during floods. Every flood adds new thin layers of silt, but with the sudden checking of flow outside the main channel, deposition is strongest along the actual banks of the river, and these banks thus tend to grow upward. In rivers with well-developed flood-plains it is thus common to find the streams running between raised banks called " levees " (Fig. 22 A). Nowadays these are generally heightened and strengthened artificially to prevent flood-waters spilling over, but in origin they are natural. Levee-development is, however, dangerous in a settled flood-plain—and most flood-plains of rivers in temperate and tropical lands are heavily settled because of the fertility of the soil—because with continued deposition on the stream-bed the water-level rises, while the surrounding alluvial lands tend to *drop* in level once the silt-supply is cut off and the deposits dry out and become compact. Thus in time the surface of the river may rise to lie well above the surrounding countryside, and in time of flood, if the retaining levee-banks are overtopped or broken through, vast quantities of water may sweep unchecked over wide areas of settled farmland. Such dangerous conditions prevail on the great flood-plains of the Whangho in China, the Mississippi, and the Po in Italy. In Britain we have analogous conditions along the Fen rivers, and here the problem is complicated by the fact that inland of the estuarine area the surface soil is composed largely of peat, laid down in the great marshes and meres that existed before this flat tract of country was drained. With drainage the peat has dried and shrunk continuously, while its surface has also fallen through bacterial decay of the peat and its removal by wind as fine dust. The ground-surface has thus dropped alarmingly—by upwards of 12 feet in places—so that not only is the Fen surface over wide areas below river-level, but the ground in the upper Fens is in some parts lower than that further

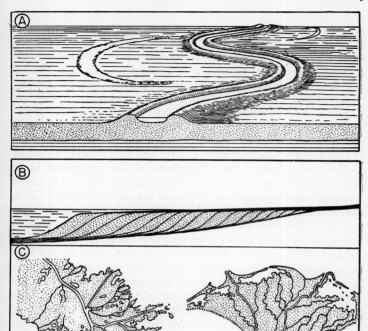

Fig. 22:

(A) " Levees " and " Ox-bow lakes " in a flood-plain.
(B) Structure of a delta.
(C) Deltas of the Mississippi (left) and Nile (right).

down towards the sea, where the flood-plains are built of river-silt. Only continuous pumping keeps the fields dry, and in bad winters there is a constant danger of a break-through of the river-banks and the flooding of wide areas, as happened in the spring of 1947. The problem is further complicated by the

D

great range of tide in the Wash, and the difficulties of carrying land-water off the flat country at high tide.

Many rivers have extended their flood-plains a long way out from the original coastline by the construction of *deltas*. On entering the sea, the river-flow is checked, and its load of sand and mud is rapidly dropped, the larger particles of sand settling first, in a band close to the coast, and the mud settling further out largely through the flocculating effect of the salt water. If the sea-conditions are fairly quiet, lacking great tidal movements and strong currents (which disperse the sediment), deposition is concentrated around the river-mouth, and a delta is built. Most of the rivers around the almost tideless Mediterranean build deltas (Nile, Rhone etc.), and we find them also where rivers flow into partly-enclosed seas, as where the Whangho enters the China Sea, and the Mississippi the Gulf of Mexico. Deltas grow by a sort of " tipping " process, like that carried out by wagons extending a railway embankment, so that the bedding in them is inclined (Fig. 22 B). Recognition of this structure in land rocks enables geologists to trace ancient sea-coast positions. As a river builds a delta outwards. however, it increases it own length and reduces the gradient of its seaward portion. The water thus finds it increasingly difficult to keep its channel clear, and for this reason rivers in crossing their deltas are very liable to frequent shifts of channel. Many break up into "distributaries " in a fan-like arrangement as the water blocks it sown path and periodically has to break out sideways. (Fig. 22 C).

Deltas grow in various shapes, not all like the classic fan-shape of the Nile Delta from which the formation takes its name (the word Delta is the Greek letter *Δ*), and they are formed elsewhere than in seas. Rivers entering lakes frequently build out deltas into their quiet waters, and these in time may fill in small lakes entirely. Lakes Crummock Water and Buttermere in the Lake District were originally one. They have been separated by the growth of a large delta flat constructed by a small stream that runs in from the east. On the tiny scale, deltas can be seen forming in the puddles that grow on any untarred road during a heavy rainstorm, as the surface runnels carry sand into them. On the large scale they build much of the Mississippi flood-plain and the lower Ganges-Brahmaputra valley.   Such vast deltas as these contain billions of tons of sediment.   The Mississippi delta is at least 2,000 feet deep.   It seems unlikely that great troughs of tectonic origin existed off the mouths of the earlier rivers to accommodate all this material, and it appears therefore that the earth's crust must have sunk down under isostatic adjustment as the weight of sediment increased, permitting further accumulation.   Gravity surveys indeed suggest that some such sinking has probably taken place.

A valley of the type we have described, having developed a sort of middle-aged spread throughout much of its course, has reached a stage of evolution which we can appropriately call " mature ", for the contrasting styles of valley are only gradually developed with backward extension of the whole river-system and slow attainment of a balance of conditions from point to point within it.   Initially the stream will have been shorter, and all its valley of immature torrent character.   We can find plenty of such immature recently-initiated valleys today in areas of recent earth-disturbance.   But even in large and old-established rivers the three distinct sections of valley-type are not always shown. Often we find little flood-plain, the "valley-tract" passing straight into the sea, perhaps through a long estuary.   Disturbance by earth-movement is often responsible in such cases, for unless checked by some abnormal occurrence or conditions, rivers appear to work towards a harmonious valley-development. This is brought out not only in the gradual change in character of their valleys upstream, but in the form attained by their beds considered in longitudinal profile.   In a mature river, this profile frequently forms a smooth curve steepening gradually upstream, and when a river has achieved this smooth " curve of water-erosion", it has been styled " graded ".[1]   Obviously much time is needed for such a regular profile to develop, for in the early stages of growth the stream-bed will follow all the inequalitites of the original land-surface.   Just how the " graded profile " is achieved and maintained is not as yet fully understood, but it clearly involves point-to-point adjustment of the stream-bed gradient to the volume of water flowing and the quantity of material being carried.   Initial " bumps " in the profile would

[1] This term has been much criticised, and needs care.   Recent studies have shown that the smooth concave profile is no necessary criterion of dynamic equilibrium (i.e. " grade ") in a river.

cause swifter flow on their downstream sides which would cause faster erosion, and as this faster erosion worked backwards the bumps would be gradually cut away. In flatter places, by contrast, the current would be checked, erosion would be slower, and there would be a tendency for material to be deposited. By means of the variable rates of erosion from point to point, in

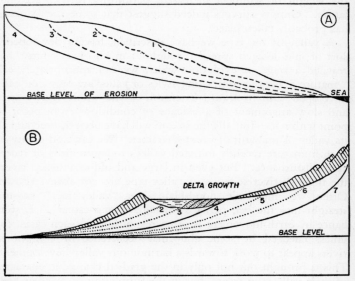

Fig. 23 :

    (*A*) *Development of a 'graded curve' in the profile of a river.* 1, 2, 3, 4 *mark successive profiles.*

    (*B*) *Elimination of a lake by river-erosion. The lake is partly drained by cutting back of the lower river* (1, 2, 3) ; *partly filled in by expansion of the delta built by the upper river. Stage 4 shows the rivers joined ; stage 7 the final graded profile.*

time the "kinks" in the profile are removed, and ultimately a nice state of balance between erosion, transport, and deposition is attained at all points in harmony with the changing conditions of volume and velocity throughout the river's course (Fig. 23 A). The theoretically perfect curve is probably never attained, because flow conditions are changing all the time, and variations in the structure and resistance of the rocks across which the river flows cause irregularities to develop and persist. By saying that a river is " graded " we therefore only imply that its profile has attained a reasonable approximation to the ideal smooth curve. Erosion does not cease when a river becomes " graded ", but it becomes slower, for any further downcutting at any point involves adjustments throughout the river as a whole. In mature rivers, effective erosion seems to go on mainly in the upper reaches, the changes lower down being slight adjustments in the distribution of the transported material. It is the lack of active downcutting that permits the wide lateral swinging and other developments we noted as characteristic of the middle and lower reaches. In time, however, while maintaining its general form, the graded curve must gradually flatten out, the rate of change becoming ever slower as the elevation of the hill feeding-grounds diminishes. The form of the whole curve is of course adjusted to sea-level which forms the " base-level " of river-erosion. Inland, each tributary stream becomes similarly graded to the level of the point of its entry into the main river, and as the profile of the latter is lowered, so the tributaries cut down their beds in harmony. Maladjustment of tributary valleys causing them to drop abruptly into the main valley, can however occur if for any reason they are unable to keep pace in downcutting with the main valley. This sometimes happens through diversion of part of the water-supplies of a tributary, but the most common cause is over-deepening of the main valley by some extraneous agency like a glacier (*see* Chap. X). Such discordant valleys, if separated by a marked " step ", are said to " hang " above the main valley.

In the main valley itself, breaks of profile may occur. The presence of a lake, for instance, will divide the river into two separate portions working to independent base-levels. In the fullness of time such breaks tend to disappear through the disappearance of the lake itself; but this may take many thousands of years. The lake will become slowly filled in by the deposition on its floor of sediment and the building of a delta by the upper river, while the outfall river will slowly cut down the level of the spill-over point and thus in time drain off the waters.

When the lake dries out, the two sections of river will join up, and the " bump " in the middle of their united profile will get gradually eliminated as the river begins to operate as a whole (Fig. 23 B).

Other breaks in river profiles are caused by the emergence of bands of unusually resistant rock across the river's path, flanked by softer formations.   As erosion proceeds, the hard bands are left standing out, and may give rise to waterfalls or sections of rapids.   Such waterfalls may persist a long time if the geological structure is favourable, e.g. if the resistant bed runs nearly horizontal or dips only gently up or downstream (Fig. 24).   The fall itself will gradually retreat by undercutting, but will often leave behind a cliff-walled gorge, the resistant bed checking the normal retreat of the valley-sides.   The classic example of such a waterfall and gorge is that of Niagara, where a thick bed of hard limestone causes the river to drop over a 160-foot cliff, whose retreat has left a gorge 7 miles long.   Many of the earth's most spectacular waterfalls are caused by rivers tumbling over the steep edges of piled volcanic flows.   The Victoria Falls are of this type, the Zambesi dropping 360 feet into a gorge 60 miles long.   In this country, as mentioned earlier, High Force in Upper Teesdale tumbles over the emergent edge of the Whin Sill.   There are breaks in river-profiles caused by other factors, like change of sea level and tectonic movements, but we may leave these aside for mention later.   To conclude this chapter, we may glance at a few further points concerning the forms of river-valleys as viewed in cross-section rather than in longitudinal profile.

In countries experiencing a rainy or " humid " climate, valley-forms evolve for the most part in close harmony with the development of the river to which they owe their primary creation.   Valleys are, however, obviously not excavated *entirely* by the rivers that flow through them.   If they were, they would remain almost vertical-walled trenches.   Retreat of the valley-sides is caused by weathering, rain-wash, soil-creep, and various other ancillary processes, and the form of a river-valley results in principle from the respective rates at which its floor is lowered by river-erosion, and its sides worn back by these secondary agencies.

But various factors may intervene to produce abnormalities. Variations in rock hardness and geological structure often produce distinctive valley-forms. Thus in horizontally-bedded strata composed of occasional resistant beds with intervening

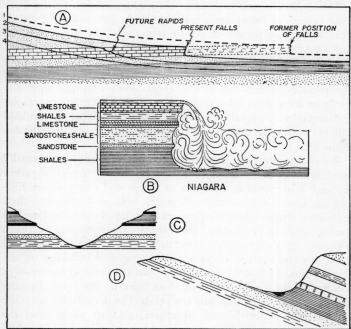

Fig. 24:
    (*A*) *Retreat and eventual elimination of a waterfall caused by the outcrop of a resistant formation dipping gently upstream.*
    (B) *Section of Niagara Falls.*
    (C, D) *Effects of different structures on valley forms.*

softer ones, we often find a stepped profile in the valley-sides due to differential retreat of the beds (Fig. 24 C.). Again, if the river works along parallel with the outcrops of tilted strata it tends to migrate down the bedding-planes, and so to develop an asymmetric valley-form (Fig. 24 D). The variations in detail are endless, and in regions of variable structure the student will find much interest and profit in noting valley-form changes and seeking for reasons in factors of rock-type and structure.

A further important factor, though one that cannot be studied in Britain, is climatic variation. In regions of dry climate such river-valleys as occur are generally deeply-cut and steep-sided. This is because the processes of rain-wash and soil-creep that contribute so much to valley-widening, and in Britain give us our characteristic flowing curves in valley-forms, are almost in abeyance. Great canyons like that of the Colorado River are the product mainly of direct river down-cutting, with the resultant rock-walls relatively little modified by other processes. If desert climate prevailed in Britain many of our gently-moulded valleys would have assumed the same rugged and precipitous character.

We may sum up this chapter by stressing that under " normal " rainy conditions of climate, hills and valleys evolve together through a harmonious complex of forms and changes, the hills coming into being as the valleys are hollowed out, and their individual shapes being the product of valley-slope formation and the weathering processes that shape their upper portions. Variable rock-types and structures guide all the erosional processes and exert in consequence a profound influence on the results, but, in Britain at any rate, we see little in the way of original " constructional " relief as built by the earth directly. Our landscapes are essentially the product of denudation working on variable materials and structures, and to understand the whole we must study not only the evolution of individual valleys, but the patterns they form and their interrelations in the landscape development. To this we turn in the next chapter.

CHAPTER VII

THE GROWTH OF RIVER-SYSTEMS AND THE WATER-CARVED LANDSCAPE

LANDSCAPES evolve very slowly by human standards, and the pattern of rivers, valleys, and hills in any mature region will only have reached its present condition by infinitely slow changes and adjustments stretched over tens or hundreds of thousands of years. To understand how such landscapes have evolved we therefore have to make deductions based on comparison of regions and features at different stages of development, on what we know of the ways in which rivers and other agencies work, and on such evidence as careful study of the landscape features will reveal about what has happened in the past. It is helpful to approach the complex realities by study first of simple idealised cases, and we may here profitably follow this line.

Let us suppose then that we could actually watch a virgin land-surface rise from beneath the sea and river-systems establish themselves on it ; say a simple oval-shaped island created by uplift of the sea-floor which warps the sedimentary rocks that have there accumulated into an elongated dome. (Fig. 25 A).

Directly such an island appeared above the waves its surface rocks would come under the attack of weathering, and when rain fell, some of it would flow off down the slopes to the sea and begin to carry off the wastes of rock-destruction. Minor irregularities in the surface would guide the water-flow along fairly well-marked lines, and soon there would emerge the framework of a fixed drainage pattern. The earliest streams (Fig. 25 B (i)), although no doubt crowded together and liable to shifts and adjustments, would run on the whole radially from the higher ground towards the sea by the shortest and steepest routes. Their directions would result directly from the initial structural slopes. Streams and rivers so aligned are termed *Consequent*.

Fairly quickly these streams would begin to carve out shallow and narrow valleys, of the immature torrent type, but as these

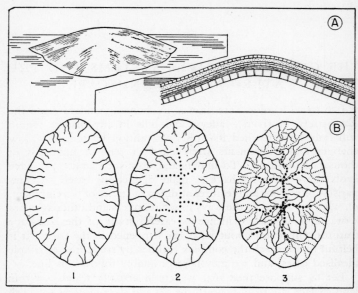

Fig. 25:

(*A*) *Outline and structure of a new island.*

(*B*) *Three stages in drainage development. The dotted lines mark the main divides.*

deepened and widened new lateral slopes would be created, and the surface runoff waters of the surrounding strips of ground would be diverted by these new slopes into the more active streams, which would thus start to develop systems of tributaries, running into them at angles to make up patterns like those of the veins in a leaf.   But even as these tributary systems developed, the initial consequent valleys would be deepening and lengthening, and as all would not increase at the same rate, in time many of the smaller would get absorbed into the larger. Thus the original crowded series of sub-parallel little streams would become amalgamated into a smaller number of vigorous young rivers, each busily engaged in deepening and expanding its own valley and spreading out branching systems of tributaries. In the earlier stages tongues of the original surface would remain practically unmodified between the various valleys, but as the drainage-systems expanded, both backwards and laterally, these would get more and more eaten into and carved up. In time, we should thus be able to draw in fairly precise lines marking the divides, or water-partings, between the various different expanding catchment areas or drainage-basins. Our island would by now have quite a well-organised drainage-system (Fig. 25 B, stage (ii)), and a time would soon come when no further expansion of the various stream-systems could take place without mutual interference and struggle for catchment-areas : (stage (iii).)

Before considering what might happen then, we may cast a glance at the pattern of relief developed by this stream-valley evolution. The original smooth rounded dome would have long since gone. Instead we would now have a radiating system of main river-valleys, still rather narrow and torrent-like in their upper courses, but lower down beginning to widen out, and towards the sea starting to build minor flood-plains and perhaps even deltas. These trunk streams would also by now be showing some tendency towards grading in the curve of their longitudinal profiles. From them would radiate branching systems of tributary valleys, each breaking down into minor sub-tributaries and streamlets in a pattern like that of the trunk, branches and twigs of a deciduous tree, and hence called " dendritic " (Greek : *Dendron*—a tree). Between these river and stream-valleys we should have residual ridges carved out of the original high-level surface, but these would by now already be cut back in places into sharp divides, and have suffered much lowering of their crests by weathering and the cutting of stream-heads into their flanks causing wash and sliding-removal of the products of weathering. In pattern the divide-ridges would be by now somewhat twisting and irregular, with notches cut into them at points where especially active headstreams were cutting back, and between these protruding spurs of higher ground. The actual pattern assumed by the watersheds would of course depend on the accidents determining the pattern of the headstreams cutting into them. If, for instance, along the main central divide the two sets of lateral rivers lay in " staggered " positions, the divide would develop a zig-zag pattern as their respective head-

streams cut backwards. More probably, however, at some
points streams would cut back directly towards one another
from each side of the main ridge, while at other points stream
inroads would be less successful. The ridge would be lowered
more rapidly at the former points, while at the latter it would

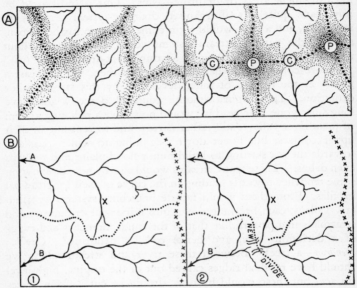

Fig. 26:

(A) Types of divides. On left, zig-zag divide created by streams cutting back in offset positions. On right, straighter divide with peaks (P), and cols (C) created by streams cutting back towards one another.

(B) Two stages in river-capture. The double bracket shows the position of the "wind-gap". Note the "elbow of capture" in the new combined stream X-X [1].

retain much of its original altitude. Thus in profile we should
find something of a saw-tooth development, " cols " or
" saddles " forming between the converging headstreams, and
higher ' peaks ' separating them (Fig. 26 A).

The details of this development of related river and divide-
patterns would clearly depend on the positions assumed by the

various streams (which could not be predicted in detail) and their respective rates of back-cutting, tributary-development, and valley-enlargement. It is extremely unlikely that all would remain equal in these respects. Early accidents in development, variations in the resistance of the rock over which they flowed, the assistance or otherwise of rock-structures like joints, and variations in water-supply, would cause variations in stream-activity, and with this, perhaps some migration in the positions of the divides. For instance, if one side of the island received more rainfall than the other, one set of streams would cut back more rapidly (having greater volume and erosive power) and the central divide might become gradually shifted laterally away from coincidence with the structural axis of the anticline. But such unequal stream activity might in time have further and more important effects. The more powerful rivers might succeed in enlarging their basins at the expense of the weaker by actually breaking through the earlier divides, and pirating areas formerly draining in another direction, and from such accessions cases of actual "river-capture" would probably result. We can illustrate this process best by a figure. In Fig. 26 B, suppose stream X, a tributary of river A, is cutting back actively into the divide separating it from the drainage-basin of river B. In time it cuts back right through the divide, and its head extends backwards very close to river B. itself, and approaches it at a lower level than that at which stands river B in that locality. A flood comes down, and some water spills over the narrow neck between the rivers. The occurrence is repeated; the head of stream X cuts back even further; and eventually the whole flow of the upper portion of river B is diverted into stream X, to swell the volume of its parent river A and still further increase its power. River B, now shorn of its headwaters and much of its former water-supply, is seriously crippled. Its beheaded trunk, with reduced water-flow, is no longer able to carry out much effective erosion, and it is left as a shrunken "misfit" stream occupying a valley too large for it. Meanwhile river A, swollen by its gains, works even more vigorously, and may in time capture even more of B's drainage-area, or territories from other streams. In river-development, as in some other spheres, nothing succeeds like success. The point at which the original capture took place remains clearly marked on the ground by the abrupt angle that the composite stream X-X' makes at this spot, a characteristic feature called an " elbow of capture ". Below it, in the valley of B, there will be initially a flat marshy area where the original river was broken, but as the beheaded stream of B contracts, and the invigorated stream X-X' cuts down its valley, the new drainage-divide will become more clearly-marked, and the effective valley of the beheaded river B will terminate in what is called a " wind-gap " ; a dry col through which the original river ran, but which now lies above its highest headwaters. Many captures, of similar or other types, would doubtless take place as the various more active river-systems fought for expansion, and by their occurrence quite new and apparently anomalous patterns would be introduced into the drainage.

River-capture, so far as we can judge from the ground, has been a very common occurrence in the development of mature river-patterns, and we have countless examples of it in Britain, some fairly recent and quite obvious, others old and rather problematical. The actual mechanism of the final capture and diversion we have to guess at, since few if any cases of river-capture have actually been seen in operation. Some authorities believe that the final step may often take place underground by seepage, without the actual surface streams meeting at all, but for this to be possible fairly pervious rock formations would be required. In regions of impervious rocks it seems more likely that the final breakthrough is made by a flood, as we have suggested. Before quoting cases of river-capture in Britain, there is, however, a further aspect of the river-evolution of our imaginary island we should note.

So far we have assumed that all the developments have been made on the same type of rock, and have neglected the effects of geological structure. On our original supposition, however, we pictured the island as built of a series of superimposed sedimentary formations, and as denudation proceeded these would in turn be gradually worn through. Let us suppose that the various beds are not of equal resistance, but that L, N, and P, for example, consist of a hard limestone, while M and O are of softer materials (Fig. 27 A). The overall denudation (neglecting the river-pattern) will work most rapidly on the higher ground, and so the original surface formation P will be first completely removed—as distinct from being cut through by individual rivers—along the anticlinal ridge. Its cut-through edges, dipping outwards, will gradually fall further and further apart as lowering of the whole island surface proceeds. Once bed P is completely cut through on the central ridge, bed O below it will be exposed, and in time it will suffer a like fate, and in turn beds N and M will be worn through in the same manner. At a late stage we would thus find the lowest (and oldest) bed L exposed in the centre of the island, and forming the central ridge, while in cross-section the higher beds M, N, O, and P would appear as symmetrically-disposed pairs of outcrops on either side (Fig. 27 A). Since the whole island is oval in shape, however, and structurally a dome, in plan the various formations would appear as a series of concentric ovals, the oldest bed L being in the middle, the youngest P forming the outer ring.

It will be noted that on the sectional view we have, however, shown a further significant change in the topography. No longer does the land slope smoothly down each way from the central ridge. There still is a central ridge (though much reduced in height) but on either side the ground is diversified with ridges and hollows. The harder formations, L, N, and P, stand up as ridges ; the softer M, and O, have been worn down into valleys. The ridges deserve note. They are asymmetric in section, having a long gentle outer slope coincident with the dip of the rock, and a short steep inward-facing slope. Such ridges, owing their creation to the differential wearing-down of inclined strata, are called " Cuestas " in America, and in Britain " Escarpments ". The steep inner slope is the " scarp " slope ; the gentle outer one the " dip " slope.

It may appear self-evident that such a ridged topography should develop, given a sequence of formations of varying resistance, but in fact the evolution of the escarpment topography is only in part due to overall weathering. In large measure its development is assisted by progressive changes in the river-pattern that occur to fit it to the new surface-structure. The original conse-

quent rivers indeed will probably retain their original courses
with little alteration during this evolution, but in their valleys
will now be found alternating wide, open, reaches where they

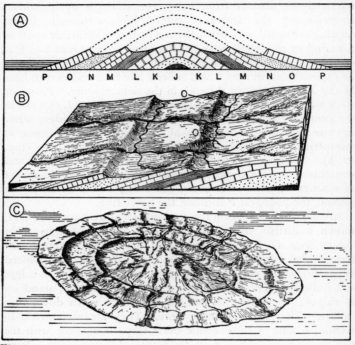

Fig. 27 :

(A) Section across island after denudation, showing development of scarp-ridges.

(B) "Trellised" drainage evolved on the escarpment relief. The consequent
stream in the foreground has been beheaded by a 'strike', or subsequent
tributary of the further stream. Obsequent streams at O.

(C) Pattern of relief and drainage developed on the island after long denudation.
Note the concentric escarpments, and the trellised pattern of the drainage, with
evidence of many stream captures.

cross the "vales" cut in the softer outcrops, and deeper and
narrower gorge-like sections where they have sawn down through
the emerging limestone ridges of beds N and P. But instead of
the original branching and tree-like pattern of tributaries, we

would now probably find a trellised pattern, with many of the main tributaries coming into the main streams at right angles. This change would have come about by adjustment of the tributaries to the variable rock-resistance.   They would gradually migrate down the dip-slopes of the harder beds, and cut back vigorously along the exposed bands of softer rock, to take up alignments along the feet of the scarp-ridges of formations N and P (Fig. 27 B).   Such tributaries, running parallel to the out-crops of banded strata, are called *Subsequent* streams. We might even find small streams now running back *inland* down the emergent scarp-slopes of the cuestas.   Such streams, opposite in direction to the original consequents, are called *Obsequent* streams.   The overall pattern of relief that has evolved by all these changes, and the adjustment of the river-system to it, is shown in the oblique aerial view of Fig 27 C.   It will be apparent that such developments are very favourable to further stream-captures, as subsequent tributaries cut back towards one another along the softer beds.   Several such captures are indicated in Fig. 27 C.

The case we have described is, of course, idealised ; but we have in Britian an example in the Weald in which the landscape evolution has not been much more complex, and in which the overall pattern shows marked similarity to our theoretical case (Fig. 28 A).   But scarpland topography, with consequent-subsequent drainage, is not confined to structural domes.   It is the typical development in all areas of simple inclined strata, and on a large scale is well displayed by the whole stretch of country making the Midlands and Eastern England.   Over the whole of this region the formations incline on the whole east and south-east, and the original rivers probably flowed in the same direc-tions.   The present Trent and Wash rivers are compound subsequent streams, developed by the cutting back of lateral tributaries along the vales of softer rocks lying between the outstanding arcuate scarp-ridges.   The pattern will be readily apparent from a glance at an atlas.   In north-east England, again, is a region where river-capture on a large scale has occurred. The rivers of west Yorkshire—the Swale, Ure, Nidd, Wharfe, Aire and Calder,—all rise in the Pennines and initially flow roughly parallel towards the east. Quite probably these rivers in earlier days continued eastwards to the sea as independent streams; but with the carving out of the Vale of York along the softer Triassic rocks, the subsequent Yorkshire Ouse worked back to capture each in turn. The anomalous Derwent, commen-

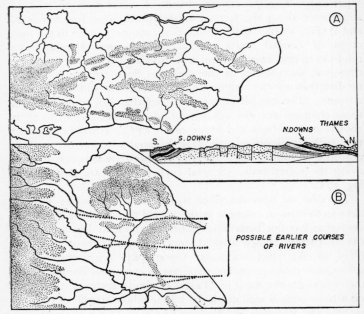

Fig. 28 :

(*A*) *Relief and drainage-pattern of the Weald, with geological section.*

(*B*) *The rivers of east Yorkshire. Dotted lines indicate diagrammatically the probable alignments of the earlier consequent rivers, captured in turn by the subsequent Yorkshire Ouse cutting back northwards along the outcrop of the soft Trias formations.*

cing near the sea and running in a great arc inland, owes its peculiar course to diversions caused by events in the Ice Age (Chap. X), (Fig. 28 B).

Many other cases of river-capture are to be found in our islands, some self-evident, some dubious and only to be proved by indirect evidence. Blockages and diversions of rivers occurred on a wide scale during the Ice Age, and movements of sea-level, and even of the land, have greatly complicated the river-patterns in many areas, so that interpretation is not always easy. Should the reader feel like trying to test his deductive powers in building up a reasoned interpretation of river-evolution, his attention is invited to the area around the Tyne Gap, between the head-waters of the Tyne and Irthing river-systems. Few areas show a more intriguing pattern.

We have so far been concerned with the adjustment of rivers to fairly simple structures. In regions of more complex earth-disturbance, as in the zones of folded mountains, the river-patterns are often intricate, and their relationships to the geo-logical structures far from obvious. Where systems of parallel folds occur, we may indeed be able to see fairly clear relationships. In such areas the main rivers would initially most likely flow along the synclinal valleys, receiving short swift lateral tributaries from the anticlinal ridges. In the long run, however, as we mentioned in Chap. III, the original anticlinal ridges may be reduced to val-leys, and the original synclinal valleys stand out as ridges. In harmony with this change, the river-system would show a sort of lateral displacement. But in regions of high parallel ridges or even pronounced mountain-chains, although the rivers on the whole may tend to flow parallel to the " grain " of the structure, we do often find cases where rivers turn and break right across the folds, or cut through the ridges transversely, often in deep gorges. Sometimes this is to be explained by the existence of large faults which have sliced across the ridges and opened ways for the rivers to cut through, but occasionally a different type of explanation must be sought. Some of the most astonishing river-features of the earth are the great gorges through which the upper Indus and Brahmaputra rivers cut right across the main chain of the Himalayas. These rivers commence high on the Tibetan plateau, and run for hundreds of miles along the foot of the unbroken mountain chains. Then suddenly they turn south and cut through the whole system in gorges thousands of feet deep. The only feasible explanation that can be advanced is that the rivers had already established these courses before the

Himalayas attained their present height.   The mountains appear
to have been slowly raised up, as it were, under the rivers, and
the latter seem to have been able to cut their beds down fast
enough to keep pace with the rising, and so escape diversion.
Features of this sort (which are somewhat rare), illustrate what
is called " Antecedent drainage ", implying that the rivers were
there before the mountains.

But in many mountainous regions we can trace little apparent
connection of any kind between the river-patterns and those of
the geological structures. Rivers cut across faults and folds
indiscriminately, at all sorts of angles.   The explanation in such
cases often proves to be that the river-system did not grow
directly on the rocks into which its valleys are now cut, but on
some overlying " blanket " formation of quite different structure, of which denudation has by now removed every trace.
The rivers have been, as it were, " let down from above ", and
have maintained their earlier courses despite the discordance
with the rocks over which they now flow.   Such systems of
drainage are called " Superimposed ", and we find them, as
might be expected, not so much in the areas of recent, or new
mountains, as in regions where the worn-down stumps of ancient
mountains have been re-elevated.   The Lake District offers an
example.   Here the present river-pattern is markedly radial, but
the old crystalline and volcanic rocks through which the rivers
cut have a grain running S.W. to N.E., and the position of the
main original axis of uplift lies well to the north of the hub of
the present river-system.   Originally the Lake District formed
part of the Caledonian mountain-system but over aeons of time
its mountains were worn down flat, the stumps drowned beneath
the sea, and new sedimentary rocks were laid down over them.
At much later date the whole area was re-elevated as a dome, and
the radial river-pattern was developed on this dome.   In time,
the cover of sedimentary rocks was completely stripped away, but
the rivers maintained their courses discordantly across the re-
exposed crystalline rocks.   Probably the river-patterns of much
of Wales and parts of the Scottish Highlands have similar
histories.   In their later development many adjustments to the
exhumed structures have been made, but the overall pattern

can only be understood if the geological history is known.

These few illustrations must suffice to indicate the many ways in which river-systems may develop, and the complexities of their relationships to the geological structures of the lands over which they run. We must now turn to some wider considerations of the progressive evolution of river-carved landscapes.

It was the great American physiographer W. M. Davis who formulated clearly the " cycle " idea of landscape development. Davis conceived (as we have done) an initial land-surface raised from the sea, and deduced its progressive development as a whole under the attack of river-sculpture and overall denudation. In the stage of "Youth" the surface is carved up by immature streams vigorously cutting deep and narrow valleys, and so the *range* of local relief increases since the valleys are cut down more rapidly than the ridges. With " Maturity ", however, a change sets in. The rivers are by now well-established, their tributaries widely-spread, and their profiles approaching the graded condition. Valley-floors are no longer being so rapidly cut down, and the rate of wastage from the crests and ridges catches up with, and outstrips, that of valley-lowering. Thus the range of relief begins to diminish, and the topography becomes more subdued. The phase of " Old Age " sees the rivers mature and sluggish. Flood-plain conditions extend far up their valleys, the hills on which they rise are now reduced to low rounded " swells ", and the inter-valley divides to gentle undulations. With the diminished relief, all the agencies of denudation lose their power, the rates of landscape-change slow down, and the late stages would see little happening at all. For this reason, one can hardly envisage any region ever being worn down literally to a flat surface at sea-level, however long the time allowed, and Davis thought the practical limit would be when the land was reduced to a low-lying "almost-plain", gently undulating and with low mounds marking the sites of earlier mountains. To this final subdued condition Davis applied the term " Peneplain ". It would persist until something happened to start off a new " cycle " of landscape evolution.

If we review the earth's land-areas today, we can see very few areas which approximate at all closely to Davis' theoretical " end-stage " peneplain, but this we might expect from the fact that relatively recently the earth experienced a worldwide and very severe epoch of crustal dislocation and upheaval, and over much of the earth landscapes are therefore still relatively immature. Geological evidence, however, reveals that at many earlier periods vast areas were, in fact, reduced to conditions of extremely low relief by sub-aerial denudation in which rivers appear to have played the leading role. Always in the end, however, some change of conditions intervened to start denudation off again. We earlier noted the sorts of disturbance to which the earth's surface is subject, and we are now in a position to comprehend how different movements are likely to affect the orderly course of landscape evolution. The effects of such interferences are clearly to be seen in many features of our present landscapes.

Since all river-work is controlled by the position of sea-level, any change in the relative levels of land and water will clearly affect the course of events. A *positive*, or upward, movement of base-level, whether occasioned by a rise of the sea, or depression of the land, will " drown " a strip of land along the coast, and so give rise to new and distinctive shore features (*See* Chap. XV.) In addition, however, it will weaken the power of inland rivers, and tend to reduce the rate of denudation. Rivers will find the gradient of their lower courses diminished, and their velocities checked. There will thus be much dumping of transported material, and a phase of building, or " aggradation " will ensue in the middle and lower river-valleys with filling-up of the lower valleys with gravel and sand. A *negative* movement, a rise in the land or fall in the sea, will have the opposite effect. Rivers will generally be steepened in gradient at their mouths, and mature sluggish streams will thereby be revived or " rejuvenated ". Active erosion will start again down at the mouth, and will work its way backward up-river as a wave of renewed down-cutting into the earlier valley-floor. The river will thus develop, in longitudinal profile, a double curve, the point at which the old and rejuvenated parts of the profile meet being called the " rejuvenation-head " or " nickpoint ". Below this point, if the renewed downcutting has been active, a distinct new inner trench will often be cut within the old valley (Fig. 29 A).

In meandering sections of river, such rejuvenation may check further meander-development, and set up renewed vertical downcutting, so that the meanders are cut down into the solid rock, and the river develops a deep canyon-like valley while

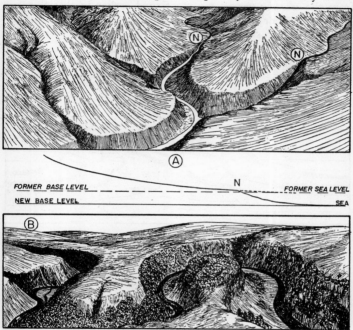

Fig. 29. *Features of rejuvenation in river-valleys.*

(*A*) '*Valley-in-valley*' *forms, with the unmodified earlier valleys remaining above the ' nick-points ' (N).*
Longitudinal profile of such a valley is shown below. Note the steep and irregular profile below the nick-point.
(B) *Incised meanders.*

preserving the twisting loops of its earlier course. An excellent example of this type of development is afforded by the River Wye in Herefordshire (Fig. 29 B).

Lower down, in the open valley and flood-plain tracts, minor rejuvenation will often create a different type of feature, *rejuven-*

ation-terraces. Renewed downcutting causes the river to cut away again much of the gravel and sand earlier deposited, but fragments of the old alluvial spreads are often left lying along the valley-sides in the form of gravel terraces. These are distinct from the *meander-terraces* we mentioned earlier in that they are generally longer and more continuous, often occur at similar heights on both sides of the valley, and, followed downstream,

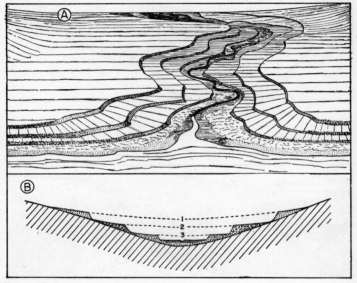

Fig. 30. *Rejuvenation-terraces :*

    (*A*) *Ideal sequence of terraces grading into raised strand-lines on the coast.*

    (*B*) *Section of triple series of terraces.*

maintain approximately the same profile as the river itself. Occasionally a whole series of such features can be found at various heights above the river. Such a series can be formed if the base-level sinks not steadily, but by a series of jerks separated by sufficiently long intervals for the waves of rejuvenation to work back far upstream. In the case illustrated in Fig. 30, caused by periodic fall in the base-level, terrace I, the highest, is the oldest, terrace III, the lowest and youngest. In the actual terrace-sequences that occur along the Thames and some other British rivers "the highest the oldest" is not always correct, for fluctuating base-levels in the past have left terraces at variable heights, and the age-sequence, and hence the sequence of movements, can only be worked out with the aid of fossils contained in the river-gravels. Ideally, such river-terraces, if continued down to the sea, should link up with old shorelines marking their respective former sea-level positions. Such cases occur for instance in the lower Rhone valley, and along the coast of Peru, but in Britain, although we have both river-terraces and raised marine beaches, the connections are obscure, and the correlations present some exceedingly difficult problems to the geologist and physical geographer.

It is to features like compound river-profiles, "valley-in-valley" forms, rejuvenation river-terraces, and the like that the physical geographer must however turn if he seeks to decipher the denudational history of landscapes. Careful study of these features has revealed that over most of Britain, if not all, our landscapes are the product of "polycyclic" past development rather than one simple and continuous evolution even since the Alpine phase of mountain-building. In more recent earth history, it would appear that conditions have seldom been stable long enough for anything like a true extensive peneplain to develop. Cycles of development have been continuously interrupted and started off again, leaving us with our present landscapes pleasantly interspersed with hills. If we look closely at our hill areas, however, we can often see interesting suggestions of widespread "levels" cut across them ; tracts of country now dissected by valleys, but in which the summits of the intervening areas all lie at about the same elevation. If in imagination you fill in all the valleys of many parts of, for instance, the Scottish Highlands or the Pennines, you are left with areas almost flat, though high above the sea. These cut-up high-level platforms are not original structures, for the surfaces cut across inclined and contorted strata. They must be old surfaces cut by *erosion*, yet erosion could not have worn them flat at their present elevations. We must interpret them, therefore, as old erosional *plains*—peneplains if you like—produced in the past by mature denudation down near sea-level, but later uplifted and carved up by the valleys of later erosional cycles. Research is revealing a multitude of such uplifted ancient erosion-surfaces, and by correlating them we are beginning to trace some of the stages by which our present scenery has evolved. The picture is still far from complete, but we know enough amply to justify the proposition set out in the opening chapter of this book : that in landscape nothing is really fixed or final. What we see is the compound product of a multitude of interwoven past cycles of scenic development, many left incomplete, and all still undergoing slow changes under the processes in operation today.

CHAPTER VIII

THE ROCK FACTOR IN LANDSCAPE:
LIMESTONE AREAS

IN tracing out the broad principles of landscape evolution, we have skimmed over many complications. Landscapes have been presented as the products of progressive sculpture of areas variously uplifted and distorted by earth activity; the differences in them as being explicable in part by the nature of the original uplift and the structures imposed on the rocks, in part by the stage of sculpture attained, and in part by the conditions guiding the sculpturing process. This last theme will be followed up in the next two chapters, but there is another " variable " that affects the results and which demands more attention than we have hitherto given it, and that is the character of the rocks from which the landscape is carved.

We earlier noted the main divisions of the earth's rocks, and here and there we have illustrated their varying reactions to the processes of denudation. In Chapter IV for instance we saw how the different resistance of igneous rocks from that of those they break through can develop highly distinctive landforms in volcanic regions as denudation proceeds. This principle clearly has general application. Wherever rocks of markedly different character—and by character we here imply resistance to denudation—occur together, the less resistant will be apt to get cut away more rapidly than the more resistant, so that the latter will be left outstanding in hills, knolls, and ridges, while the former are worn into hollows and valleys. The ribbed topography of scarplands illustrates this principle on a regional scale. It can be studied in detail where complex folded or faulted structures have produced a more intimate alternation of rock-types. The indented pattern of cliffed coasts illustrates it most effectively where marine erosion is eating into regions of complex structure (Chap. XV). In old regions of worn-down mountains we frequently find that the hills no longer coincide with structural axes at all, but with the exposures of more enduring rock, left outstanding in the overall reduction. Thus many Scottish hills are built of quartzite, one of the most resistant of rocks, while bands of shale are cut into valleys. Of great importance in guiding the detailed pattern of landscape development, rock-character, however, seldom assumes the position of a predominant scenic control. Only one group of rocks which occurs widely reacts to denudation sufficiently distinctively to " produce its own scenery ", irrespective—in favourable circumstances —of all but the most extreme conditions of structure and climate. That group is the limestones which, when sufficiently thick and pure, do often produce a highly individual type of land surface.

The distinctive features of well-developed limestone scenery result from the unusually large part played by solution processes in the denudation of this rock. Limestones vary much in their character and mode of formation, but all are of sedimentary origin and contain a high percentage of lime (calcium carbonate). The most extensive formations grew on sea-floors, and were built largely of the shells, skeletons, and other hard limey parts of marine organisms, large and small. We have shelly limestones, built of large shells and fossils, others built of corals, others again, like the Chalk, composed largely of extremely tiny shells of minute organisms called foraminifera. Many limestones on the other hand are compact and massive, having grown by chemical precipitation from lime-rich waters, and some of the shelly ones have been compacted by the internal percolation of water and deposition of lime cements. So far as landscape effects are concerned, however, it is enough to draw a distinction between the soft limestones like the Chalk, and hard massive limestones, and to distinguish regions where extensive beds of thick and pure limestone occur from those built of " half-and-half " rocks such as sandstones with a lime cement, or those where only thin beds of limestone occur between intercalated beds of sandstone and shale. As might be expected, it is only where we have thick and fairly pure limestones that we find the rock factor beginning to dominate the scenery.

The chemical nature of the attack of natural waters upon limestones we noted in Chap. V. We turn now to its results. Most limestones contain well-developed systems of joints, and it is down these joints and other cracks that the solution-attack is concentrated. Rainwater, working down the fissures, enlarges them by solution, and so in time opens up passages by which it can flow away underground.—In well-developed limestone country we thus find a marked lack of surface drainage. Streams developed on outcrops of other rocks, or on patches of impervious clay on the limestone surface, seep away underground directly they pass on to the bare limestone itself, or tumble into open fissures or vertical " swallow-holes ". No orderly pattern of surface drainage thus gets a chance to develop, and denudation proceeds by general weathering and the chemical solution effected by rainwaters on their way downward into the rock. The pattern of surface features thus tends to be somewhat chaotic, inequalities reflecting differences in the resistance of the rock to solution rather than systematic stream-sculpture. In the hollows residual soils accumulate, built of the insoluble clay particles left as the limestone dissolves, but the soils tend to be thin and the vegetation remains scanty. Trees are often almost lacking because of the lack of surface water, and harsh dry grasses clothe the hillsides. But often at every turn the bare rock breaks through the scanty soil cover, carved into a variety of fantastic shapes. Where the bedding is fairly horizontal extensive rock-pavements may develop, cut up by deep gullies into separate blocks. Such are the " clints " and " grikes " of the Yorkshire limestone moors, the gullies being simply enlarged joints (Fig. 31 A).

Scattered about the hillsides and bare grassy slopes are often to be found round or funnel-shaped hollows, in the Pennines known as " shake-holes ", which reflect more concentrated solution down vertical pipes, or subsidence of the surface over underground cavities. These are interspersed with occasional gaping holes that plunge vertically into the ground and may drop hundreds of feet. Downwards these " swallow-holes " frequently enlarge into enormous caverns and grottoes. Alum Pot and Gaping Gill on Ingleborough are well-known examples, the great chamber in Gaping Gill being large enough to contain York Minster. From such caverns ramifying tunnels and galleries may lead miles underground, sometimes emerging in caves opening into the hillside.   In many of these subterranean channels large streams race along, dropping in waterfalls where

Fig. 31. Features of limestone country :
   (A) Limestone pavement with ' clints ' and ' grikes', above Malham Cove, Craven area.
   (B) Malham Cove.

the galleries change level, and sometimes opening into underground lakes.   The explorations of " pot-holers ", and tests made by putting colouring matter into streams where they tumble underground and tracing where the coloured water emerges, have enabled the underground watercourses to be mapped in some regions, and it is clear that complete river-systems may exist far down below the harsh and waterless surface. Swallow-holes, caverns, and passages alike have been hollowed out over the centuries by the dissolving power of the water, which has dug its way ever deeper below the surface. It must not be overlooked, however, that both hydraulic action and active stone-corrasion go on in these underground streams, the latter involving true pot-hole cutting through the agency of stones dropping in down the shafts. Within the caverns, however, rock is formed as well as destroyed. Water charged with lime, dripping from the roofs, builds the picturesque aprons, stalactites, and stalagmites that give many of these grottoes their chief attraction. The rock composing them, a form of limestone called calcareous tufa, is identical with the " fur " that forms in the kettles of those who live in regions of hard water.

The limits to which this downward migration of the drainage can penetrate are determined by the elevation of the ground sur-face and the geological structure. Obviously the features described can only develop on fairly high ground, for limestones situated near sea-level remain saturated with water to near the ground-surface and streams cannot dissolve their way downwards. Thus we find the most distinctive limestone scenery in areas like the Mendips and the Craven uplands in Britain, the high " Cau-sses " of south-central France, and the " Karst " hill-tracts of Dalmatia. The thicker the limestone, the deeper the penetration can go, but it is frequently checked by a change of rock. Often limestones overlie impervious formations like shales, and at the junction the water is held up. Along the outcrop of such rock-junctions on the hill-slopes the underground waters emerge as springs or fully-grown streams issuing from caverns. Spec-tacular " coves " may surround such emergences. The " Fon-taine ", of Vaucluse in Provence is a classic French example, paralleled in England by Malham Cove (Fig. 31 B).

In some limestone tracts, like the Causses of France, rivers rising beyond the limits of the limestone areas cut right across the latter. They now run on the underlying impervious clays, but traverse spectacular gorges left by their earlier erosion, the

limestone cliffs rising sheer and bold because of the lack of surface waterflow to wear them back. Gorges, with similar cliff-
like walls but now entirely dry, also occur frequently in limestone
areas. Familiar British examples are Cheddar Gorge and
Burrington Combe in the Mendips, and the gorge above Malham

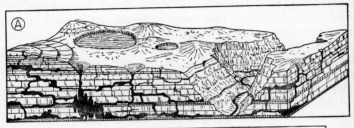

Fig. 32 :
   (*A*) *Features of " Karst" country (schematic). Underground solution-channels and
   caverns in solid black. The higher ones would now be abandoned, the water
   seeping out along the floor of the river-gorge which has cut down to an impervious
   formation.*
   (*B*) *Limestone gorge of the R. Jonte, " Causse" country, central France.*

Cove in Craven. These may have been cut by surface streams
in times past when the saturation-level of the rock was higher
than it is today, or they may represent old underground caverns
in which the roofs have been dissolved away or have collapsed.
We cannot be sure.

The most extensive tract of highly-evolved limestone " solu-
tion-scenery " in Europe is that of the Karst zone of Istria and
northern Jugo-Slavia. Despite heavy rainfall this region is virtually a stone desert, lacking systematic surface drainage, and in
places modelled into a chaos of pits, hollows, and residual
ridges. Much of it is bare rock, and aerial photographs show
the surface to be pitted with solution cavities until it resembles
Gruyere cheese. Apart from the features earlier listed, this
area contains numerous large flat-floored depressions called
" Poljes " which seem to be partly of tectonic origin. Many
contain fertile soil in which water is retained, so they are generally
dotted with farms and intensively cultivated, forming oases in
the arid stony wilderness around. Indeed, by reason of its lack
of surface water, well-developed Karst-type country has a good
deal in common with the deserts. The Yucatan peninsula, for
instance, although receiving heavy tropical rainfall is largely
barren and unsettled because of the permeability of its limestone
platforms.

Limestone scenery cannot be left without some brief mention
of the " soft " varieties, well represented in Britain by the
Chalk. Friable, soft, and offering only limited resistance to
mechanical abrasion, the Chalk of southern and eastern England
yet stands up in many hills and escarpments above the surrounding
rocks. This hill-building capacity results in the main from its
permeability. Full of joints, and fairly porous (*See* Chap. XIII)
it absorbs water greedily and its higher tracts are markedly
deficient in surface water save where covered by impermeable
clays. The Chalk country, however, shows none of the harsh
angular features of Karst scenery. Instead its outlines are highly
distinctive by reason of their smooth delicate flowing curves.
The homogeneity of the rock, its purity, and the part played by
overall solution in its weathering are responsible for this characteristic. The most intriguing feature of the Chalk country,
however, is the presence of numerous dry valleys scoring its
surface ; valleys manifestly cut by streams but now carrying no
water-flow. Two types of explanation have been offered for
the origin of these valleys. One is that they were cut by surface
streams when the ground was so full of water that the streams

E

could not soak away, i.e. the " water-table " (*See* Chap. XIII) was much higher than it is now. The fall in the water-table is believed to have been caused not by any marked diminution of rainfall, but by the progress of denudation which has caused the Chalk escarpments to retreat, the scarps to become higher, and the " spring-line " or level at which the water comes out on top of the impermeable Gault Clay that underlies the Chalk in consequence to fall deeper below the plateau-surface. Alternatively it has been suggested that many of these valleys were cut during the Great Ice Age, when southern Britain experienced a sub-arctic climate so that the ground was frozen and streams could flow over the normally permeable Chalk without sinking away. Both theories may contain elements of the truth; but the case is instructive in revealing how, to explain landscape features, we often have to appeal to past changes of climate. This takes us on to the subject of the next two chapters.

CHAPTER IX

THE LANDSCAPES OF DESERTS

IN studying landscapes we have so far restricted our attention to areas where rivers and streams form the spear-head of the sculpturing process, as in our familiar landscapes of Britain. Since such conditions prevail over the greater part of the earth's lands we can justifiably regard the river-carved landscape as the " normal " type ; but nearly a quarter of the earth's land-surface is so dry that permanent streams are entirely lacking, and further great areas are so cold that although water exists in plenty it is held locked in the relatively immobile forms of snow and ice. In both types of region the " normal " balance of earth-sculpturing processes is upset, and highly distinctive types of scenery develop in consequence. We will review these two distinctive "abnormals" in turn.

Arid regions, or deserts, owe their existence quite simply to insufficient rainfall. Not, be it noted, a total lack of rainfall, for there is probably no spot on earth where rain (or snow) *never* falls. Arid deserts are defined by their relative, or effective, dryness, judged by their lack of normal vegetation. Rainfall figures alone will not define desert conditions satisfactorily. Ten inches of rain in the year will almost inevitably mean true desert in the Tropics, but the same amount in high latitudes may allow quite a lot of vegetation to grow. Much depends on the many factors which govern what happens to rainfall and how much of it becomes available for plant growth—the conditions of temperature (which govern the evaporation-rate), how and when the rain falls, and the nature and constitution of the ground, which helps to determine what proportion of any rainfall flows away over the surface, soaks gently into the soil, or sinks in too deeply for plants to get at it. In view of all these variables there is clearly no one simple numerical criterion by which we can define the beginnings of desert country, and indeed in nature conditions hardly ever change abruptly along fixed lines.

Climate changes by gradual transition, so that the earth's most arid tracts are mostly surrounded by wide zones of lesser aridity linking them almost imperceptibly with better-watered regions. For our present purpose, however, we can limit our discussion to areas in which (*a*) rainfall is very scanty, irregular, and insufficient to maintain any co-ordinated system of permanent streams and rivers ; (*b*) evaporation is dominant, to the extent that far more water would evaporate from the land (were it present) than is actually supplied by rainfall (this is, of course, the reason for the lack of permanent rivers) ; and (*c*) in consequence of the lack of available water, vegetation is very sparse and limited to

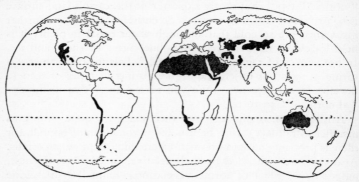

Fig. 33. Distribution of the earth's arid regions.

scattered special drought-resisting types. There is no continuous ' carpet '.

Since the largest areas exhibiting these conditions occur in the Tropics (we shall examine later the reasons for this) the earth's great deserts are predominantly *hot* deserts, and for them we can add the following general characteristics to our list :—

(*d*) Normally the skies are cloudless, and the air extremely dry. By day the sun beats down on the naked ground and temperatures reach extreme figures, 120°F in the shade being common in summer. By night, however, because of the clear skies and dry air, temperatures fall sharply. Frost may occur after a midday temperature of over 100°F. The hot deserts thus typically

THE LANDSCAPES OF DESERTS

experience great daily ranges of temperature. (e) Finally, most deserts are notably windy regions, and the open landscapes and lack of vegetation give optimum conditions for wind to work on the desiccated surfaces.

Excluding the Polar regions, nearly a third of the earth's lands experiences these conditions in greater or lesser degree. Australia is the worst-off continent, having 43% of its area classed as " arid ", but Africa runs it close with 40% and a far larger actual area of desert country. The Sahara alone is as big as the whole United States. Asia has 23% arid, including some extensive deserts, and large deserts occur in both the Americas, although in neither continent is the percentage over 10. In Europe we have only a small patch of truly arid country around the Caspian Sea. Fig. 33 shows the distribution of the world's desert areas.

When we examine the landscape characteristics of deserts, the effects of the conditions described become immediately apparent, for desert scenery shows many strongly distinctive features wherever it occurs. Variation is due chiefly to differences in geological structure and tectonic history. The N. American deserts, for instance, are largely mountainous, for geologically the land is young, and folded mountains and block-faulted " basin-and-range " structures predominate. Some of the Asian deserts are also mountainous, but in Africa and Australia the desert lands are geologically old, and the imprint of aridity is set on vast monotonous plains cut by aeons of denudation across ancient crystalline rocks and little-disturbed sedimentaries. Leaving aside such structural differences, we can say that desert scenery is typically harsh and angular. Level plains are abruptly broken by jagged escarpments and gaunt ribbed mountains, and there is an almost total absence of the smooth flowing curves so prevalent in the humid landscape. Valleys, where they occur, are steep-sided, rocky, and irregular, their floors cumbered with boulders and rock fragments—the type of the American canyon, the North African wadi, and the Indian nullah (Fig. 34 A). The ground lacks any true soil cover, and carries at best a sparse sprinkling of stunted shrubs and dry grasses, at worst no vegetation whatsoever. Bare rock

Fig. 34 :

(*A*) *Wadi, eastern desert of Egypt.*

(*B*) *Typical scenery in the sandstone country, Libyan Desert, with numerous conical relict hills.*

is exposed everywhere in the hills, and is littered with loose angular debris. On the plains, surfaces of naked rock (the Saharan ' hamada ') alternate with areas covered with pebbles or small rock chips (the Saharan ' serir '), or with sand. Contrary to popular belief the great deserts are by no means uniformly covered with drifting sand, but great patches of sand-desert do occur, and the sand may be built into systematic patterns of dunes. Surface water is, of course, almost entirely lacking, but where the ground drops low enough underground water may come within reach of the surface, and in such spots oases occur. Some have open pools, maintained by spring-flow despite the intense evaporation. A few permanent rivers also cross the great deserts, like the Nile and Colorado, but these draw their water-supplies from beyond the desert confines. Elsewhere, as in central Asia and Australia, rivers flowing into the desert from surrounding mountains dry up and disappear, or flow only for short periods after heavy rains or snow-melt in the mountains. Some such rivers lead to interior lakes and marshes which have no outlet, like Lake Chad, Lake Eyre, Lake Balkash and the Caspian Sea. Evaporation prevents such lakes from overflowing, and many periodically dry out completely leaving tracts of saline mud. These lakes exist because many desert areas contain vast shallow depressions of structural origin, from which rivers have never been able to cut outlets to the sea. The great deserts, indeed, are predominantly regions of " interior-drainage ", in so far as any surface drainage exists at all.

Finally, we may add that the strangeness of the desert land-scape to European eyes is partly a matter of colour. Unrelieved by vegetation, the harsh browns, yellows and greys look dead and forbidding, the whole aspect often calling to mind the surface of the moon. After some weeks in the desert the eyes ache for the restful greens of our own countryside.

To account for the features of desert scenery we may start with this very lack of vegetation. Without it, no true soils develop, and the wastes of weathering remain loose and friable, the finer particles being continually sifted out by the wind. Over great areas the bare rock is continuously exposed, so that weathering has an unusually large surface of bedrock to work on. Lack of water hampers it, but the extreme changes of temperature accelerate mechanical disintegration of the rocks. From the universal occurrence of sharp fractured debris it is generally concluded that temperature-shattering dominates the weathering processes of deserts, but chemical decay also plays an important part, for despite the surface dryness, moisture from the occasional rains and night dews can linger inside the rocks, decay their minerals, and so help to disintegrate them. Sandstones crumble away to release the raw material for dune-building. Limestones break down into dust. The massive igneous rocks like granite typically weather into enormous rounded boulders by exfoliation (*see* Fig. 16 A). In addition, mineral crusts often form on the rock surface. These, sometimes called " desert varnish ", are apparently formed by the surface crystallization of dissolved mineral salts drawn out from inside the rock by the intense evaporation. In general, unchecked weathering on rock surfaces widely exposed creates continuously a surface veneer of loose residues. What happens to all this material ?

Because of the lack of surface water, gravitational sliding of the loose material downhill is checked. The great resistance of dry friction has to be overcome, and thus except on very steep slopes loose fragments tend to remain where they are to decay in situ. This greater friction does much to explain the steep slopes of desert hills, and the abrupt angles at which they rise from the plains. There is none of the persistent soil creep that smoothes out our own hillsides. Wind, however, is always at work winnowing out and carrying away the finer dust as it forms. As we noted in Chap. V, this dust is mostly carried right out of the deserts, to fall in moister regions or on the seas. The coarser sand grains are not so readily moved, for, being much heavier, they cannot be carried in true suspension. They are rolled or bounced along, and move relatively slowly[1]. In time, however, the wind can move great masses of sand long distances, to accumulate it in localities where factors of topography and wind conditions check the movement. Here are built the great systems of dunes.

Apart from carrying away the loose sand and dust, however, wind does carry out some direct land-sculpture, although its powers in this respect are restricted. It used to be thought that many features of rocky deserts like undercut cliffs, pinnacle rocks, natural arches and the like had been carved out by wind-driven sand. The effectiveness of the natural " sand-blast " action that certainly does go on in deserts has, however, been questioned. It can certainly burnish iron telegraph poles, and

[1] Even in a sand storm the sand is not in true suspension. Experimental work has shown that the grains fly with a bouncing motion off the ground, and only in exceptional winds do they rise more than a few feet.

cut through walls of sun-dried bricks, while in a sandstorm paint is quickly removed from a motor-car. But its direct erosive effects on the ground seem to be limited to the grooving and polishing of bare rock surfaces, and the carving of gullies in soft friable formations. The latter sometimes leave between them long streamlined ridges called, in central Asia, " Yardangs ". The spectacular natural arches and pinnacle rocks of arid regions familiar to cinema-goers from " western " films, are now thought to owe their creation rather to slow differential weathering. Wind, however, does appear to have been responsible for carving out one important type of landscape feature. Often in deserts we find large enclosed depressions cut below the general surface, such as the Qattara Depression south of El Alamein, and the hollows in which lie the desert oases of Egypt. No other agency than wind can have scoured out these great hollows, for wind alone (apart from moving ice, hardly to be appealed to in the Sahara) can lift rock-wastes *upwards* and so cut an enclosed depression. Minor effects of the persistent wind-action can be seen in the rounding of the actual sand-grains (grains of desert sand are typically rounded, in contrast to the " sharp " sand found in river-beds) and in the facets often cut by sand-blast action on pebbles to convert them into shapes like Brazil nuts. Such pebbles, called " Dreikanter " (German : three-edged), are an unmistakable sign of persistent sand-blowing. You can pick them up on the Culbin Sands of the Moray Firth and else-where around our coasts, and found in ancient sandstones they tell geologists that the rock was formed from consolidated desert sand.

If the wind plays a relatively minor role in the sculpture of desert landscapes, however, how are we to account for the many distinctive eroded forms ? Contradictory as it may appear, we must attribute many of them to the action of running water. As we stressed earlier, rain does fall in deserts, and although intervals of several years may elapse between showers it is a peculiarity of desert rainfall that when it does come it generally falls in torrential downpours. These may completely flood the desert surface, (the suburbs of Cairo are often flooded by desert storms) and paradoxical as it sounds people have on occasion been drowned in deserts through camping in a dry stream-bed that has turned in a few minutes into a raging torrent. These violent rainstorms can produce devastating effects. Their power is much increased by the lack of vegetation to break the force of the fall, and of plants and organic litter on the ground to absorb the water and check its swift runoff. The percentage of a rainshower that flows away over the ground surface during a desert storm is thus generally much greater than that in humid regions. By such surface flows, vast quantities of the loose stones, sand, and dust that cumber the hillsides are periodically swept down and out into the plains. Often the flow becomes liquid mud, with no water visible at all. On the gentler ground, however, such " sheet-flows " are soon checked as the water evaporates and sinks away, and the jumbled mass of material is dumped. By this process great alluvial cones and benches are built out along mountain-fronts, and in hilly country the basins between hills may get completely filled in with such material in the course of time. But not only do these floods sweep loose material down on to the plains and hollows. In the mountains and foothills, where confined to definite channels, they rip out the great canyons and wadis, and, in the long run, may cut away the ridges between them. The action is intermittent, but over centuries none the less effective. Being violent and spasmodic, it creates irregular and un-graded valleys, but although when the traveller views such canyons nothing seems to be happening in them, in the long run the lower outlying parts of the mountains are planed away by their growth, and in their retreat leave flattish bevelled-off rock-platforms, thinly veneered with debris, grading out into the filled-in hollows. Such planed-off rock-platforms encircle many of the desert mountains in the N. American deserts, where they are called " pediments ", and although views differ about the exact mechanism of their evolution, it seems likely that the mountains are gradually cut away by their inward extension. In this way, as W. M. Davis saw it, a " cycle " of landscape development goes on with progressive reduction and cutting-back of the mountains, the infilling of hollows with waste, and the extension of wide undulating plains. The end-product of a cycle of erosion he conceived would be a variable " denudational surface " of very low relief analagous to the peneplain of the humid lands.

Before the final achievement of such a featureless surface, however, we should expect to see many isolated residual mounds and hills still outstanding, separated by wide stretches of flattish erosion-surface. Such, indeed, is the typical landscape of many desert regions (Fig. 34 B). The processes at work appear to cut away the hills by eating into them around the edges, and for this reason the hills often rise abruptly from the level plains. Typical of great areas of arid and sub-arid Africa are landscapes of wide flat plains dotted over with peculiar abruptly-rising hills like haystacks, called " Inselbergs " (German : island-mountain). These are the relics of older, higher-level surfaces now almost completely cut away. But we find similar isolated abrupt hills in much wetter areas in the Tropics, like Nigeria and Mozambique (Fig. 35 I). and most authorities now believe that true inselbergs are not really a product of desert conditions at all. We come here to one of the great problems about deserts. To what extent are the features we now see in them the product of really " arid " processes and conditions, and to what extent have they been inherited from earlier periods of wetter climate ?

That the climate of many (if not all) desert areas has been wetter in the past there can be no doubt. In the interior Sahara we find great " fossil " rivers hundreds of miles long that are now bone dry. The mud deposits of long-vanished lakes can be found today being carved away by wind in interior Libya. In the same region, as everywhere over the Sahara, we find remains of prehistoric man, and his rock paintings often depict scenes of cattle-herding in regions now without a blade of vegetation. We even find small crocodiles in the pools of the Tibesti mountains that must have got there by water, though the mountains are now isolated by hundreds of miles of waterless desert. The evidence indicates that the wetter periods of the past very likely coincided in time with epochs when much of Europe was buried under ice (*See* Chap. X), but we do not yet know just how wet the climate was, nor how long the humid conditions persisted. Clearly, however, we have to make allowance for such past changes when interpreting the scenery,

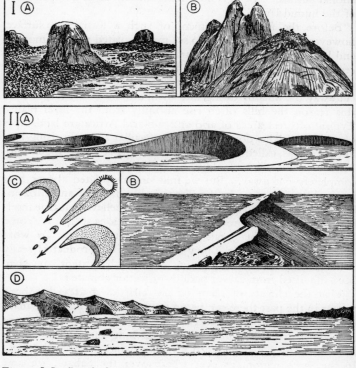

Fig. 35. I. Inselberg landscapes :
   (A) Rounded inselbergs of granite, northern Nigeria.
   (B) Close-up of a granite inselberg showing exfoliation of the rock.
   II. Desert sand-dunes :
   (A) Barchans.
   (B) A ' sand-shadow ' dune, in the lee of an obstacle.
   (C) Barchans and sand-shadow dune in relation to wind direction.
   (D) " Seif " dune chains in the Libyan Desert. The scale is indicated by the two
       motor-cars in the foreground.

and one of the most interesting problems in the physical geography of the great deserts is to elucidate what is due to present conditions, and what is an inheritance from different conditions in the past. Conversely, we find in some regions of humid climate today traces of past desert conditions. Deserts covered most of Britain in the remote geological periods of the Permian and Triassic, but much more recently, in some phases of the Great Ice Age, there were periods of extremely dry (though cool) climate in western Europe during which deposits of wind-blown " loess " were laid down across the centre of the continent, and great sand-dunes were built across the plains of northern Germany and Poland. These " fossil " sand-dunes account for various patches of heath-country in these regions, and comparable grown-over dunes in northern Nigeria reveal that in some period of the past the southern edge of the Sahara was a good deal further south than it is today. Whether the Sahara has changed its boundaries during more recent times is a problem much argued. There are some who hold that it is continuously extending, but the evidence is far from certain. We will touch on the interesting and important matter of historical climatic change later on, but before leaving deserts we must say a few words about their most distinctive and best-known feature—their various sand-formations.

The sand-areas of the great deserts, as we said, make up only a fraction of their total area, but exhibit a variety of different features. The sand itself is the residue of ages of slow weathering, being released mainly by the breakdown of sandstone rocks, themselves sometimes the consolidated dunes of some remote geological period. Drifted by the wind, and with the finer dust sifted out of it, this sand accumulates in favourable localities (often areas of low relief, or great depressions) and there is piled up into many distinct types of formation. Thus in north Africa we can distinguish between :—

(a) " Sand sheet " areas, flat plains uniformly veneered with a thin flat covering of hard sand which makes an ideal surface to motor over.

(b) Regions where the sand is deeply piled up, and thrown into tempestuous waves. Such are the great " ergs " of the French Sahara, sometimes a hundred miles across and very difficult to traverse.

(c) Other regions deeply buried under sand where it is shaped into gigantic elongated ridges often hundreds of feet high and a mile or more across, sometimes called " whalebacks ".

(*d*) Belts of more regular types of true dunes.

The last are of two main varieties. " Barchans " are separate rounded mounds of sand with a bite taken out of the down-wind side. They generally occur in groups or strings, and migrate slowly down-wind as the sand is blown up the windward side of the mound and slips down the steep concave " slip-face ". The two " horns " are built out because of the reduced frictional retardation of the wind around the edges of the pile. Barchans occur locally in most of the great deserts, and range in size from a few yards to a quarter of a mile or so in diameter (Fig. 35 (II). More spectacular, however, are the great longitudinal dunes like gigantic railway embankments which in Egypt are called " Seif " (Arabic : sword) dunes. These run and grow parallel with the prevailing wind, extending by accretion at the down-wind end. In the western desert of Egypt huge belts of these dunes occur, each dune rising 100 or 200 feet in height, and continuing straight and unbroken sometimes for fifty miles or more. Similar, though smaller, longitudinal dunes cover large tracts of the Australian deserts, but in other continents linear dunes are known which build transversely across the main wind direction. There are also many miscellaneous types of sand accumulation built in the lee of obstacles where pockets of " dead air " occur.

Just why sand dunes in deserts assume these markedly different shapes in different areas is a problem not yet fully understood. We know the basic laws relating sand-movement to wind-velocity, and the mechanisms by which sand is moved, but why the sand should be spread indiscriminately abroad in one area, and in another piled up neatly into geometrically regular dunes as though swept up with a broom ; and why the barchan shape occurs in one locality, and the longitudinal shape in another, are still to some degree mysteries. In both the Sahara and Australia enormous simple arcuate patterns are revealed by the dune-systems extending over thousands of miles, and these must clearly relate to the prevailing wind-systems, for wind alone builds these great " free " dunes of the desert ; but just how dunes and air movements are related will need much further study to answer with certainty. Fascinating to the physical geographer, dunes, however, can be a curse when they start invading cultivated land or blocking railways (as they often do), and the understanding of their mechanism of growth has much more than an academic interest.

CHAPTER X

LANDSCAPES UNDER SNOW AND ICE

CONTRASTING sharply with the hot deserts are the lands where snow and ice permanently cover the ground. Such conditions occur most extensively in the Polar regions, but smaller tracts of glacial country occur on the higher mountains in all latitudes, even on the Equator and among the hot deserts. This fact badly puzzled the ancients, but the explanation is simple. For snow to lie permanently on the ground demands conditions in which the rate of supply equals the rate of removal. Fallen snow is removed by direct evaporation, by melting, and by rain-washing, and the lower the temperature the less active these processes become. The essential condition for permanent snows is thus low temperature, especially in summer, and low temperatures are not the monopoly of the Polar zones. Temperatures at which fallen snow will melt and evaporate too slowly to clear the ground before the next fall can be found anywhere on earth provided you climb high enough, for everywhere temperature falls away steadily with altitude. The level above which such conditions obtain is called the " snowline ", and its height varies over the earth roughly in accordance with variation in sea-level temperatures. At the Equator it stands at some 16 to 18,000 feet, and only the few Andean and East African peaks which project above this level carry permanent snowcaps. To North and South it gently declines in height, dropping to about 9,000 feet in the western Alps, some 5,000 feet in southern Norway, and approaching sea-level within the Polar Circles. In Scotland it just clears the highest hills. Were Ben Nevis a few hundred feet higher, the snow-patches which linger in its shaded north-face gullies each year well into the autumn would form parts of a true permanent snowcap. The position of the snowline is not, however, a simple function of latitude. Since it reflects a balance between supply and loss of snow its height varies locally with factors of snowfall, topography, exposure and so on. Thus in the Alps it is about 2,000 feet lower in the wetter western mountains than in the drier east, and generally some 1,000 to 2,000 feet lower on the shaded northern slopes than on the sunny slopes facing south.   But there is a general decline in height towards the high latitudes, and only there do we find really extensive areas permanently ice and snow-covered.

The largest land-area affected is the Antarctic continent.   The greater part of this huge land-mass stands above the snowline, and on it, for an unknown period, the annual snows have accumulated and buried the land completely save for the higher peripheral mountains.   Under its own weight the snow has consolidated into ice, and the form of the ice-mantle at once tells us one interesting thing about land-ice—that it is in some measure plastic.   Were it completely rigid it would have grown up and up until the slopes of the gigantic dome were too steep for new snow to rest on them.   In fact, however, although so extensive, the Antarctic ice-sheet seems to be relatively thin (its maximum depth is believed to be about 6,000 feet), and in form it is a very flattened dome.   This flattened shape, and the fact that the ice comes right down to the coast below the snowline almost everywhere, shows that there must be some general flowage outward. The pieces which break away from the edges to float off as icebergs are a consequence of this outward flowage[1].   In the Ross Sea the main sheet is extended into the great ice platform of the Ross Barrier, which is at least partly afloat and rises and falls with the tide.   The Barrier appears to be mainly self-nourished, largely no doubt by snowfall on its surface, but also perhaps in part by the freezing of sea-water on to its base in winter.   The occurrence of sea-floor muds lying undisturbed on its surface, which have apparently worked their way up through the ice, suggests that this mechanism may make a major contribution to maintaining the Barrier.   Seawards the Barrier terminates in huge ice-cliffs, from which fragments periodically break away as tabular icebergs.   Those who saw the film " Scott of the Antarctic " will have a better idea than any words can convey of the beauty and majesty of this strange ice-scenery.

[1] Recent investigations indicate that the whole formation may now be shrinking in size and if so movement in the ice is probably slight.

In the Arctic conditions are different, for the area round the Pole is all sea. The sea-surface is permanently frozen, but the marine pack-ice never grows very thick, and is broken up and moved about by currents. On the huge island of Greenland, however, a second vast land ice-sheet is located. Greenland stands high, and although the snowline is still up at 2,000 feet at its southern tip, most of the land stands above that level. The snowfall over Greenland is also much greater than in the Antarctic, and three-quarters of the whole island is covered by a huge ice-cap which is in places 6,000 feet thick. Its surface rises in a flattened dome to over 10,000 feet, but around the edges isolated mountain peaks called " nunatakkr " emerge, and the ranges of coastal mountains are clear. Again we have evidence of flowage, for between them tongues of ice lead down from the ice-plateau as valley-glaciers, some descending below sea-level and periodically calving off icebergs. These icebergs carry away the surplus snowfall of Greenland which cannot be disposed of in other ways.

We cannot in this short book look closely at the many intriguing problems presented by these huge masses of ice, but one point about Greenland deserves mention. " Echo-sounding " through the ice has indicated that the land surface below the ice-cap may drop into a saucer-like hollow, and if this is so, it may well be a creation of the ice itself, the land having sunk isostatically under the enormous weight. This is of interest in relation to past vertical movements between land and sea in north-west Europe which, as we suggested in Chap. II, may have been caused by the past glaciation of that region. Before leaving the high latitudes, however, it is perhaps as well to stress that by no means all the land north of the Arctic Circle is ice-covered. The low-lying plains and islands of northern Canada, and the vast tundras of northern Siberia, although experiencing even colder winters than southern Greenland, receive insufficient snow for ice to form. In the short but warm summers the thin winter snows melt away, and although the ground a few feet down remains permanently frozen (borings in north-eastern Siberia reveal that it is frozen in places to depths of over 400 feet), the surface soil in summer is converted into a morass from which, because of the frozen subsoil, water cannot drain away. Liquid water is, for a short time, master of the land. Vast floods cover the areas round the rivers, and such roads as exist have to be built on a log foundation so that in summer they will " float ". In Spitzbergen and Iceland, however, which stand higher, we again find smaller icecaps on the high ground with valley-glaciers descending from them.

We may now turn to the more accessible and familiar tracts of mountain-glaciers like those of the Alps and Norway. In such high but dissected mountains not all the ground above the snowline is snow-covered (Fig. 36). The high peaks stick out with their steeper cliffs bare and rugged, snow only clinging to their gentler slopes and gullies; but between them the flatter saddles and cols are deeply buried. These areas serve as feeding-grounds for valley-glaciers. Snow falling on them lies where it falls and builds up a stratified accumulation. The pressure of the overlying layers, aided by melting and refreezing, gradually transforms the lower layers into transitional forms called " névé " and " firn ", from which the little air pockets are gradually squeezed out so that the whole mass is converted into tough granular ice. From the growing accumulation on the snowfields the surplus flows slowly off in divergent tongues of ice down the valleys to form the valley-glaciers whose snouts can be seen glittering above St. Moritz and Chamonix. It was proved long ago that these ice-tongues move forward, for stakes stuck in the ice slowly advanced. Also, stakes set out in line across a glacier were pulled out into a curve, showing that the movement was most rapid in the middle, where the ice is thickest. The reality of flow in glaciers is also demonstrated by the patterns of cracks or " crevasses " that develop in them where they pass over uneven places in the floor. At the head of such a glacier, where it leaves the snowfield there are generally several major cracks called " bergschrunds ", which mark the place where movement becomes appreciable. The rate of advance, although it varies much between different glaciers, is always of course relatively slow. Advance of several hundred feet a year is fast; often the annual movement is only 150 feet or so.

The mechanism by which glaciers move offers many problems, and is by no means yet completely understood. Glacier ice is a semi-crystalline solid. How then can it flow? In steep

Fig. 36. High ridges in the Alps. Above: Névéfield (gathering-ground of a glacier) with frost-sharpened 'arête' ridges and rock pinnacles (aiguilles) rising above. (Chamonix area, western Alps). Below: Frost-sharpened pinnacles in limestone (Dirupi di Larsec, Dolomites). Note the different appearance of the pinnacles in the two cases, due to contrast in rock-type.

glaciers there is clearly often some mass-sliding of the whole structure under gravity, but as the glacier adapts itself to curves and irregularities in its bed there must also be some type of differential movement within the ice. This may involve a sort of rolling of the component crystals over one another, in the manner of a pile of shot poured down an inclined board, but recent work suggests that differential sliding of segments of ice along shear-planes, or along thin layers of ice where the crystals are so arranged as to make movement easy, may play a major part. Whatever the exact mechanism or mechanisms, the ice advances under gravity until a point is reached at which the rate of melting in the advanced portion is sufficient to remove the amount of ice being brought forward, and at this point, generally far below the snowline, is located the " snout " of the glacier. In physical terms, the radiating glaciers of a high-level snowfield thus serve to prevent undue accumulation of snow by carrying off the surplus to lower and warmer levels where it can melt away. But in their slow movement the glaciers carry out important work in sculpturing the landscape.

If you examine any valley-glacier you will find that it is by no means all ice. On its surface lie many fragments of rock, concentrated along the edges where they may form continuous banks called " moraines ". The rock-fragments come from the steep rock-walls of the glacier valley, whence they are prised off by frost action to fall on to the glacier and get carried along with it. Hence the concentration along the edges. When two glaciers flow together, however, a central or " median " moraine may be formed by the union of the two adjacent lateral moraines. (Fig. 37 A). At the snout, all this material is deposited, and it is then revealed that a great deal more rock debris has been carried within the main body of the ice, and especially in its lower layers. As the ice melts this material builds crescentic mounds around the glacier snout called " terminal moraines ". Streams of melt-water issuing from the glacier sift through this material and comb out the smaller stones and sand into sheets called " outwash fans ", which may combine to form extensive " outwash plains " (Fig. 37 B). These are well illustrated today in southern Iceland, where multiple streams from the edges of the ice-sheet on Vatnajökull braid across the ten-mile wide outwash plain they have built. But the water also carries off in suspension vast quantities of finely pulverised rock waste which makes all glacial streams milky-white in colour. This fine " rock-flour " comes from within and below the glacier. It is a product of mechanical corrasion, and demonstrates the great erosive power of glaciers. While land deeply buried under snow or motionless ice is protected from the elements, and so undergoes little if

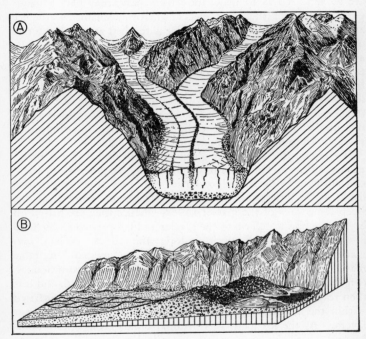

Fig. 37:

(*A*) *Valley-glacier, showing moraines and crevasses.*

(*B*) *Depositional features around a glacier-snout after retreat of the ice. Note the crescentic ridges of moraine, combed out by stream-flow into outwash plains, the small lake occupying the hollow where the glacier-tongue lay, and the rounded mounds of boulder-clay (drumlins).*

any attack, directly the ice begins to move the surface is scraped away as though by a gigantic file. The abrasive power of moving ice increases with increasing rate of movement, and the thicker the ice, the greater its erosive effect. Much of the abrasion is done by the sharp rock-fragments embedded in the sole of the ice, which act as cutting-tools—even as a river uses stones and boulders to wear away its bed—but the ice also seems able to tear away pieces of solid rock by a process called " plucking ", the mechanism of which is not yet thoroughly understood.   About the efficacy of glacier-erosion, however, there can be no doubt, for examination of the ground-features in any glacier valley yields evidence to convince the most sceptical.

In the Alps it is obvious to the discerning eye that in earlier days the glaciers were very much bigger and longer than they are now, for miles below their present snouts we encounter belts of old terminal moraine marking former limits.   Along the southern flanks of the Alps, such old morainic mounds have been in large measure responsible for the creation of many of the North Italian lakes.   But ascending any of the Alpine valleys above these outer ramparts a host of features catch the eye which differentiate these valleys sharply from the normal type of river-valley described in Chap. VI.   Instead of being V-shaped in cross section, these valleys have the form of a deep rounded " U ", often opening out at higher levels into a flattened " V " (*see* Fig. 38).   But not only is the cross-section different.   For long stretches these valleys run " unnaturally " straight, and all their lateral spurs seem to have been cut away.   Tributary valleys for the most part enter high up the steep valley-sides, and from their mouths streams tumble in waterfalls into the main valleys. These " hanging " tributary valleys indicate great overdeepening of the main valleys, which can hardly have been effected by normal river-erosion.   Study of the valley-floors reveals further peculiarities.   There is generally a great deal of bare rock exposed, most of the soil and loose debris having been stripped away, and the exposed rock-surfaces are markedly smooth and polished and occasionally scored with deep scratches called " striae " which are systematically aligned down-valley.   Protruding rock-bosses reveal smoothing and polishing on the up-valley side, although the down-valley side may be jagged and suggest that angular blocks have been torn away from it.   Finally, on the larger scale, these valleys advance upwards not in the smooth curve of the river-cut valley, but in a series of irregular steps

linked by breaks which may be steep enough to cause waterfalls
in the modern streams (Fig. 38 B).

There can be no question that these modifications are the work
of ice, and indeed you can see identical features immediately in
advance of the present glacier-snouts in areas that have only in

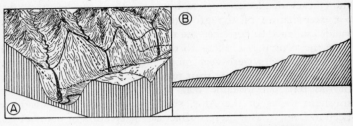

Fig. 38. Modification of a valley by glacier-action.
> (A) *Diagram of glaciated valley, showing over-deepening (broken lines indicate*
>   *previous profile), hanging tributary valleys etc. (modified after W. M. Davis).*
> (B) *Longitudinal profile of a glaciated valley, showing steps and rock-basin lakes.*
> (C) *The Lauterbrunnen valley, Switzerland, a classic example of a glaciated*
>   *mountain-valley. The Staubbach waterfall, on the right-hand side of the*
>   *valley, is nearly 1,000 feet high.*

recent years been uncovered by the glacier-retreat that has been
so marked a feature of the Alps and Norway in modern times.
Glaciers, when confined within enclosed valleys, clearly have
considerable powers of erosion. In their slow movement they
grind away their valley-floors, tear off protuberances, wear away

the outstanding spurs, and gradually gouge out a very distinctive valley-type, often hollowed deeply below the pre-existing valley in which they grew. Glaciers even seem to be able to dig out enclosed hollows in their valley-floors, for we find lakes in many valleys formerly occupied by glaciers which fill hollows carved in the solid rock that could have been excavated by no other agency. This deep erosion and rounding and polishing of the valley-floors, however, contrasts strongly with the forms displayed on upper ridges and peaks. There everything is jagged and sharp, the ridges carved into knife-edge " arêtes ", the peaks into precipices and needles. On these higher portions slopes are too steep for a protective blanket of snow to lie, and they stood above the level of glacier-erosion even when the glaciers were much larger. Frost action dominates their forms, and the piles of angular fragments that line the glaciers testify to the power of its relentless whittling away of the higher ridges (*See* Fig. 36).

Such, in brief, are the main features of the glaciated landscape in such a region as the Alps. But we need not go so far afield to study these features. Snow and ice are indeed now absent, but at every turn you can see in the hills of the Lake District, in N. Wales, or in the Highlands, just the same scenic modifications ; somewhat softened perhaps by weathering and stream-action since the departure of the ice, but quite unmistakable. Most of the larger valleys in these areas display the " U " cross-section and the over-deepening of glacial erosion. Hanging tributary valleys with streams descending from them in waterfalls can be found in scores. The rounded bosses of rock called " roches moutonnées " are to be seen in every Lake District valley, and with little trouble you can find rock surfaces scored by stones carried by past glaciers. We have in Loch Coruisk in Skye a perfect example of a lake occupying an ice-carved rock-basin (any reader knowing Skye will recall the scoured-down rock bar separating Coruisk from the sea), while above it the Cuillins, in their jagged peaks, rock needles, and knife-edge ridges, reflect frost-cutting far more severe than any affecting them today. Most convincing of all, perhaps, are the peculiar hemispherical hollows called " Cwms " in Wales, and " Coires " or " Corries " in Scotland, for which the French names " Cirques " has been generally adopted in technical works. These are to be found eaten into the mountain-sides in all our higher northern and western hill-areas. By encroaching on Snowdon from all sides they have created the narrow summit ridge of Crib Goch, while on Helvellyn they have left, by their backward and sideways extension, the knife-edge ridge of Striding Edge. No ordinary process of weathering or stream-cutting can account for these great hollows, but in the Alps or Norway you can see their mode of origin clearly demonstrated. There many still contain small steep glaciers or permanent snow-patches, which typically rise to an almost vertical " back wall ". It is believed that frost, snow, and ice alone have cut out these hollows. Possibly they originate by alternate freezing and thawing around and under a small patch of snow which gradually creates a shallow hollow in the hillside. Accumulating in this growing hollow, eventually sufficient snow collects for it to be converted into ice. Periodic sliding of this ice and snow abrades the rock-floor below and carries away loosened fragments, but it also opens up crevasses at the back of the ice-patch down which air can penetrate and attack the rock by frost-action. By this localised frost-shattering, and clearing away of the debris by the ice as it moves forward, the hollow is deepened and cut backward, the undercutting at the rear gradually creating the steep cliffed back wall. Many cirques as we see them today have an actual hollow in their floors containing a small tarn. Sometimes this is contained by a morainic dam, built by the cirque-glacier, but in some cases the solid rock is cut into a hollow. When the glacier was steep, such " hollowing-out " may be explained by a type of rotational slipping in segments of the cirque-glacier which concentrated the erosion downwards and left a rock-sill at the mouth of the hollow. Cirques can grow to a great size, and if they attack a mountain from all sides they can cut it back into a pyramidal peak. The Matterhorn is the classic example of a peak formed in this way. Snowdon and Helvellyn show successively less complete stages of the same process (see Fig. 39).

It was partly the similarity in features between our British hill-areas and the Alps that led geologists to the belief that in the geologically recent past our hills had nourished valley-glaciers, but the evidence of past glaciation in Britain is much more extensive than that.   All over the country north of the line Bristol Channel to Thames can be found what are called " erratics ";

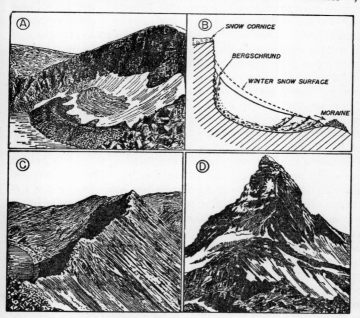

Fig. 39. Cirques and associated features.

    (*A*) *An active cirque, containing a small glacier (Skautböe, Jotunheim, Norway).*

    (*B*) *Possible mechanism of cirque excavation. The rock-wall is shattered by frost-action and ice ' plucking ', the cirque-floor smoothed by the motion of the ice. Fragments carried up the thrust-planes make the arcuate lines seen on the exposed ice in (A).*

    (*C*) *Striding Edge, Helvellyn, an arete formed by backward cutting of cirques.*

    (*D*) *The Matterhorn, a pyramid peak.*

stones and rock fragments lying about on the surface or contained in the surface deposits which are of totally different material from the local bedrock. Many can be traced to their points of origin, and we find, for instance, blocks of Lake District granite now perched on top of the southern Pennines, and fragments of Scottish rocks in East Anglia. The only conceivable agency that could have transported these rock-fragments is ice, and this means that not only the hill-areas, but the greater part of all Britain must have been ice-covered. Revolutionary as this idea was to the earlier geologists, confirmatory evidence rapidly accumulated. Over much of Britain the solid rocks are obscured by a layer of material called "drift". This varies in thickness from a few inches up to hundreds of feet, and is typically composed of a heterogeneous mass of sticky clay, sand, and angular stones. Study showed this material to be very similar to the "boulder clay" dumped by melting glaciers, and this above all convinced sceptics of the reality of past glaciation. Comparable evidence accumulated from all northern Europe, and from much of N. America, and today it is unquestioned that during the Pleistocene or Quaternary period, commencing roughly a million years ago and ending, in northern Europe, only 10 to 15,000 years ago, the climate of these regions was much colder, and ice-sheets similar to those of present-day Greenland covered the ground. Erratics of Scandinavian origin found on our east coasts show that at one stage the ice-sheets crossed the North Sea basin to impinge on Britain from the east and to jostle with our local glaciers. At the same time vastly extended glaciers spread out from the Alps and other higher mountains further south. But detailed studies have shown that the glaciation was not just one single event. In the Alps and over much of Europe we have evidence of at least four main phases of cold climate and ice growth, with intervening phases of milder climate when the ice-sheets dwindled and may have disappeared entirely. One of these "inter-glacial" phases is estimated to have been of some 200,000 years duration, or ten times as long as all "post-glacial" time, and at periods within the whole Ice Age the climate of Britain was warmer than it is now. Indeed many authorities believe we are still within the Ice Age, that our present mild climate is but another phase of recession, and that in the future the ice will return. We cannot pursue this controversial topic here, but it seems probable that the past phases of wetter climate in the Sahara that we noted in the last chapter were connected with the glacial phases further north. Indeed there are probably few landscapes on earth which do not still reveal some modifications inherited from the very different conditions that obtained during the Great Ice Age.

The story is exceedingly complex, and we cannot do more in this book than touch on a few selected points. What caused these fluctuations of climate is still unknown. Of the many theories that have been advanced, that attributing the changes to variations in solar radiation is perhaps the most plausible. Whatever the cause, most widespread repercussions ensued. The vast quantities of water withdrawn from circulation and locked up in the ice-sheets must have caused a world-wide lowering of sea-level. We shall see in Chap. XIV that there is much evidence that this did occur, and that life in the oceans was profoundly affected, with effects upon the growth-patterns of ocean-floor sediment, and upon the life-history of coral islands in tropical seas. It is probable, too, that the land areas affected sank down isostatically under the great weight of ice, even as central Greenland seems to be depressed today, and as we mentioned earlier, both movements of the land and movement of the ocean-level may well be reflected in the raised beaches and submerged shorelines we find around our coasts today. But we must leave these intriguing topics to return to more direct effects of the glaciation. We have touched on the modifications imposed on the hill-areas by glacier erosion. What of other areas ?

The over-deepening of valleys, cutting of corries, and carving out of rock-basins are naturally restricted to the regions of higher dissected hills and harder rocks, where the ice was constricted to narrow channels. On the smoother uplands, like the Pennines, the ice-sheets spread more widely, and their erosional effect was less severe. But everywhere pre-existing soils were stripped off, and in their place were eventually dumped sheets of boulder-clay. New soils have scarcely had time to mature fully on these heavy clays in northern Britain, as gardeners in that area will be all too well aware. The boulder-clay, however, completely filled and blocked many of the pre-existing river-valleys, so that when the ice finally disappeared new rivers established themselves in positions often considerably displaced from their earlier courses. The tracks of such old filled-in river-valleys have frequently been revealed by mining operations. When the ice was melting, also, vast quantities of water were released, and because of the blocking of pre-existing drainage-lines by boulder-clay, moraines, and unmelted masses of the ice itself, widespread systems of lakes came into existence in many parts of the country. The well-known "Parallel Roads" of Glen Roy, near Fort William, are ancient beaches left by an ice-blocked lake which stood at several different levels, while vast lakes covered the Vale of York, the lower Trent Valley, the Fens, the plains of Cheshire, and other areas. In the hillier districts the overflow waters from such lakes impounded in the valleys often cut deep and distinctive escape-channels across the old divides, which now remain as anomalous high-level dry valleys in form like gigantic railway cuttings. These can be found in profusion in the North York Moors (where Newton Dale is a giant example—See Fig. 40 A.), in the Pennines, and elsewhere, and their mode of origin was a complete puzzle until their connection with the events of the Ice Age was deduced. Some such lake-overflow channels at lower levels were later adopted by permanent rivers, with consequent marked changes in the drainage-pattern of the country. For instance, it seems likely that in pre-glacial times the present upper Severn continued northward to join the Dee and drain into the Irish Sea (Fig. 40 B). Ice standing in the Irish Sea and along the coast, however, ponded back its waters to form a great lake (Lake Lapworth) which drained over the earlier divide southward, the overflow waters cutting the gorge at Ironbridge. When the lake was finally drained the re-established Severn continued to follow this course, to drain to the Bristol Channel.

On the lowland areas, the ice-sheets have left few marked erosional effects, but we inherit many features created by variable deposition of the material ploughed up and re-deposited by the ice. Apart from the great spreads of boulder-clay, which give generally monotonous scenery, we have a considerable variety of more distinctive forms. In the Solway area, the Clyde valley, and best of all in central Ireland (to cite only a few areas), are to be seen groups of "drumlins", smooth oval mounds and hills

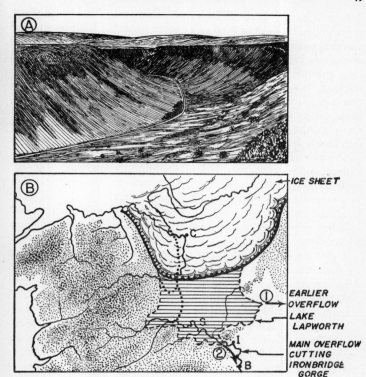

Fig. 40 :
  (A) Newton Dale, a large glacier-lake overflow channel (spillway) in the North York Moors.
  (B) Diversion of the Severn by the creation of glacial Lake Lapworth. Dotted line shows the earlier course of the river. The lake first spilled over eastwards, then as the level dropped the main overflow went south, cutting the gorge at Ironbridge through which the river was diverted when the ice disappeared. Note that other ice-sheets, on the mountains, and in the Irish Sea basin, have been omitted for simplicity.

built of boulder-clay and generally disposed all with their long axes parallel. These are thought to have been moulded under the ice-sheets, but the mechanism is little understood. Here and there, again, we find great spreads of gravel and sand among the

drift, and locally these are built into distinctive hills. " Kames "
are rounded hillocks of sand and gravel, probably built by streams
washing against the edges of a melting ice-sheet. Examples are
numerous in the valleys of northern Britain. Less common are
long sinuous sandy ridges called " eskers ". Possibly built by
streams flowing in tunnels under the ice, or as backward-
extending deltas where streams issued from retreating ice-edges,
these ridges are well-displayed in Finland where they comprise
many of the necks of wooded land that twist between the innumerable lakes of that country. Sand and gravel washed out
of the glacial drifts also covers the floors of many British river-
valleys, and is extensively worked for building material. Indeed,
such fluvio-glacial deposits, together with the more distinctive
kames and eskers, comprise the main source of such materials.
It is not too much to say that the sand and gravel extraction
industry of this country is primarily based on the results of the
Pleistocene glaciation.

It will be clear even from this short survey that the topographic
effects of glaciation are many, and that the repercussions of the

Lakes are the final group of topographic features we may note
in connection with glaciation. Enormous numbers of lakes
were created during the melting-phases of the ice-sheets, and
although many of these long ago disappeared, myriads still
remain. Probably the majority of all the earth's existing lakes
owe their creation to the effects of glaciation. The deep lochs
of the Scottish glens had their basins at least in part excavated by
valley-glaciers. Windermere is held up by a morainic dam, as
are many of the Alpine lakes, while the innumerable lakes of
North Germany, Poland, and Finland are in the main the result
of uneven deposition of boulder-clay over the flat countryside
and the general disorganisation of drainage that ensued. Glaciation also played a large part in the evolution of the Great Lakes
of N. America, themselves but shrunken remnants of the enormous bodies that existed when the ice-sheets were melting.

It will be clear even from this short survey that the topographic
effects of glaciation are many, and that the repercussions of the
Great Ice Age were far-reaching and not confined to areas actually
ice-covered. Although subsequent denudation, the spread of
vegetation, and the hand of man have partly obscured the effects
in Britain, the imprint of the glacial period is still set deeply on

our lands, and has markedly affected the patterns of land-use and economic development. In a country like Norway the influence of past glaciation is still more apparent. Agriculture, severely hampered by climate, is further handicapped by the steep dissected relief, the lack of soils, and the infertile character of the jumbled moraines, sands and boulder-clays that mask the naked rock on the lower patches. Cultivation would indeed be in a sad case were it not for the coastal strips of clay-covered sea-floor that have risen above the waves through isostatic uplift consequent on the melting of the ice. Much of Norway's agriculture is concentrated on these narrow coastal strips of flatter ground. The numerous rivers, in part nourished by melting glaciers in summer, owe their tumultuous character and many falls in large measure to glacial modifications of the landscape, and on these, in the absence of coal, most Norwegian industry depends for electric power. The indented fiord coast and fringe of "skerries" afford numerous good harbours and sheltered coastal waters, to which we can relate the high development of modern Norwegian maritime activity and fishing no less than the historic exploits of the Vikings. Indeed, wherever you look in Norway, the influence of past glaciation can be seen, not only on the ground, but in the adaptations of human life to the conditions it helped to create. Again we are impressed, in studying any of the earth's landscapes, with the necessity of taking into account the evolutionary history and features inherited from earlier phases of different climate. Climate indeed emerges as a prime determinant of scenery, and to climate and its variations we must now turn.

F

CHAPTER XI

THE HEATING OF THE EARTH AND THE CIRCULATION OF THE ATMOSPHERE

Everyone knows that climatic conditions vary considerably over the earth's surface, but the enormous importance of the variations is seldom fully realised. It is not too much to say, however, that the influence of climate is virtually all-pervasive. By controlling the processes of weathering, climate is largely responsible for the regional differences between soils. Soils and climate between them control the distribution and character of all the earth's natural vegetation, and despite all our science, exercise a decisive influence upon the patterns and prosperity of our agriculture. Weather and climate hamper our movements no less than do mountains and seas; the distribution of many diseases and pests is closely governed by climatic factors; while climate and weather even affect appreciably how we feel day by day, and so may influence our habits of thought and the very texture of our civilisations. Some authorities indeed would grant climate the leading role in guiding all human history. Such themes are beyond the scope of this book, but it is pertinent to recall that extreme climatic conditions withhold a good third of the earth's lands from our use, and render the exploitation of vast additional areas exceedingly costly in human health and effort. Climate, however, is not a thing apart from the solid earth. Landscapes themselves, as we have seen, are in large measure the product of ages of slow sculpture by air and water, whose patterns of activity are controlled directly by climatic conditions. Everywhere scenery thus reflects to the discerning eye the climate under which it has evolved, so that we can say that climate is built into every landscape. But the connections are by no means all one way. The variation of climate over the earth is itself in some degree produced by the pattern of land and water, and over the lands highly distinctive climatic conditions are created by the very relief features they help to carve out and destroy. Land, water, and air are inseparable interacting components in the physical diversity of the earth, and change in the local features of any one inevitably results in changes in the conditions and activities of the others.

The terms " weather " and " climate " are too familiar to need elaborate definition. Both refer to physical conditions in the lower atmosphere, but whereas *weather* implies the conditions that exist at some particular time and place, *climate* deals rather with average seasonal conditions, ranges of departure from such averages, and the variation in these matters over the earth. The study of weather demands careful simultaneous observations of all significant phenomena over the desired area; but the realities of climate, and its variations, only emerge when we extract from the mass of daily weather observations taken at meteorological stations all over the earth such quantities as the average temperature at each place during each month in the year, the normal monthly totals of rainfall, and the comparative totals in the year. Plotted on maps, such data allow us to see the patterns of climatic variation, and to classify the great diversity of conditions. There are, of course, no hard-and-fast dividing lines, for climate changes over the earth by gradual transition; but comprehensible patterns emerge, and we find that the differences from place to place are systematic and governed by definite physical principles. In the last analysis climate is just the total of day to day weather—put into summarised form—and any study of climate must be based on an understanding of the various phenomena of meteorology; but in the world view the individual storm or fog belt is unimportant. What matters is the variation in average conditions, and range of conditions, from place to place. In this book we shall therefore concentrate on the climatic aspect. Inevitably the study of climate involves statistics, but these will be kept to a minimum, attention being directed rather at the working principles and causes. The detailed facts of climate for any country, should the reader require them, are readily available in climatic atlases and text-books.

Since climate defines conditions in the atmosphere, we must start with a brief examination of this most distinctive element of our planet. Totally enclosing the solid globe like an impalpable blanket, the atmosphere is composed of an intimate mixture of gases in which nitrogen (78% by volume) and oxygen (21%) make up nearly the whole. Among the minor constituents we may note the small quantity of carbon dioxide (average 0.03%), for this is vital to plant life, plants taking it in to extract the carbon and return the oxygen to the atmosphere. This biological process, in company with weathering and some solution of the gas in the ocean, is responsible for the fact that the carbon dioxide percentage remains so small despite the large quantities emitted by volcanoes and contributed by many organic processes including our own breathing. In addition to its gaseous components, however, the atmosphere contains alien matter derived mainly from the earth below. Solid matter includes dust (mainly from deserts and volcanoes, but including meteoric dust), soot (from chimneys and forest fires), organic particles like spores and bacteria and salt particles (from evaporated ocean spray). Some of this solid matter plays an important part in many weather phenomena. Much more important, however, is the small quantity of water held in the atmosphere: indeed so vital is this that we shall devote most of the next chapter to it. Although never exceeding about 4% (by volume), there is always some water-vapour present in natural air, but since, like most of the solid particles, it is derived from the earth below, it is concentrated in the layers of air near the ground. Little extends above the first three miles, and half of the total amount is in the first mile of air above the ground-surface.

This prompts the question, how high does the atmosphere extend? No precise answer can be given, for being very compressible the air becomes less and less dense upwards (as the weight of air on it decreases), and at the outer edges it no doubt diffuses imperceptibly into space. Traces of atmospheric gases may attain heights of several 100 miles, but this matter need not detain us since virtually all the phenomena of weather that affect the earth's surface occur in the lowest three miles. The compressibility of the atmosphere does, however, introduce an important matter, which is that of the pressure it exerts. Although so tenuous air is of course pulled down by gravity, and by its weight it exerts a definite pressure (about 15 pounds per square inch) on every object on the earth's surface.

We on that surface have to support this pressure continuously, just as crabs and lobsters, on the sea-floor, have to support the weight of the water above them. Atmospheric pressure is measured by the length of the column of mercury it will support in balance in the tube of a barometer. This is, on average, 29.9 inches.[1] Were the earth a perfect sphere, and the atmosphere around it everywhere at rest, this pressure would be the same at every point over the surface, and would everywhere decrease upwards at exactly the same rate. Since the earth is not quite spherical, however, there is a variation in sea-level pressure with latitude, while over the irregular surfaces of the lands pressure varies inversely with elevation. This fact is made use of by surveyors as a rough guide to the height of the ground, through the medium of the aneroid barometer, and the aircraft altimeter uses the same principle. Unfortunately neither instrument is very reliable, the main reason being that our basic condition, complete stability and rest of the atmosphere, is never fulfilled. Even at the same level pressure is *not* the same everywhere over the earth, and throughout the year, if not from day to day, its value changes at any place appreciably. Great patches of persistently low and high pressure exist in certain latitudes, shifting their positions slightly as the seasons change. But over the continents marked fluctuations of pressure occur throughout the year, and on top of these major systems a host of transitory irregular patches of relatively low and high pressure—the familiar " depressions " and " anticyclones "—develop, move about, and disappear again, rather like eddies in water. These are more strongly developed in certain parts of the earth than in others. It is all these pressure differences that are responsible for the movements in the air that we call winds, for whenever the pressure is different from place to place *at the same level* in the atmosphere, air moves from the region of higher pressure to that of lower in an effort to cancel out the difference. Near the earth, however, despite all the activity of the air the pressure differences remain, or are constantly re-created, and so the air is kept in

---

[1] This figure applies to the British Isles. Nowadays pressure is more commonly recorded in millibars. The millibar is a unit of pressure, not of length, 1 millibar being a force of 1,000 dynes per square centimetre. 1,000 millibars (1 bar) are equivalent to 29.53" of mercury at 32°F. in lat. 45°N.

perpetual restless turmoil. Some of the movements are large-scale and regular, relating to the more permanent pressure differences over the earth; others are irregular and produced by changeable local conditions, but the ultimate factor responsible for all this activity is the variable heating of the earth's surface and lower atmosphere. Not only does this maintain the temperatures to which our bodies are biologically adjusted, but it drives the whole machine of the atmospheric circulation which in turn underlies the constant stream of weather changes; and the energy responsible for all this activity is that of the sun.

As we noted earlier, there is much heat locked up within the earth, but this leaks out so slowly that were no other source of heating available the surface would remain frozen and lifeless. To the sun we owe the fact that our planet is habitable at all, and it is variation in the amount of solar energy received on different parts of the earth's surface that is the basic cause of all climatic variation. With its surface temperature of some 10,000°F. the sun continuously radiates out to space a fabulous amount of energy. Only a tiny fraction of this—less than 1/2,000,000,000th part of the total output—strikes the earth, and of this 57% is abstracted in passing through the atmosphere by reflection, scattering, and absorbtion. It is the 43% that gets through, however, that is vital, for of the incoming solar radiation only the 14% that is absorbed by the atmosphere raises its temperature directly. The radiation striking the ground, however, is mainly absorbed and transformed into heat; and as the ground warms up, it in turn begins to radiate out energy, but this time in the form of long heat-waves which are readily absorbed by the air and raise *its* temperature. The atmosphere thus acts rather like the glass in a greenhouse, letting the solar radiation in, but trapping the heat that it generates, and the clouds and moisture in the lower atmosphere greatly increase the trapping effect. It is now apparent why, as we noted in the last chapter, temperature decreases steadily upward from the earth's surface; it is because the air is heated mainly from *below*. Variation in air temperatures over the earth must therefore be directly related to the differential heating of its surface by incident solar energy, and this is governed by two basic factors: the angle at which the sun's rays strike the ground, and the length of time during which solar energy, or "insolation", is received. The former factor varies over the earth with latitude, while because of the earth's movements both factors vary in every latitude through the year. We must briefly examine the causes of these variations.

Fig 41 shows that because the earth is spherical in shape, the heating effect of the sun's rays becomes progressively less outward from the Equator, because on the Equator the rays strike the earth squarely (i.e. at midday the sun appears vertically overhead) while as the latitude increases the rays strike the ground more and

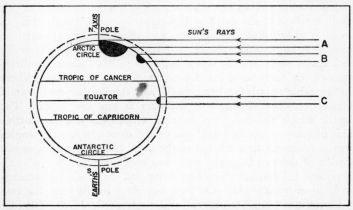

Fig. 41. *Variation of insolation with Latitude. The three columns of sunlight, A, B, and C, are of equal cross-section area. The black semi-circles illustrate the respective areas of ground they fall upon.*

more obliquely. Equal amounts of solar energy are thus spread over progressively greater areas of ground and their heating power becomes very much less. The spherical shape of the earth is thus responsible for the primary geographical pattern of insolation-receipt and hence temperature, a progressive diminution from Equator to Poles. The earth, however, is not stationary. It turns daily on its axis, so that although at any one moment one complete hemisphere is receiving no insolation at all, each point on the surface is regularly brought into the sunlight for some part of the twenty-four hours. During this

daylight period the angle of incidence of the sun's rays continually
changes as the sun " rises " to its highest altitude of the day at
noon and drops away again to set at night, so that irrespective
of the latitude variation, every place experiences a daily cycle of
heating.   This naturally results in a daily cycle of temperature
change, and when other factors do not intervene we experience
the highest temperatures in the twentyfour hours an hour or
two after noon (the delay is due to time-lag in heating up the
surface and transferring the heat to the air), the lowest just
after dawn after the night hours in which heat has been steadily
radiated away.   But, as a glance back at Fig. 41 will show, this
daily rotation of the earth, although introducing a daily cycle of
heating and cooling, would in no way affect the regular variation
of sun-ray angle and insolation with latitude, *provided that the earth's
axis always remained as we have drawn it*, at right angles to the direction of the sun's rays, for day and night would be everywhere
of the same length (12 hours each) and the heating-cycle would
remain constant throughout the year at any one place.   The
factor which produces the seasonal changes is that the earth's
axis of rotation is tilted $23\frac{1}{2}°$ out of the direction at right angles
to the earth-sun line, so that as the earth proceeds on its annual
circuit of the sun both the noon angle of incidence of the sun's
rays, and the relative duration of day and night, alter systematically in every latitude.   On only two days in the year, the two
" Equinoxes " on March 21st and Sept. 23rd, do the relationships in Fig. 41 exactly apply.   After March 21st the North Pole
begins to turn in towards the sun, and throughout the northern
hemisphere days become longer, nights shorter, the suns climbs
daily higher in the sky, and the amount of insolation received in
each latitude steadily increases.   The climax is reached on
June 21st, when the sun is vertically overhead at midday on the
northern Tropic and $23\frac{1}{2}°$ above the horizon at the North Pole,
while north of the Arctic Circle there are 24 hours of continuous
daylight.   Thereafter the reverse change sets in until the balanced
position is reached again on Sept. 23rd, after which, in the north
ern hemisphere winter half-year, the same cycle of changes occurs
in reverse—the southern hemisphere now receiving progressively
more insolation, the northern one less, up to Dec. 21st, after which

again conditions slowly return to the symmetrical state on March
21st. These changes are summarised diagrammatically in Fig. 42.
Their net result is that although on annual balance both hemispheres receive approximately the same amount of insolation
(there is a small difference due to variation in the distance
between earth and sun at different times of the year) in each there
is a progressive diminution of insolation received from the
Equator outward towards the Poles, while in every latitude
there is a regular seasonal variation. The difference between

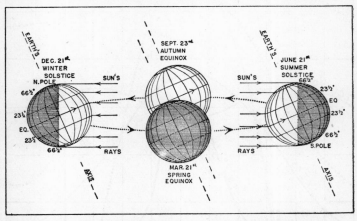

*Fig. 42. The progress of the seasons. The sun is supposed to be in the central position,
so far from the earth that its rays fall parallel in all latitudes. The diagram
shows how the angle of incidence of the sun's rays, and the proportions of daylight
and darkness, vary throughout the year.*

low and high latitudes is, however, much increased by the
effects of the atmosphere, which we have hitherto neglected. In
low latitudes the sun's rays strike squarely and have a minimum
thickness of air to pass through, but towards the Poles they pass
through the atmosphere obliquely and a much higher proportion
of the radiation is absorbed and reflected away. The effects
are shown in the graphs in Fig. 43, where the enormous loss at
the Poles is clearly brought out. It will be noted that the
Equatorial intake shows a double peak, the peaks corresponding

F*

to the overhead positions of the sun at the Equinoxes. Points within the Tropics also have a double-peak curve, but the peaks move together as the Tropics are approached, and outside them

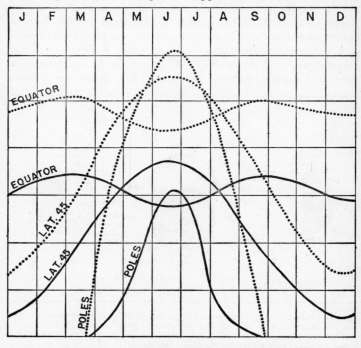

J F M A M J J A S O N D

EQUATOR

EQUATOR

LAT. 45

LAT. 45

POLES

POLES

•••••••••• **RADIATION RECEIVED AT OUTER LIMITS OF THE ATMOSPHERE**

———— **RADIATION RECEIVED AT THE EARTH'S SURFACE**

Fig. 43. Annual variation in insolation at the Equator, 45°, and the Poles. The results of Fig. 42. Note the much greater loss of insolation through atmospheric interference at the Poles than at the Equator.

the annual insolation-curve has only one peak. At the Poles no radiation at all is received for half the year, but then continuously for the next six months. Of the total amount received by the outer atmosphere, however, relatively little gets through to the ground, and in fact over the year the Poles lose more heat by outward radiation in winter than they receive in summer, while in the Tropics the reverse is the case. However, so far as we can tell the earth as a whole is getting neither hotter nor colder year by year, so that the total energy received over the whole surface must ultimately be balanced by that radiated out again to space. The excess heat of the Tropics must therefore be transferred somehow to the Polar regions to make good their deficiency. This is achieved by the circulation of the atmosphere. It is indeed fundamentally the differential heating of the earth's surface that sets up and maintains this circulation, and in it are based almost all of the phenomena of our daily weather.

We can now turn to the actual temperature-patterns we find over the earth as a result of these astronomically-produced variations in heating. As used in climatology the word temperature implies the temperature of the air, in the shade, a standard height (4 feet) above the ground. This air temperature is basically governed by the temperature of the ground below, but there is always some time-lag in the heating of the air from the ground, the ground itself reacts differently to solar radiation according to its nature, and the air itself is generally in motion. Thus we cannot expect, and do not find, any exact and simple correspondence between actual air temperatures and the theoretical distribution of insolation. There is a rough correspondence, but two factors in particular upset it— the mobility of the air, and differences in temperature-reaction between land and water areas. The latter factor is the more important.

The materials that make up land surfaces are mainly fixed and solid, reflect back relatively little solar radiation, are poor conductors of heat and have low specific heat values. They therefore respond to insolation with a rapid rise of surface temperature, but equally they lose heat again rapidly when insolation ceases. Because of its mobility, its greater specific heat, the deeper penetration of insolation into it, and because some energy is used up in evaporating its surface, water heats up more slowly, but retains its heat longer. In summer, land-areas therefore heat up more rapidly, and to higher temperatures, than do water-areas, but in winter they cool more quickly and so fall to lower temperatures. Large water-bodies like lakes and seas thus act as temperature-stabilisers, damping down the annual fluctuations. Were the earth's surface all land, its seasonal temperature changes would be much more violent than they in fact are. As it is, in the Tropics, where heat receipt is in excess, we find that the average annual temperature is higher over the lands than over the oceans, and in summer the lands are markedly hotter. In higher latitudes, however, although the summer temperatures are still higher over the lands than over the seas, the winter temperatures are very much lower, so that on annual average the lands are cooler than the waters.

To map such differences we make use of *isotherms*, which are lines drawn on a map to pass through all places experiencing the same temperature (just as *isohyets* mark lines of equal rainfall, *isobars* lines of equal air pressure, and so on). Since in climate we often deal with generalities and averages, we plot not isotherms of actual recorded temperatures at any one time, but average monthly, seasonal, or even annual temperatures. But, as we saw, temperature is affected by elevation, and if the average figures are worked out from the values actually recorded at different places, the world-patterns resulting from the astronomical factors and the distribution of land and sea would be obscured to some extent by the effects of variable relief. To eliminate this, for analytical work the temperatures are all " reduced to sea-level ", i.e. the recorded values are diminished by an amount proportional to the elevation of the station at which they were taken. On a world map of such reduced average isotherms for the whole year, the effects of the land and sea pattern are clearly brought out. The isotherms bend poleward over the lands in the Tropics (the lands being hotter), equatorward over the lands in the high latitudes ; but when we examine seasonal maps of average temperatures throughout the year we can see how the whole temperature-pattern shifts north and south throughout the year. In the hemisphere experiencing summer, great " poles " of heat develop over the lands around the Tropic, while in that experiencing winter the larger land-masses develop poles of cold in somewhat higher latitudes. From the temperature point of view we can therefore make a primary distinction between *oceanic* (or coastal) climates, and *continental* climates.

The former have only moderately warm summers, but relatively mild winters (appropriate to their latitudes); the latter much hotter summers, but also much colder winters, or a greater annual temperature range.

The hottest areas on earth, in the northern summer, occur around the northern Tropic in the interiors of the great land-masses : south-western U.S.A., the interior Sahara, and a great belt running from interior Arabia to northern India. In the southern summer the hottest areas lie in interior Brazil, central and southern Africa, and western Australia. The coldest areas on earth, by contrast, lie (as we should expect) around the Poles; but in the northern winter the large areas of land around 60° north, in Arctic Canada and northern Siberia, being far from the moderating influence of the ocean and losing heat rapidly by radiation, become abnormally cold for their latitude. The lowest recorded land temperature,—94°F., was experienced at Verkhoyansk in N. E. Siberia, where the *average* January temperature is—58°F, or 90° of frost. [1] By contrast the highest recorded shade temperature of 136°F was experienced in the interior of Libya, with Death Valley California (134°F) not far behind.

It would be tedious to describe in detail the pattern of temperature over the earth at the different seasons, but it will be apparent that every place has its own characteristic annual " curve " of temperature-change, in which the *shape and mean value* depend mainly on its latitude, the *emphasis in seasonal differences* mainly on its position relative to the oceans. We can illustrate some of the main variants (Fig. 44). (i) *PARA* (Brazil) illustrates the Equatorial temperature regime. It is hot all the year round, with no cool season, but two slight peaks of heat marking the passage of the " vertical sun ". (ii) *KHARTOUM* (A-E Sudan) illustrates a tropical inland station. Here there is a much more marked variation between the seasons, although the annual mean is even higher than at Para. As Khartoum is inside the Tropics, there are again two " peaks " of heat, but they lie close together. (iii) *BISMARCK* (U.S.A.) shows a continental site in middle latitudes. Here there is only one period of maximum temperature, and one season of cold, but the range between the two is very great. Winters are becoming very cold. (iv) *VICTORIA*

[1] Lower temperatures have now been recorded in Antarctica (1961).

(Vancouver Island) exemplifies coastal conditions in similar latitudes. The annual mean temperature is nearly ten degrees higher, while the range between winter and summer is very much less. The moderating influence of the ocean is clearly brought out. This graph and the last illustrate in principle the difference

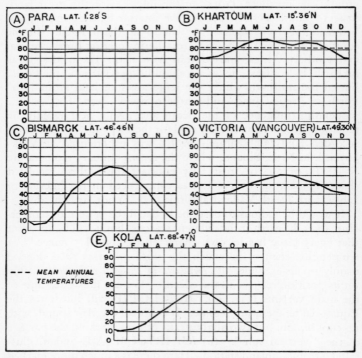

Fig. 44. Annual temperature-curves in five selected types of climate.

in annual temperature regime between Britain and southern Poland or western Russia. (v) Finally *KOLA* (north coast of the U.S.S.R.) illustrates the annual temperature curve in the high latitudes. Winter is very cold and prolonged; summer short and cool.

These few illustrations show how the mean annual temperature drops away towards the Poles, but equally they emphasise the fact that mean annual temperature figures may be dangerously misleading as a guide to actual climatic conditions. Edinburgh (47.6°F) and Boston, Mass. (48.8°F) have much the same annual average, but the seasonal values reveal a very considerable contrast in actual climate, Edinburgh having a January average of 39.0°F and a July average of 58.8°F, Boston corresponding figures of 27.8°F and 72.0°F. Indeed, when we consider climates in detail we have to go beyond even seasonal averages down to mean monthly temperatures, and within these note the expectable upper and lower limits in each month, the average duration and incidence of frosts, and so on, to make climatic data useful to the farmer and other practical men. The precision, and degree of detail given, however, must obviously be adjusted to the purpose for which the information is wanted, and here we can only deal with generalities.

Latitude and position with regard to the ocean are not, however, the only factors governing temperature. The air is by no means static, and by its own movements it modifies the pattern of temperature distribution to an important degree, carrying heat from regions of high temperature to warm up those naturally colder, or cooling down areas that would otherwise experience much higher temperatures. In Britain we all know the painful difference between the winter days when icy winds from the continent blow across our islands, and those on which warm moist air coming up from the Tropics makes us shed our overcoats. Moving " air-masses ", acquiring characteristics of temperature and moisture in regions where they linger for some time, carry those conditions with them for long distances, and so " import " extraneous conditions to areas far distant. Our climate in Britain is dominated by the changing incidence of air-streams coming from different directions, and so bringing us one day sub-tropical conditions, and a few days after conditions appropriate to lands near the Arctic Circle. The whole circulation of the atmosphere, itself basically driven by differences of heating over the earth's surface, is thus instrumental in modifying the temperature pattern, and in some parts of the earth—including our islands—its influence is often paramount. We are thus naturally led on to inquire into the nature and mechanisms of the atmospheric circulation, but we can conveniently approach this by examining first the other major factor influencing the distribution of temperature, which is altitude of the land.

We earlier noted that the atmosphere is heated mainly from below, by radiation outwards from the earth's surface, and that for this reason there is everywhere (normally) a steady fall in temperature upwards. The average rate is 1°F for each 300 feet or so, or 3.3°F per 1,000 feet. The main factor producing this cooling-off with elevation is the " heat-trapping " effect of the dust and moisture in the layers of air near the earth; higher up the air becomes clearer and drier, and loss of heat outwards by radiation at night is more marked. On regions standing high, like the great mountains and plateaux, average temperatures are thus consistently lower than on the plains around, and as one climbs higher so the temperatures drop. As we saw earlier, if the ground rises high enough, eventually it becomes cold enough for snow to lie on it permanently. Mountains thus in large degree create their own climates, irrespective of latitude, and over the great mountains climate is arranged in altitude zones. Travelling up from the Pacific coast to La Paz, the capital of Bolivia, which stands at an altitude of 12,000 feet, one thus passes through a succession of temperature zones to equal which you would have to travel some 2,000 miles southwards at sea-level. In all the Andean countries of S. America altitude overrides latitude as a climatic control, as it does in other high mountain areas. Apart from lowered average temperatures, such regions experience exaggerated temperature differences between day and night (as do the great deserts) because the clearer and thinner air permits more rapid loss of heat by night radiation. The lowered air pressure also makes such regions as the high plateaux of Bolivia and Tibet very trying to live in. Europeans are often taken ill on first ascending to them, and although some acclimatisation is attained in time, the effects upon health, energy and temperament are by no means negligible.

Apart from its effects upon the climate of high-altitude regions, however, the fall of temperature upwards is very closely tied up with the circulation and movements of the atmosphere. When air is warmed it expands and becomes lighter, so that the warming of the layers of air near the ground, if sufficient to overcome their naturally greater density (due to the weight of air above them), gives them a tendency to rise.   Such rising is called " convectional ", and because of its basic importance in the circulation of the atmosphere we must examine its mechanism fairly closely. At first glance, it is difficult to see why a mass of air at ground level, if heated sufficiently to start it rising, should ever stop; for if it maintained its temperature, as it rose it would progressively find itself ever warmer (and hence lighter) than the surrounding air, and its rate of rise would thus continuously accelerate.   This however does not happen, because even as the air rises it is automatically cooled.   Moving up into layers of reduced pressure it continuously expands, and this expansion uses up heat and cools it down.   (The fact that air is cooled by expansion you can easily check by putting your finger in the expanding air rushing out of a punctured toy balloon: the converse effect of heating by compression will be even more familiar to anyone in the habit of blowing up bicycle tyres.)   Moreover, the rate of cooling by rising and expansion is appreciably more rapid than is the rate of temperature-fall with height in the atmosphere in general.   A rising mass of dry air cools by 1°F for every 180 feet of ascent, whereas as we saw the rate of temperature-fall in the free atmosphere is only 1° for each 300 feet of height.   Thus heated air cannot rise indefinitely.   Fairly soon it is cooled by its own expansion to the point at which its temperature (and hence density) are the same as those of the air round about, and then it comes to a halt.   The extent of its convectional rising will clearly depend on the degree to which it is initially heated up, but it will also depend on the moisture-content of the air, for damp air cools with rising more slowly than dry air.   For air " saturated " with moisture (this term is explained in the next chapter) the rate of cooling by rising and expansion is only 1°F for each 300 feet of ascent.[1]   Thus damp air will rise when heated further than dry air, and the optimum conditions for convectional rising are where moist air near the ground is strongly and persistently

[1] This is an average figure: the rate varies with the original temperature of the air, being about 1°F for each 350-400 feet for warm saturated air.

heated.   Such conditions occur on the large scale around the
Equator, and thus we have in the Equatorial regions permanent

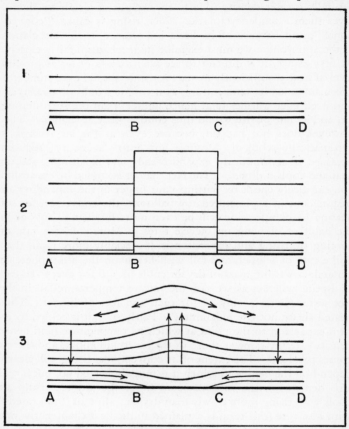

*Fig. 45. Convectional circulation. The ground between B and C is heated; the
planes of pressure rise as the air expands, and air movements are set up as in the
third diagram (After Kendrew).*

conditions of strong vertical rising in the lower atmosphere.
But such movements obviously must have repercussions.   When

air rises the pressure-distribution in the atmosphere round about is upset, for air is abstracted from the foot of the rising column, and in it pressure is lowered. Air thus moves inward from round about to equalize the pressure-distribution, so that near ground-level sets of inwardly-converging air-streams (or winds) are set up. But in the higher atmosphere, where the rising is checked, air will accumulate, pressure will increase over the area of rising, and so a flow outward will result. With continued local heating, we thus get a great double system of convectional circulation, air in the outer areas slowly settling downwards to replace that drawn in towards the rising column at ground-level (Fig. 45).

This is, in fact, what happens round the Equator where, as we pointed out earlier, there is an excess of heat-intake. Around the Poles, by contrast, the lower air is chilled by the widespread snow and ice, and becomes dense and heavy. There is therefore a tendency for down-settling of air towards the lowest levels. Did no other factors intervene, we could thus expect a vast double system of atmospheric circulation symmetrically disposed about the Equator, the rising air in low latitudes flowing outward at higher levels, and being replaced by air drawn inwards along the surface from around the Poles. Surface winds, in short would blow consistently inwards towards the Equator (Fig. 46 A). Observation shows that there is indeed a strong tendency for this to happen, but over the vast distances involved, and with a rotating earth, various modifications are introduced.

In the first place, the general fall of temperature upwards is not maintained through the full depth of the atmosphere. Over the Equator it ceases at about $10\frac{1}{2}$ miles up, and over the Poles at about 5 miles up. Thereafter there is no further consistent fall of temperature with height, and indeed at great heights temperature seems to increase again. There is thus a plane of discontinuity in the atmosphere, highest over the Equator, and sloping down towards the Poles. This is called the " Tropopause ". The relatively thin layer of atmosphere below is the " Troposphere ", and the convectional circulation, clouds, and all the familiar elements of our weather are virtually confined to this layer. In the " Stratosphere " above conditions are much

more tranquil, which is why aircraft designers have been striving
to develop types than can cruise in these peaceful regions high
aloft, there attaining much greater speeds because of the reduced
air resistance. But the variable height of the Tropopause
affects the distribution of pressure at the earth's surface, and
hence the air-movements nearer the ground. Although the

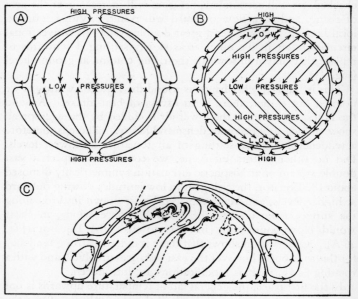

Fig. 46. *The circulation of the atmosphere.*
  (*A*) *Theoretical simple circulation on a non-rotating uniform globe.*
  (*B*) *The effects of rotation—the circulation is broken up into zones.*
  (*C*) *Schematic representation of the actual circulation (after Bjerknes).*

lower air is colder over the Poles than over the Equator, height
for height, at comparable heights the upper air is warmer over
the Poles than over the Equator; and since air density varies
with temperature, and the pressure at the surface is the sum of
that in the Troposphere and in the Stratosphere, the distribution
of pressure at ground level is affected. But deflection of the

moving air-streams also affects it. Pressure is indeed, as we should expect because of the heating, low along the Equatorial belt, but there are zones of markedly higher pressure located around 30-35° North and South. These sub-tropical high pressure zones appear to be caused mainly by a "piling up" of air at higher levels due to increasing eastward deflection of the upper air streams moving out from the Equatorial zone. Beyond there is a decrease again to zones of relatively low pressure around 40-50° North and South, while over the Polar regions pressure is again comparatively high. This banded pressure distribution is only clearly developed over the oceans, for over the continents the marked differences of temperature between summer and winter set up seasonally-reversed high and low pressure systems which cut across the planetary zones ; but were the surface all water it would probably obtain uniformly. From it we should deduce " zones " of fairly permanent winds blowing outwards towards the low-pressure belts from the zones of higher pressure, and neglecting the continental interference this in fact we do find. But the winds do not blow directly north and south. Because of the earth's rotation they are deflected by the " Coriolis " force, to the right in the northern hemisphere, to the left in the southern.[1] Thus we arrive at an idealised arrangement of surface pressure-belts and associated winds like that in Fig. 46 B. Over the Equator is a persistent strip of low pressure, with rising air, and light and variable surface winds : the " Doldrums " of ill-repute in the days of sailing-ships. In towards this, from N.E. and S.E. blow the " Trade Winds ", the most constant and regular winds on earth. These commence in the sub-Tropical zones of high pressure, the " Horse Latitudes ". Poleward lie the zones of the " West Winds ", wide drifts of air moving from the S.W. in the northern hemisphere, from the N.W. in the southern. From the Poles, cold heavy air tends to drift outwards. In practice this idealised arrangement is, however, much modified by the variable dis-

[1] The explanation of this deflection, which affects all bodies moving freely over the earth's surface, is too complex to be given here. A very clear exposition will be found in P. Lake's "Physical Geography", 2nd Edn. 1949, pp. 12-21.

tribution of land and sea. Over the continents the pressure zones and wind-belts break up, overmastered by the local developments (*see* Fig. 47 A). Thus over the Atlantic the Trade Winds emanate from large " pools " of high pressure, the northern one being familiar as the Azores anticyclone. Then the westerlies are nothing like so strongly-marked or consistent as the Trade Winds, at least in the northern hemisphere, where superimposed on the general drift of air from south-west to north-east we have a constant string of smaller moving pressure-systems —the familiar cyclonic depressions, with their intervening patches of higher pressure. In the southern hemisphere, with less interference from land, the west-wind belt is more strongly developed, being known as the " Roaring Forties ". At their Poleward edges the two zones of westerly air-drift meet, and are in continual conflict with, the cold heavy air moving out from the Polar regions, and it is the constant swaying battle between these great masses of air of very different origin and character that gives birth to the unending stream of cyclonic depressions which dominates the weather of the northern Atlantic and Pacific, and the comparable latitudes in the southern ocean. Lying right in the path of these moving air-whirls, especially in winter, we in Britain owe to them much of the inconstancy and fickleness of our weather. These conflict-zones are called the " Polar Fronts ", and they are in essence " air-convergences " analagous to the ocean-current convergences mentioned in Chap. XIV. Around the Equator lies a similar zone of converging air-streams in which occur the " Inter-Tropical Fronts." Over the oceans the variable Doldrums may intervene at ground-level, but over the lands the air-streams often meet and mingle with results of great importance in the initiation of rainfall.

The movements we have described are those near the ground-surface, but counterbalancing movements naturally go on in reverse directions up above to complete the circulations. The details are complex and not yet fully known, but Fig. 46 C will give the reader an idea of the general nature of what is believed to occur. Even from this simplified figure it will be apparent why the wind in the upper air is often entirely different, both in direction and force, to that near ground-level; a fact which obviously complicates air-navigation.

There remain for examination the modifications imposed on this general system of world air-circulation (which swings north and south to some degree with the annual swing of the temper-

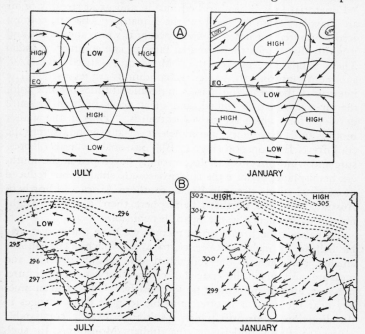

Fig. 47. *The influence of land and ocean on the planetary circulation.*
  (*A*) *Schematic distribution of pressure and winds over a continent and neighbouring oceans in summer and winter (after Köppen).*
  (B) *Pressure and air movements of the Indian Monsoon.*

ature-zones) by the great continental land-masses. To varying degree these set up their own seasonally-alternating pressure and wind systems (Fig. 47 A). As the continental interiors heat up in summer, so the air over them is warmed, expands, and rises. Pressure near the surface is lowered, and air is drawn in from all round. The effect is naturally most marked in Tropical and sub-Tropical latitudes (where the heating is strongest) and in the largest land-masses ; thus we see it best in operation in the northern summer over the western United States and N.W. India. The latter area develops so intense a patch of low pressure that the " Equatorial Low " is absorbed into it, and great streams of air are drawn in from far south of the Equator. This air, coming across hundreds of miles of warm ocean, is warm and moist, and it is this that brings the torrential rains of late summer to India. These winds are, in fact, the " Monsoon"—strictly the S.W. summer monsoon. In winter the conditions are reversed. The interiors of the great land-masses in middle latitudes become cold, the air over them is chilled, and great pools of high pressure develop from which air moves outwards. Thus in the winter months India experiences a complete reversal of wind, having the cool dry N.E. Monsoon (Fig. 47 B). Seasonal reversals of pressure and wind-direction are less strongly developed in the southern hemisphere, because the land-masses are smaller, but reduced monsoonal effects occur in Brazil, southern Africa and northern Australia. In the northern hemisphere there is even a slight monsoonal tendency in the Spanish peninsula.

To balance the broad world picture we have outlined it may be helpful to include reference to a few phenomena on the smaller scale which the individual can readily observe and measure, and which illustrate the relations between temperature, pressure, and air movement no less clearly. On a calm summer day near the coast it is often possible to note daily changes in the direction of air-drift which result from exactly comparable causes to those underlying the Indian Monsoon. In such conditions, light breezes commonly spring up during the day blowing in from the sea, while at night these are replaced by breezes blowing out to sea off the land. The cause is again differential heating. By day the land heats up, pressure over it falls, and air moves inwards off the cooler sea. At night, however, with strong radiation, the land is quickly chilled ; the air above it is cooled and becomes more dense, and a drift of air is set up from land to sea (Fig. 48A). Much more pronounced and regular " land and sea breezes " are a feature of the climate of many coastal regions in the Tropics. Local " mountain and valley " winds are another type of small-scale air-movement set up by differential heating and cooling. If a mountain rises abruptly from a plain, in calm weather the day air temperatures near the mountain will be rather higher than those at the same levels out over the low ground (because of the heat radiated from the mountain), and hence currents of air will tend

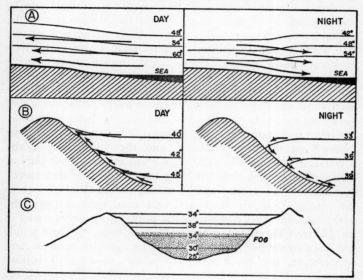

Fig. 48 :
(A) Mechanism of land and sea breezes.
(B) Mechanism of mountain and valley breezes.
(C) Inversion of temperature in a mountain valley.

to move up the mountain-sides, cooler air from further out flowing in to replace them. At night the reverse tendency sets in. The air near the slopes is chilled by the rapidly-cooling rocks, becomes denser and heavier, and flows downhill towards the plains (Fig. 48 B). But topography can affect pressure-distributions and winds on a much larger scale than this. High mountain-chains often act as pressure-divides, high pressure building up on one side while pressure remains relatively low on the other. In such situations an air-flow may start over the mountain-tops and through the high passes, and with a marked pressure-difference may pour down the reverse slopes and valleys with considerable violence. Moreover, the temperature of the air may be considerably altered during its passage, loss of moisture caused by the chilling of enforced rise up the slopes on the high-pressure side permitting a more than equivalent warming-up by compression as it pours downhill on the low-pressure side, so that reaching low ground again, such air is often much warmer than when it started. Warm dry descending winds of this type are known in the Alps as " Föhn " winds, similar winds blowing down from the Rocky Mountains towards the interior plains of Canada and the United States being called the " Chinook ". Such winds occurring in Spring are often instrumental in melting the snows with abnormal rapidity, and causing disastrous floods. But other mountain winds are of very different character, like the " Bora " of the Adriatic coast, and the " Mistral " of the Riviera. These are caused by the coincidence of a great pool of higher-pressure cold Polar air lying over the land while a travelling depression (or low-pressure centre) moves along the sea to the south. Cold air is then drawn southward through the mountains and rages down over the normally sheltered coasts in icy blasts. There are innumerable varieties of local winds produced by varying circumstances of topography, pressure, and temperature, but space will not permit mention of further examples. We may end this chapter by referring to one other point about temperature which is often of great local importance.

Normally, as we noted, the air becomes colder as height increases, but occasionally " temperature inversion " occurs with the air above warmer than that at ground-level (Fig. 48 C). Such conditions are generally produced by abnormal chilling of the air near the ground. For this, calm weather conditions are necessary, with clear skies at night. In the winter half-year, when we get a spell of settled anticyclonic weather, temperature inversion in quite a frequent development. Each night the ground loses heat rapidly by radiation, and the heat-intake next day is insufficient to make good the loss. The ground thus gets steadily colder, and the lower air is progressively chilled. As chilling increases the density of the air, such conditions naturally lead to stability in the atmosphere, and the colder the lower air becomes, the more difficult it is to break up the conditions. Severe and protracted frosts are likely when temperature inversion is strongly developed, and the conditions also favour the formation of fog. Partially-enclosed valleys and hollows are particularly liable to temperature-inversion conditions, for the cold heavy air from surrounding slopes drains into them and cannot get away. The Klagenfurt basin in the eastern Alps is notorious in this respect, its floor being often swathed in fog and under hard frost while the mountain-sides are frost-free and enjoying bright sunshine. In Britain many deep valleys are similarly afflicted, the " frost-hollow " at Rickmansworth having frost on the average about twice as often during the year as the open country round about. Fruit-growers are particularly liable to suffer heavy losses by severe frosts in Spring, and in areas liable to temperature-inversion often choose valley-side locations for orchards in preference to the valley-floors for this reason. A less severe type of temperature inversion, which most readers will no doubt have noticed, is commonly experienced when cycling across undulating ground on a calm autumn evening. On the hill-tops the air remains warm long after the sun has dropped, but in the valleys it is already cold. The cause is again rapid radiation of heat as dusk falls and chilling of the lower air, with draining of the cold heavy air as it forms down into the valleys.

Within the world pattern of temperature, pressure, and air-movement, we thus have a wide range of smaller-scale variations and distinctive local phenomena. In many mountainous countries, as in the Alps and Norway, farms and cultivation must be carefully sited to avoid blighting winds and severe frosts, and equally to take advantage of sunny locations and sheltered nooks. Examination of maps of such regions will reveal many close connections between the patterns of settlement and those of local climatic conditions, and will demonstrate how closely our relations with the earth are governed by the climatic factor, particularly in the " marginal " areas of cultivation. In the sphere of local climatology—the study of minor climatic variations over small areas—there is an enormous field for original observation, and one in which the amateur with the simplest equipment can not only find much of interest, but can make valuable contributions to our existing knowledge. Temperature, and its related air movements, are, however, only half of climate. We must now turn to the other half.

CHAPTER XII

THE CIRCULATION OF WATER. PART I: IN THE AIR

WHILE temperature is certainly the most important factor in climate, rainfall, or atmospheric precipitation to be more accurate, runs it very close. Life cannot exist without water, but there would be no water whatever on any of the earth's lands, and life on them would be impossible, were it not for rainfall. Water only exists on land at all because it is continuously supplied, and since lands only are lands because they stand above the ocean level, water cannot reach them by direct flow. The only route of supply is from above, through the atmosphere. Ceaselessly raising water from the oceans, carrying it about over the length and breadth of the earth, and dropping it back as rain or snow, the atmosphere thus acts as a gigantic natural agency of water-distribution, and from some points of view this is its most important function. We are inclined to be critical of the distribution-system, for the deliveries are seldom very regular, and while some areas get far more than they need others get so little that life in them is scarcely possible; but viewed as a machine for distributing water the atmosphere is really wonderfully efficient. Every year it carries over 100,000 cubic *miles* of water about the earth, a quantity sufficient to give every place the adequate rainfall of 30 inches in the year (were it evenly distributed), yet at any one moment the air holds enough water for only two or three days' supply. " Pickup " is thus as continuous as transport and delivery in the atmospheric water-distribution, which itself makes up but part of the wider closed circulation of water over the earth that is called the " Hydrological Cycle ". It is this aspect of the atmospheric activity, and its effects upon climate, that we will examine in this chapter.

We start with the way in which water gets into the atmosphere at all. It was earlier remarked that natural air is never entirely dry, and the reason is, in simple terms, that totally dry air has a great natural affinity for water. When the two come into contact, water passes into the air by a process of molecular transfer called *evaporation*, becoming an invisible vapour which spreads evenly and intimately through the whole volume of the gaseous mixture. Once in the air, water vapour acts like any of its other gaseous components, so long as it remains vaporous : but under varying conditions the balance of movement of water into the air and out again may alter. Wherever liquid water is exposed to air, evaporation will always go on, provided that the air can still take up more water ; but there is a limit to its capacity. The amount of water any volume of air can hold in vapour form is strictly controlled by its temperature. The warmer the air, the more it can hold, and vice versa. Thus the apparent dampness of air, and equally its real drying-power, depend as much on its temperature as on the actual amount of water in it. Hot air will feel drier than cold, even when it really contains more water. The total amount of water contained never reaches high figures— it varies in nature from only traces to about 4% of the air's volume—but in relation to evaporation this *absolute humidity* (defined by weight of water per unit volume of air) is of minor importance. What *is* important is the *relative humidity*, or the ratio of the actual amount of water present to the maximum amount the air could hold at its existing temperature. This is expressed as a percentage, and when the value is 100, whatever its temperature, air is *saturated*. Unless warmed up, it can take in no more water vapour, and if it is cooled, some of the water it already contains must be released. This comes out of the vapour state as liquid drops (or, if the temperature is below freezing-point, as ice crystals) by the process of *condensation*, and the temperature at which condensation starts in any particular volume of air is called its *dew-point*. Condensation is thus a necessary preliminary to the return of evaporated water from atmosphere to earth by one of the various forms of *precipitation*, of which the most important are rain and snow.

Condensation need not, however, produce appreciable precipitation. All clouds are composed of condensed water— tiny liquid droplets, or ice crystals,—but it is common observation that not all clouds bring rain. What is critical for rainfall is

that the water-drops in a cloud should grow large enough for
the pull of gravity on them to overcome the supporting-power
of the air, and until this happens large amounts of water can
stay up in the air in liquid or solid form.   Water in such forms
is, indeed, carried long distances and may evaporate again without
ever falling to earth.   Nevertheless the bulk of the atmospheric
water is always in the invisible vapour state, and as such it may
travel several times round the world before coming back to
ground.

The factors governing the rate of evaporation (or the amount
of water going into the atmosphere) are firstly the relative
humidity of the air, and secondly the temperatures, of both air
and ground—for the higher the temperature, the more active is
the molecular transfer on which evaporation depends.   Air
pressure affects the matter to some extent, but more important
is the degree of air movement, for if the air is stagnant the layers
in contact with the ground soon become nearly saturated and the
process slows down, but if winds keep the air mixed and in
motion, new drier air is always coming along to replace that
which has taken up moisture.   These facts are familiar, in their
effects at least, to every housewife.   The " good drying day "
is the one on which bright sunshine, warm dry air, and a fresh
breeze are combined ;   on the overcast, calm, and muggy day
clothes never seem to dry—and if the air were truly saturated
they would literally never dry at all.   Applying these principles,
it is clear that evaporation must be most active in the Tropics,
least active in the Polar regions, and that the highest rates could
be expected where great heat, cloudless skies, and constant winds
are combined.   These conditions characterise the great deserts,
and in them, as we saw, the evaporation-rate is in fact extreme.
Were open water-bodies present, 90 to 100 inches of water would
be sucked out of them by evaporation in a year in the central
Sahara or western Australia.   Since there is seldom any free
surface water about, however, the contribution to the atmospheric water made by the great deserts is small, and the greatest
quantities are undoubtedly drawn from the ocean surfaces in the
hot latitudes.   Evaporation does, of course, go on the world
over all the time, but when we recall that two-thirds of the surface

is ocean, it will be obvious that most of the water drawn into the air must come from this source. Indeed, if we neglect the smaller quantities that circulate direct from moist land-surfaces into the air, and back again, we may justifiably regard all the water, in the long run, as coming from the oceans, and meteorological opinion generally believes that the bulk of the rain that falls, even in the interiors of continents, comes directly from the seas. A great deal of rain falls, of course, on the oceans, completing another kind of minor closed cycle of movement, but in principle we may neglect these complexities. The " supply " end of the distribution-system we may consider to be primarily evaporation from the oceans. The transportation part we have already dealt with in the last chapter, for the water is carried about as an incidental in the general circulation of the atmosphere. We may thus now proceed to the delivery end, and here we have two matters to consider : how the processes of condensation and precipitation occur, and why they occur where they do. The former to a large degree explains the latter.

The only known method by which large-scale condensation can be brought about in the atmosphere is by the cooling of masses of moist air below their dew-points. Air nearly saturated needs little cooling before condensation sets in ; drier air needs much more. Hence there is always greater likelihood of effective condensation and precipitation where the air is humid, provided that adequate cooling mechanisms can operate. There are, however, various distinct ways in which such cooling may occur.

In the first place, chilling of the air below its dew-point, with condensation and some precipitation, can occur at ground-level. This happens every night on which there is a dew, dews being most common in spring and autumn during calm clear weather. In such conditions the ground loses heat rapidly at night by radiation, heat is withdrawn from the overlying air, and if the latter is fairly moist its temperature may fall below the dew-point with a resulting precipitation of drops of liquid water over the ground-surface. A comparable effect is produced in winter inside houses when, after a spell of cold weather, unusually warm and moist air suddenly arrives. Before the walls can warm up, they chill the air in contact with them below the dew-point, and dew is deposited on them, giving streaming walls, be-dewed window panes, and limp wall-paper. In the open, if favourable conditions for condensation occur on a cold night in winter, the dew-point may not be reached until the temperature has fallen below the freezing-point, and hoar-frost is the result. " Radiation-weather ", with calm air and a clear sky, is clearly conducive to winter frosts, and the same conditions often produce low fog, of which mist is a minor, thin, and often discontinuous variant. True radiation fog occurs when the ground gets very cold by night, but when there is just sufficient turbulence in the lower air to carry the chilling through a layer of air of appreciable thickness. Condensation, when the dew-point is reached, then takes place throughout this layer, producing a sort of cloud at ground-level. The conditions favouring persistent and intense radiation-fog are thus like those producing inversion of temperature, and indeed this often accompanies winter fogs. The warmer overlying air then forms a sort of lid over the fog and checks the development of large-scale turbulence, so that the conditions often intensify day by day, especially in midwinter when the sun has not sufficient power to evaporate the water droplets even at noon. Dispersion may only come with a marked change in the weather, and the arrival of warm air or strong winds. Over large towns and industrial areas such persistent fogs are often darkened by smoke-particles and soot, prevented from escaping by the temperature inversion. The term " smog " (smoke-fog) has been coined to describe such conditions, which may occasionally be dangerous if factories emitting poisonous fumes are in the area affected. Many cases are on record in which many people have been taken ill as a result of such conditions. The " London Special " is a classic case of smoke-darkened fog, but it is now seldom experienced in its earlier virulence.

Since cold air drains downhill, radiation fog is most common and persistent in winter on low ground, and in valleys and other semi-enclosed areas where pools of cold air tend to form. It remains one of the most formidable natural obstacles to transport, and a major menace to airfields, which, although necessarily

G

located on level ground, are generally carefully sited with an eye to minimum fog interference. Many local factors indeed appreciably affect fog incidence, and the site of London Airport (Heath Row), although in the Thames valley, is claimed to be tolerably fog-free. Little can be done to combat fog by artificial means, the wartime device of dissipating it on airfields by burning petrol being far too expensive for general adoption.

A somewhat different type of fog, called "advection fog", occurs when warm, moist, air is chilled by drifting over a cold surface and mingling with the cold air above it. On land this is frequently experienced during snow-thaw as the warm air that melts the snow itself gets chilled. At sea, dense banks of fog tend to occur where warm and cold waters meet. The frequent fogs over the Grand Banks off Newfoundland are of this character. Relatively little actual precipitation results from most fogs, which are built of very small water-droplets which float in the air. Very similar is the type of cloud called "stratus" which so frequently blankets the whole sky in a dull uniform sheet in winter, stratus clouds being really high-level fog, and like it giving little precipitation. They are formed by the mixing of warmer and colder air along the junction-zone of two air-layers of different character.

While the cooling of moist air by direct contact with cold ground, or by local mixing with cold air, can thus give rise to various distinctive forms of condensation, the precipitation afforded is generally negligible. Effective precipitation is almost entirely in the forms of rain and snow, and the mass-cooling necessary for their formation seems to be brought about only by the *rising* of large masses of air. As we noted earlier, whenever air rises it expands, and this expansion uses up energy, so that the internal temperature of the air-mass is lowered. The cooling effect occurs throughout the whole volume of the air, and if continued long enough brings it below the dew-point so that great volumes of water condense to give various types of cloud, from which, in favourable circumstances, precipitation may occur. There are three principal ways in which such rising can be brought about.

The first we have met already. It is convectional rising

occasioned by heating from below.   This occurs all the time in the equatorial zone, and as the evaporation-rate there is high owing to the great heat, the rising air is not only warm but very moist.   As it rises it cools, condensation sets in, and great clouds of the " cumulus " type develop ; clouds with high vertical development, in appearance like cauliflowers.   The great height developed in these clouds shows clearly the strength of the upward air-currents, to which the moisture of the air materially contributes ; for once condensation starts a good deal of additional heat is liberated which maintains the temperature of the rising air-column and assists its ascent.   (This release of heat during condensation, the reverse of the heat-intake required to cause evaporation, is the reason why moist air cools on rising more slowly than does dry air : vide p. 163).   The typical Equatorial day, in the monotonous conditions of heat and high humidity, thus follows a standard pattern.   In the morning the sky may be clear and calm, but as the day's heat builds up, so the upward convectional rising begins and towering cumulus clouds develop which lead to regular afternoon downpours of heavy rain.   Convectional rainfall is thus characteristic of the hotter regions of the earth, and in cooler lands, of summer.   In the continental interiors rainfall is predominantly of the summer convectional type, for as the ground heats up the high pressures of winter are broken down, the air becomes unstable, rising currents start, and convectional uplift becomes general.   This in turn leads to lowered pressures, and moist air is drawn in from the oceanic areas round about.   Under the cold conditions and high pressures of winter, convectional rainfall can obviously seldom occur.   The oceanic margins of the cooler lands do not get much convectional rain, since they seldom experience high enough temperatures, but in Britain our summer rainfall is in part of convectional type, being associated with the typical cumulus clouds which reveal convectional rising.   The rain associated with convectional movements is typically heavy, localised, and composed of big drops falling more or less vertically.   It generally accompanies summer thunderstorms, which themselves are a product of convectional turbulence. When the uprush of air is very rapid, water-drops may grow

quite large within the stream without being able to fall to earth.
Such drops readily get broken up, and in the process the minute
electrical charges they carry are separated, the negative charge
going to the air, the positive to the water. Multiplication of
this process can build up enormous electrical potentials, until a
flash jumps considerable distances within the cloud, between
clouds, or from cloud to ground. The accompanying " roll "
of thunder is caused by reverberations of the noise made by the
lightning flash from other cloud surfaces. Thunderstorms
can occur at any time of year, but as they require unstable air
conditions they are most common in summer. Closely associated with them is the most destructive form of precipitation,
hail, which although its stones are composed of concentric
layers of clear ice and part-melted and re-frozen snow, occurs
mainly in the summer months. Hailstones as large as pigeons-
eggs not infrequently fall, and an unlucky shower can ruin a
whole orchard or vineyard. Hailstorms are particularly characteristic of the interiors of continents in spring and early summer,
when the ground is heating up rapidly and the air is least stable.
To understand the mechanism we must say a further word about
the actual formation of rain and snow.

Condensation is not quite the simple phenomenon it appears.
Experiments show that in perfectly pure air considerable cooling
below the dew-point can go on without any condensation
occurring, to produce " super-saturation." For free and
extensive condensation it seems that the air must contain minute
solid particles to form nuclei around which the water can
condense. The hygroscopic particles of sea-salt, carried into
the air by spray, seem to be the most important nuclei in the
atmosphere. Around these grow tiny water droplets which may
be as small as 1/100th millimetre in diameter. The gentlest of
air turbulence is sufficient to keep these floating—hence the
many clouds from which no rain falls. Growth to a size at
which gravity can pull them down involves problems not yet
thoroughly understood, for very small water-droplets tend to
repel one another rather than coalesce, and their high surface-
tension makes it difficult for them to grow by absorbing further
molecules of water-vapour. Growth, however, clearly does go

on in some way, and eventually the drops become large enough to overcome the supporting-power of the air, and so fall to earth. The character and duration of the fall naturally vary with the rapidity of the uplift producing the condensation, and the extent to which it is continued. From a mass of air being gently and gradually lifted, rain will fall as soon as drops reach the size of about 1 millimetre, and the rain will reach the earth as a light drizzle. In strong convectional uplift, however, the drops may have to grow to 5 mm. or more in diameter before they will fall through the uprush of air, and such big drops, once clear of the ascending air-stream, naturally fall much faster. So-called "cloudbursts" are often caused by the sudden checking of a great mass of rapidly-ascending air and cloud, heavy rain then pouring down without warning. If rising continues until the temperature in the cloud falls to below 32 °F. the water-droplets freeze, and further condensation is in the solid state. Snow-flakes may then be built up from the tiny ice-crystals formed. Hail is created in strong uprushes of air in which water-drops get swept up to freezing heights, there to freeze and have further ice deposited on them before they fall again. Often they fall and are swept up again many times, growing in size all the time, and developing the typical composite structure of layers of clear ice separated by layers of mushy snow with much included air. It is only by such repeated uplifts, in all probability, that hailstones can grow to large size. In relation to ice-condensation it may here be remarked that the upper parts of many clouds are, in part at least, composed of ice-crystals, but that often some degree of "super-cooling" exists in them which checks the growth of ice-crystals and snow. In such conditions, however, ice may be rapidly deposited on any foreign body, and aircraft often suffer great peril in traversing such clouds through the weight of ice deposited on their wings, although de-icing equipment can now combat this danger. The highest clouds of all, the fine wispy trails called "cirrus", are probably made up entirely of ice-crystals.

The second way in which large masses of air can be raised and large-scale condensation and precipitation effected, is by topo-graphic obstacles. If a low-level stream of warm, moist air strikes a mountain-chain lying across its path it may be forced to climb over it, and exactly the same mechanism of cooling and condensation comes into operation (Fig. 49). The cooling is generally more gradual, so that the rain starts with a drizzle, becoming heavier as altitude increases. If the barrier is very high, however, after a certain point the rainfall may decrease again. This effect is common on high mountains in tropical latitudes. In temperate latitudes, a proportion of the higher-altitude precipitation is likely to occur as snow, even in summer. Precipitation caused by the presence of high land is called " *Orographic* ". It is worldwide in distribution, occurring

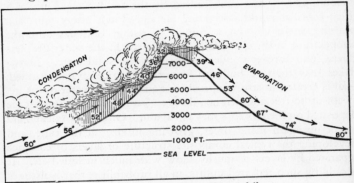

Fig. 49. Mechanism of a ' Föhn', and of orographic rainfall.

wherever an obstacle sufficiently high to cause effective condensation opposes the drift of moist air. A glance at any world rainfall map, and comparison with the relief map, will show clearly how great is the control of relief over rainfall. It is a common saying that " hills attract the rain ', and in Britain it is well-known that the hills of the north and west have far higher rainfall totals than the lower country of the midlands and east. This is partly because most of the moist rain-bringing air flows over our islands from west to east, but the higher relief in the west plays a dominant part in bringing the rain down. The Lake District hills, the hills of N. Wales, and the western highlands of Scotland are the wettest parts of Britain, some places having annual totals of over 100 inches of rainfall, whereas East Anglia and the Thames estuary get less than 25 inches. Gross contrasts in rainfall between places quite close together are often caused by high dissected relief. Good examples are to be found in British Columbia, where the Rocky Mountains oppose the drift inland of moist air from the Pacific; down the west side of the Andes in S. America, where desert conditions along the coast are replaced by abundant rain and forest growth at higher levels; and along the high west coasts of Britain and Norway. In the Hawaiian Islands, located in the zone of the N.E. Trade Winds, rainfall figures of perhaps 20 inches on the low coastal plains contrast with figures exceeding 200 inches on the windward side of higher mountains. The inblowing S.W. Monsoon of India, loaded with moisture after its trip across the warm Equatorial seas, pours torrents of water along the abrupt rise of the Western Ghats (Calicut has 116 inches of monsoonal rain), and even more on the higher hills of Assam, where Cherrapunji, with 426 inches of rain a year, has the highest recorded rainfall on earth.

The effects of relief on rainfall are not, however, entirely one-way. Although causing heavy rainfall on their windward sides, mountain-chains opposing the drift of moist air often create belts of deficient rainfall in their lee. Having overtopped the crest the air-currents no longer rise, and may even roll down again; and if they do they become compressed, warmed, and dried. The clouds evaporate, and in the lee of the mountains the ground may in consequence be parched. "Rain-shadow" zones, sometimes so marked as to amount to local deserts, thus frequently occur in low-lying basins within mountain-systems (as in central Asia), or on the lee side of great chains which oppose regular wind-systems. The effect is well illustrated in Argentine Patagonia, where sub-desert conditions extend in the lee of the Andes where they block the westerly wind-drift. Here we may amplify the note included in the last chapter about the "Föhn" wind of the Alps. As it climbs uphill, the air loses much moisture by condensation and rainfall, but as this process releases heat, cooling goes on at the "wet adiabatic lapse-rate" (to use the technical term) of c.3 °F per 1,000 feet. On coming down the other side, however, the air warms up by compression at the

" dry adiabatic " rate of 5.4°F per 1,000 feet, i.e. it warms up on descending much more rapidly than it cooled in climbing. This rapid warming of course tends to check its descent, but in suitable conditions strong currents will blow down the valleys as unusually warm descending winds. The air is extremely dry, and tends to melt snow, dry up moisture, and even parch wood to such an extent that fires are to be guarded against. Fig. 49 illustrates the principle.

The third major mechanism whereby air is cooled, and rain formed, is by the rising incidental to the creation and movement of cyclones, or depressions. Such rainfall, called "*Cyclonic*",[1] is the type we most commonly experience in Britain. In this case the warm moist air is forced to climb up over colder dense air by the swirling movement of the air-streams in the cyclonic structure. A cyclone or depression is, in principle, a sort of gigantic eddy in the atmosphere, with low pressure at its centre into which air tends to move from all round. The deflection caused by the rotation of the earth gives the inward-blowing air currents a spiral motion, anticlockwise in the northern hemisphere, clockwise in the southern. For a long time it had been known that these moving centres of low pressure and in-blowing winds usually brought clouds, rain, and blustery weather, but just why was only discovered by the researches of Norwegian meteorologists into the origin, growth and structure of these pressure systems during the first World War.

The depressions we experience so frequently in Britain appear to originate as "waves" in the junction-zone of the moist warm air of the Westerlies belt with the cold heavy air drifting down from the Arctic ; the zone we earlier styled the " Polar Front ". The stages in growth are illustrated diagrammatically in Fig. 50. Warm air from the south pushes a " bulge " into the cold, which circles round behind it as the structure travels along. Gradually the bulge grows, and the air-currents in and around it become stronger. In vertical section, inclined junction-planes, or " fronts " are formed between the two different types of air, and as the whole structure drifts along, the warm moist air in the middle is forced to climb up over the more sluggish cold air in advance of it, while colder air swirling round in the

1 Or "Frontal".

rear tends to undercut the warm air from behind and lift it off the ground. "Lines of discontinuity" occur in the weather conditions at ground-level where these inclined planes between the two different types of air intersect the ground-surface, and these are reflected on weather-maps in abrupt changes in direction

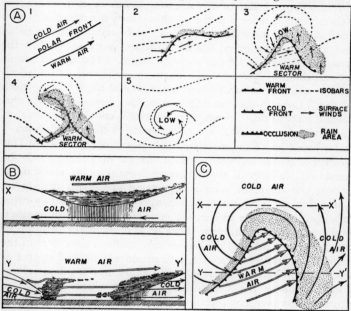

Fig. 50 :

(A) 1-5. *The birth, growth and disappearance of a depression.*
(B) *Vertical structure of a frontal depression. The sections run along the lines X-X' and Y-Y' in (C).*
(C) *Structure of a frontal depression when well developed.*

(*After Kendrew and Bjerknes.*)

in the isobars, and by sharp alterations in temperature and wind direction. The sequence of weather experienced as such a well-developed depression, with marked "fronts" in it, drifts across the British Isles, is something as follows. (We assume the observer to be south of the centre of the depression). Winds

G*

are at first south-easterly, gradually veering to south, and high thin cirrus clouds spread over the sky, followed by thickening lower clouds of alto-stratus type as the " Warm Front " approaches. Drizzling rain commences, gradually becoming heavier with the approach of low " nimbus " rain-clouds. As the " Warm Front " line of discontinuity passes over, there is often a sharp change of wind to the south-westerly quarter, heavy rain, and (in winter) generally a marked rise of temperature with an increase of air humidity, for within this " warm sector " of the structure the air is of sub-tropical origin. The clouds might lift and the rain ease off as the warm sector passed, but piled-up nimbus clouds and further heavy rain would mark the approach of the " Cold Front " in the rear of the depression. As this passed, a sharp drop in temperature would coincide with a shift of wind to the N.W., stronger winds, " clearing showers ", and a break up of the clouds to give place to blue skies. This weather-sequence is very familiar to us in Britain, and the interested reader will find many opportunities of checking it against the travel of such a depression across his district by comparing the actual weather-changes with the weather-maps published in the daily papers. The detailed sequence of weather, however, varies at different times of year, with the position of the observer relative to the line of movement of the centre of the depression, and with the size, rate of movement, and degree of development of the depression. Some slow-moving depressions, and particularly the " occluded " ones in which the mass of warm air has been completely undercut by cold and lifted off the ground (so that no linear " fronts " at ground-level appear on the weather-maps at all), merely give prolonged heavy rain without any sharp weather changes. Smaller " secondary depressions " are liable to travel faster, and to produce stronger winds and gales ; but for the weather types associated with these, and with the various other distinctive travelling pressure-structures that contribute to the variety of our British weather, the reader must be referred to the many excellent popular books on meteorology now available. Cyclonic rainfall, the main source of our British supplies (although orographic factors strongly affect its distribution) occurs mainly in the earth's zones of westerly wind-drift in the middle and higher latitudes, where the necessary conjunction of warm and cold air-streams is present on a large scale.   Tropical cyclones, hurricanes, and typhoons are, however, often accompanied by torrential rain.   These are much more violent gyratory storms in which wind velocities often reach 100 m.p.h.   Originating generally along the edges of the Doldrums they may inflict appalling damage and travel long distances before dying out.

Such, then, are the main mechanisms by which atmospheric water is returned to the earth.   The amount falling in any area is measured in the rain-gauges maintained at all meteorological stations, and is recorded in inches of water, snowfall being reduced to its water equivalent.   From an understanding of the mechanisms, combined with a general knowledge of the earth distribution of temperature and air circulation, it is not difficult to appreciate the pattern of rainfall over the earth, and the seasonal incidence at different places.   On this factual matter only a brief outline can be attempted here.   The details can be found in climatic atlases and works of reference.

Study of a world map of annual rainfall reveals that, in general, the hottest regions get the largest rainfall totals, their rainfall being mainly convectional and orographic.   Thus the wettest points in the tropics have about twice as much rain as the wettest places in temperate latitudes (over 400 inches as against some 200 inches).   This is clearly in harmony with the much greater evaporation-rate in the Tropics, and the more rapid " turnover " of the atmospheric water.   The pattern of rainfall distribution within the Tropics, however, reveals the influence of the major pressure systems and related air movements, while as everywhere the influence of ground-relief and altitude can clearly be seen. Coastal regions in areas experiencing strong monsoonal developments generally have heavy rainfall (especially where mountains occur near the coast), while the regions of more consistently high pressure and off-shore winds are markedly drier.   The great deserts occur systematically in the interiors and on the western margins of the continents in the zone of sub-tropical high pressures and Trade Winds.   Poleward of the Trade Wind belts and the sub-tropical high pressures, rainfall shows a marked dimi-

nution inland from the coasts towards the continental interiors,
while in latitudes 40° to 55° north and south, where the air
movement is generally from west to east, the western margins
of the continents receive more rain than the eastern. The
rainfall here is mainly cyclonic and orographic, but in the
continental interiors it is mainly convectional and occurs in
summer. In winter, as the reader will recall, these regions are
very cold, and have high pressures and an outward drift of air.
The atmosphere is stable; there is a tendency for " down-
settling "; and moving cyclones cannot penetrate far against the
high pressures. In summer, however, temperatures rise fast,
turbulence and convectional rising are set up in the air, with
convectional rain and the entry of damp air from the oceanic
regions round about. In the high latitudes precipitation is
generally scanty, and occurs mainly as snow; but since the
evaporation rate is so low because of the low temperatures, the
snow lies long on the ground and the ground remains moist all
summer, so that where temperatures permit plant growth can go
on with much smaller amounts of precipitation than is the case in
the Tropics. Mention of scanty precipitation introduces one
further general point that is of importance. On the whole
(though there are exceptions) the regularity and reliability of
rainfall diminish with decrease in its total amount. Highly
irregular rainfall, no less than minute annual quantities, character-
ises the great deserts, and it is the uncertainty of rain even more
than its small quantity that makes the exploitation of marginal
sub-arid lands such a chancy business. In western Australia,
for example, places with an average annual rainfall of 15 inches
have been known to get as much as 40 inches in one year, but at
other times no rain at all for several years. Clearly in the matter
of rainfall, as with temperature, annual averages can be dangerously misleading as guides to actual conditions. The practical
farmer or irrigation engineer must take account of reliability,
character, and seasonal incidence of rainfall no less than average
annual amount.

Seasonal incidence is the last aspect of precipitation that we
need note; and it shows almost as wide a range of variation as
total annual amount. Some regions have most of their rain in

winter, some most in summer, some most in autumn or spring. Almost continuous and even rainfall all the year round at one extreme contrasts with heavy showers over a few weeks only and total drought for the rest of the year at the other. We cannot describe all the variants, but a few notes on the more distinctive types of annual regime may be included.

(1) *Equatorial type.* Abundant convectional rainfall, with constantly humid air, occurs all the year round. Rainfall totals vary with location, but an average amount is 80 inches. Just as there is no cool season, so there is no dry season, although " peaks " of rainfall may mark the temperature maxima.

(2) *Savanna type.* Savanna is a term used to describe the open " bush " vegetation, consisting of scrub, tall coarse grasses, and occasional trees, that covers the drier lands around the rain-forests of the Equatorial regions. It reflects diminishing rainfall (average figures 35 to 60 inches), and the onset of a definite dry season. Heavy rains of the Equatorial-convectional type occur in summer, but in winter there is often complete drought. Such conditions prevail over much of tropical Africa, between the Congo and Guinea coast rain-forests and the dry scrub and desert country.

(3) *Monsoon type.* The pressure and wind reversals which make up a monsoon were described in the last chapter. Rain comes in summer with the inblowing monsoon, after a dry winter season. In India, where the monsoon is most strongly developed, the moist oceanic air breaks in about June in the south, bringing torrential rains which spread steadily northwards and last until about October. The amounts vary much with elevation and situation, but include some of the highest totals on earth. Indonesia and S.E. Asia generally experience monsoonal rains, which also affect southern China. Slight monsoonal effects are experienced in E. Africa, in Brazil, and in Central America and the S.E. U.S.A.

(4) *Tropical Desert and Steppe.* The Savanna conditions gradually tail out with the summer rains becoming shorter, slighter, and less regular, until sub-arid transition zones give place to the virtually rainless desert tracts of the Trade Wind

zones. The air comes from regions of " down-settlement ",
and is hence initially dry, while as it blows towards the Tropics
it becomes ever warmer and drier. From the Sahara a great
extension of arid country runs east into central Asia where the
Himalayas and other high mountains prevent the summer
monsoon from carrying rain further inland. Central and western
Australia lie in the sub-tropical arid zone, as do S.W. Africa,
northern Chile and Peru, the S.W. States of the U.S.A. and
northern Mexico.

(5) *Mediterranean type*. Around the shores of the Mediterranean
Sea, and over limited tracts on the western sides of other continents in similar latitudes (California; C. Chile; C. of Good Hope;
Swanland in W. Australia) a most unusual rainfall regime is
found. With the seasonal " swings " north and south of the
climatic belts, these marginal regions fall in summer under
the edge of the Trade Wind desert conditions, in winter
under the edge of the westerlies-cyclonic zone. Long dry
sunny summers thus alternate with warm winters in which
some cyclonic rain falls, affording (in the more temperate spots)
one of the pleasantest climates on earth.

(6) *Mid-latitude West coast type*. Britain and N.W. Europe,
lying within the westerlies zone, experience rain at all seasons,
the amount varying with exposure and elevation. The rain is
mainly cyclonic and orographic. British Columbia and Southern
Chile have similar rainfall regimes.

(7) *Temperate Continental Interior*. From the humid west coasts
rainfall decreases in amount inland in Eurasia and Canada, while
winters become rather dry. Such rain as falls comes mainly in
spring and late summer, being largely convectional in character.

(8) *Temperate East Coast*. New England, the Canadian eastern
maritime provinces, and the N.E. coastlands of Asia have
moderate rainfalls, somewhat irregularly distributed; N.E.
Asia receiving mostly summer rain (produced by an extension
of the monsoon effect), New England mainly cyclonic rain
better distributed through the year. Southern Patagonia, the
only southern hemisphere land area in this group by position,

gets little rain because of the rain-barrier presented by the Andes to the westerly winds.

(9) *Polar type*. Within the Arctic Circles precipitation is mainly in the form of snow. There is probably more in the Arctic than in the Antarctic, owing to the stronger high-pressure system over the Antarctic ice-cap, but information on amounts and seasonal distribution is still scanty.

It is by combination of figures and regimes of temperature and rainfall, with some occasional reference to winds, cloudiness and so on, that climatologists attempt to describe and sub-divide the total complex panorama of climatic variation over the earth. Many systems of classification have been suggested, varying in degree of sub-division, and according to where the dividing-lines are drawn, but any classification must be to some degree arbitrary, since in nature one set of conditions blends gradually into another; there are no clear and sharp dividing-lines. As this book does not set out to be a work of reference, no formal description of any selected system of climatic classification will be given, but the reader will find the more popular systems illustrated in Atlas maps, and in the standard text-books. We may here perhaps more usefully include a few words upon the stability of our climatic system.

In treating the heating of the earth, it was said that the earth appears to be getting neither hotter nor colder year by year; but that was a short-term statement. When we review the whole vista of geological time, it is clear that both the average conditions, and the regional distribution, of climate have varied a good deal in different eras. In the Cretaceous period, for instance, climate was quite genial in Greenland, where a rich vegetation flourished, while in the earlier Permian and Triassic periods the area now western Europe was an extensive desert. However, it is clear that through most of its history the climate of the earth has been at once more genial and more uniform than it is today. The events of the Pleistocene Ice Age, which we outlined briefly in Chap. X, although involving large areas of the earth and introducing great changes in conditions particularly in the high latitudes, in proportion to the whole extent of geological time represent but a brief "cold snap". Similar cold snaps had occurred before, probably the most severe being that of later Carboniferous times, but against total earth-history these cold phases appear as but trivial episodes. Early in this book we noted that in somewhat similar fashion periods of marked earth-activity and high continental relief have been relatively few and short-lived. At the present time, with ice-capped Poles, snow-clad mountains, a marked diversity of climate, some 500 active volcanoes, and a highly diversified relief, earth-conditions are distinctly abnormal, and we have good reason to suppose that they are changing relatively fast by geological standards. In north-western Europe the big ice-sheets of the last Pleistocene glacial advance only melted away some 10-15,000 years ago, and climate has been by no means uniform since. On the contrary, there have been very marked fluctuations. In later prehistoric times (post-glacial), climate in Europe varied from warm and wet to cold and dry, with several minor readvances of the glaciers. We can trace the sequence of the fluctuations by analysing the changing character of the predominant types of tree-pollen contained in superimposed beds of peat, for the pollen reflects the dominant vegetation type, and vegetation is a delicate recorder of climatic change. Even in historic times the situation has been by no means static. One of the best sources of evidence about climatic fluctuation is change in the positions of glacier-snouts, and from this evidence it would appear that about 4,000 years ago western Europe was definitely warmer that it is now. When the Vikings colonised Iceland and Greenland they occupied lands which were still much more genial than we now know them, for Viking settlements were later covered by ice, and some have only quite recently been exhumed again by glacier withdrawal. The same sort of evidence occurs in the Alps. There we can find ruins of villages now being re-exposed which were overwhelmed by glacier advance in the 16th century. In general, it would appear that a phase of colder climate set in about A.D. 1200-1300. Viking settlers were driven out of Greenland, glaciers advanced in Iceland, and in Scandinavia the cultivation of barley in many areas was abandoned for that of oats. Fluctuating glacier advance continued, in Greenland the maximum positions being recorded in the late 18th and early 19th centuries, while in the Alps a considerable ice-advance which set in in the 16th century again culminated, after many fluctuations, in the early 19th. Old forests were buried, and many villages progressively abandoned. The Nile attained its maximum flow of modern times in 1850, while old-lived Sequoia trees show a widening of their annual rings corresponding to this period, this indicating moister conditions. Since 1850 or so, however, there is widespread evidence of amelioration of winter temperatures, and perhaps some decrease of rainfall in certain areas. Since the turn of this century, at least, glaciers throughout the northern hemisphere have been in retreat, and in some areas quite rapid retreat. Old temperature records confirm the change. Winters in Holland are today on average 4° warmer than they were in the early 19th century, and Lancashire records reveal a comparable change. The popular impression that our winters are getting less severe is thus confirmed, and all sorts of interesting correlated changes are being revealed by the most diverse lines of research. For instance, since the turn of the century cod, formerly almost unknown off southern Greenland, have been appearing in those waters in large numbers, and have by now become a staple article of local diet. It seems likely that a slight rise in water temperatures may be responsible for this change in habits of the cod, and various other obscure migrations of fish may also be attributable to slight changes in water-temperatures and the flow of currents relating to slight changes in earth-climate.

On this evidence it appears justifiable to conclude that we are living in a period of climatic instability; possibly that of " recovery " from the last glaciation, possibly even in a mild phase *within* that glaciation. The changes, to be sure, are slow and slight, and no one can be sure whether they will continue, or whether present trends will be reversed. If the former, however, in time they could alter living conditions on the earth quite significantly. It has been calculated that an increase of only 2°F in the *mean* temperature of the earth would suffice to clear all ice from the Polar seas, while a decrease of only a few degrees in mean summer temperature in the higher latitudes would result in vast additional areas becoming ice-covered. Disproportionate results and unforeseen complications can result from even slight changes where natural conditions are delicately balanced, and a realisation of this, and of the intricate interaction of natural forces and processes, is perhaps the most valuable lesson that physical geography has to teach. We will return to this point in the concluding chapter; but as regards climatic change, it must not be thought that we need worry much about possible changes in the foreseeable future. Only in the " marginal " areas is it likely to produce perceptible changes in conditions within decades, even if the present suspected tendencies persist. Yet even now the commercial promoters of hydro-electric power-stations in the Alps and Norway are concerned about the glacier-wastage which threatens the water-supplies of their all-important streams. As regards climate we thus end on the note with which we started: its unexpected intrusion into almost every aspect of human life and welfare.

CHAPTER XIII

THE CIRCULATION OF WATER. PART II: ON THE GROUND

"All the rivers run into the sea; yet the sea is not full; unto the place from whence the rivers come, thither they return again."

ECCLESIASTES, I. 7.

OUR theme in the last chapter was the outward or delivery part of the Hydrological Cycle, the part carried out by the atmosphere. We must now follow up what happens to the water it distributes which falls on land. For the large quantities of rain which fall at sea, clearly the story is at an end; but lands have a great capacity for storing water, and even when their capacity is surfeited the return-flow from them is relatively slow. All the waters that we find on land are elements in this combined storage and slow return—glaciers and snowfields, lakes and swamps, springs and rivers, the moisture in soils, and the water in the rocks underground—and all exist only because of the water-retaining power of land and because the rainfall-supply exceeds the constant counter-withdrawal by atmospheric evaporation. Although much water is retained on land permanently, there is a turnover in virtually all land-waters, slow or fast, and over a period of years as much water returns to the oceans as is lifted from them; for despite the constant activity of the atmosphere the ocean level does not drop, nor do the lands become progressively more waterlogged. The return flow takes place through two channels. The more important is again through the atmosphere, for evaporation takes its toll of all exposed water on land, and probably some 70 to 80% of all land rainfall evaporates again. The remaining 20 to 30% flows back to the oceans in liquid or solid form through rivers and glaciers, but so far as rivers are concerned, relatively little of this flow is direct ground-surface runoff. Most of it is " spillover " from the various land water-reservoirs, and this explains the curious fact that despite the highly irregular incidence of rainfall in time and place, the total volume of water returned to the ocean by the world's rivers varies relatively little throughout the year. The atmosphere has to work fast, for it can hold only enough water for about two or three days' precipitation, but land can store up the accumulated rainfall of weeks and months, releasing the surplus slowly and steadily. We again emphasise, however, that water is not an essential component of land, and that all forms of land-water reflect a state of balance between supply and withdrawal. The relative abundance of water in any country depends, in the last analysis, on its climatic conditions.

The water which falls from clouds upon land-surfaces seldom stays long where it falls. Usually the bulk of it is rapidly dispersed and there are three ways in which this dispersal is brought about. The first is by evaporation. Even while it is falling rain is subject to evaporation-losses, and these continue all the time the water is exposed on the land surface. Of the remaining water, some may run off over the surface to join streams and rivers, and so return eventually to the sea, while the rest soaks into the soil, there to maintain soil-moisture and to replenish the water-supplies held in the underlying rocks. The proportions between these three modes of dispersal in any rain-shower vary enormously in different circumstances, and it is difficult to generalise about them. We can, however, examine the factors which affect the outcome.

Taking evaporation first, since for the whole earth this is by far the most important mode of rain-water dispersal, we have already noted the factors which govern its activity : temperature, of the air and ground ; relative humidity ; wind ; and some minor factors like air pressure. In hot regions of dry air and infrequent rain, like the Sahara, evaporation is so dominant that liquid water seldom occurs on the ground at all. It is not uncommon to see rain evaporating away completely before it even reaches the ground. The precipitation has to be very intense to set up any appreciable surface flow, and as we saw in Chap. IX, such flows quickly peter out. They do so mainly by evaporation, relatively little of the water soaking into the rocks because being bone-dry these are full of air which the water cannot rapidly displace. Over the arid quarter of the earth's lands, indeed, virtually none of the oceanic water that is occasionally precipitated as rain returns direct to the ocean. The only return is through the atmosphere.

At the other extreme stand the Polar regions, studied in Chap. X, where the bulk of the precipitation, being in the solid form, accumulates on the surface. Infiltration into the ground can only go on when some of the snow melts, and even then the frozen soils prevent free ingress. Evaporation certainly removes some of the water (the reader will have noticed that snow slowly disappears even during continuous frost), but in the prevailing low temperatures its rate is much reduced. Runoff is also severely hampered by the solid condition of the water, and can only occur effectively where the ground is steep, or when the " water " has piled up to such a thickness that it flows outward under its own weight. In the glacial regions therefore vast quantities of water remain on the land surface. It is of some interest to note the extreme slowness of the " turnover " in these ice accumulations. It has been calculated that it may take 10,000 years for a particle of ice, deposited as snow in the middle of the Greenland ice-cap, to work down into a coastal glacier and emerge in a sea-borne iceberg. Icebergs now floating down from Greenland may thus contain water deposited as snow during the Great Ice Age.

Between these extremes of no surface water and maximum surface retention lie the rainy temperate lands. In them although much rainfall returns by evaporation, a good deal soaks into the ground, and the surplus flows off in numerous surface streams. Evaporation withdrawals are everywhere greatest in summer, which accounts for the drier condition of soils and the lower river-levels in that season, (unless the rainfall in summer is very heavy and winter dry), but the detailed percentages of losses by evaporation vary greatly. It is to be noted also that the water running off in streams, and even that soaking into the ground, is not immune to evaporation-losses. These continue in rivers all the way down to the sea, and evaporation takes back much water that earlier soaked into the soil. The surface films of water

soon disappear after a rain-shower, but by the process of capillary
rising water continues to be sucked up through the soil and
evaporated on the surface. It is by this mechanism that the
upper soil is kept damp. If the intervals between rains are long,
great quantities of water may be drawn up out of the ground by
this means, and the underground reservoirs seriously depleted.
The rate of such evaporation-losses from the ground is governed
not only by the external conditions of temperature, humidity, and
wind. The texture of the soil, and the nature of its surface, affect
the rate appreciably. An open-textured sandy soil which allows
water to pass through it easily will drink in rainfall rapidly but
will also readily disgorge it again, so drying out more quickly,
and to greater depth, during " evaporation-weather ", than a
compact clay in which the pore-spaces are too small to allow
water to move easily through it. Vegetation also influences the
rate of evaporation from the ground-surface considerably. All
plants need water, but they can take in very little directly from
the air. Most of their needs are drawn up from the soil through
their roots, while water is continually passed back to the atmosphere through their leaves by a process called transpiration.
The rates at which plants transpire water are affected by their
rhythms of growth and also by the external air conditions, but
with a dense coverage of growing vegetation the quantities of
water drawn up from the soil and returned to the atmosphere by
this means are considerable. In dense tropical forest the greater
part of all evaporation losses of ground-water is by plant-
transpiration, and even in temperate climates this may be the
case. On the other hand, to offset its transpiration activities,
vegetation cuts down the rate of direct physical evaporation
from the soil. Plants and trees, by shading the ground, reduce its
temperature ; they help to maintain a higher air humidity near
the ground than occurs over bare soil ; and they greatly reduce
the wind velocity near ground-level. But dense vegetation
also prevents an appreciable amount of rainfall from reaching the
ground at all (it hangs on the leaves and evaporates off them
again) ; yet of the rain which does penetrate, it retains a great
deal in the leaf-mould and organic litter that it drops on the
ground, so helping to reduce both runoff and immediate evapor-

ation-losses. It will be apparent that the effects of vegetation on the disposal of rain-waters are many and complex. But the common idea that forests by their very presence attract rainfall has received little scientific support. The mechanisms that create rain take place well up in the atmosphere, and the only significant way in which vegetation could affect them might be in the case of orographic rain, where tall forest, by increasing the effective height of a hill-range by perhaps 100 feet, might cause slightly increased air uplift and precipitation. The importance of vegetation lies much more in its influence on what happens to the rainwater that reaches the ground.

The second mode of rainwater dispersal is surface runoff. For this to start, the rate of supply of water to the surface must exceed the rates of abstraction by evaporation and soil-absorption combined. Water will flow over the most open-textured and absorbent sand if the slope is steep enough and the rainfall sufficiently intense, but with light showers of limited duration factors of ground-slope and porosity of the soil obviously determine whether any surface runoff occurs or not. The readiness with which any soil or rock will drink in water depends on the materials of which it is made and their arrangement. Open-textured materials like sand and gravel take it in fast; fine-grained compact clays admit it much more slowly; and truly compact solid rocks may not admit it at all. But the percentage of water passing over it that sinks into any rock surface depends not only on its porosity or perviousness, but upon the time during which the water stays on its surface, which is another way of saying the speed of flow; and here surface texture becomes an important governing factor as well as ground-slope. A rough-surfaced soil or rock checks rapid water-flow over it, so enhancing the water-losses by both evaporation and infiltration, while smooth surfaces allow the water to pass over them more rapidly and hence cut down these incidental losses. In this context vegetation again assumes great importance. In the first place, a close vegetation-cover breaks the force of rain beating, which by itself can hammer the soil into a compact impervious mass which stimulates surface runoff. Then if surface flow does start, the stems and roots check its velocity, and allow the maximum

amount of water to sink in down the openings maintained by
root-systems.   The litter of mould, rotting branches, leaves and
so on also absorbs large quantities of water, while the humus it
creates increases the absorbtive capacity of the soil itself.   In all
these ways vegetation helps to check surface runoff and retain
the maximum amount of water in the soil, and its influence in
this matter may be of supreme importance.   American studies
have shown that on land of moderate slopes carrying full undisturbed natural forest, little if any water from normal rains runs
off over the ground surface at all.   Only with abnormal rains
does surface flow start, and it is greatly hampered.   On burned-
over forest land, by contrast, 50 or 60% of quite normal rain-
showers may run off over the surface, being lost to the soil, and
scoring it away in the gullies it carves out.   Clearly here is a
matter of the utmost significance to the menace of soil-erosion
that has already ruined vast areas of good farm-land in many
parts of the world.   We shall touch on this matter again in the
last chapter.   But even now we have not exhausted the factors
influencing runoff.   Since it is the result of the balance between
relative rates of rainfall and water-removal by other means, the
rate—or intensity—of the precipitation is clearly significant.
On the same ground runoff will be copious from an inch of rain
falling in half a day, when it would not occur at all with the same
amount falling over a week.   The water-situation in the ground
is also important, for once completely saturated with water, the
most absorbent materials will allow surface-flow to pass over
them.   And finally, we may note that a thin layer of frozen soil
on the surface will transform the most pervious formations into
" waterproofed " surfaces over which water will run with little
loss.   Clearly with so many variable factors affecting the outcome
one cannot safely generalise about the percentages of rainfall
that are likely to move away as surface flow after any rainstorm,
but for Britain as a whole it is probably true to say that only a
small fraction of our total rainfall does so, and that mainly
confined to the steeper hill areas.   After evaporation-losses, in
most parts of the world by far the most important mode of
rainwater-disposal is by absorption into the ground.

The part of rainwater that sinks in is, from nearly every point of view, the most important. It alone maintains in soils the moisture that permits plant-growth. It alone replenishes the underground water-reservoirs, on which we largely depend for domestic consumption. And equally it is this fraction that principally maintains the flow of our rivers, reaching them by slow subterranean seepage. Direct runoff of rainwater over the ground surface, in a country like Britain, only contributes to river-flow effectively in the steep hill areas or after abnormally heavy rains, augmenting the normal flow to produce floods and spates. The steady flow, maintained with little diminution through weeks of complete drought, comes from the underground reservoirs through springs and seepages. In most regions far more water is held permanently below the ground than ever appears on the surface.

That buried rock formations can take in, hold, transmit, and release great quantities of water depends on features of their internal structure and disposition, and rocks vary greatly in this respect. In discussing this matter we must first clarify a few common terms. Rocks like sandstone, made up of small separate particles stuck together, have an appreciable percentage of their total volume made up of tiny inter-connected air spaces, or pores. Such rocks are called *porous*. They can take in, and hold, considerable quantities of water, as can a sponge. The quantity they can absorb depends on the size of the individual particles, their arrangement, and the extent to which the pore-spaces between them are filled with bonding cements. A moderately coarse-grained rock, well-sorted, and without much cement, will hold much water. Well-screened gravel is a good example. Angular grains pack more closely than round ; an ill-sorted material will have much of its potential pore-space filled with tiny grains ; while in a well-cemented rock the cement itself will fill much of the air-space (*See* Fig. 51 A). Thus among porous rocks clean washed loose sand will hold much more water than a mixed sand-silt alluvium, while a strongly-cemented sandstone will generally be less porous than one weakly cemented. But a rock may be porous, in the sense that it will drink in much water, and may yet prevent the free passage of water through it and only yield up its water reluctantly. The critical factor here is grain size. Clay is highly porous, but the pore-spaces are so small that the water clings by molecular attraction around the tiny grains, so that the rock will yield up little water, and may not allow *any*

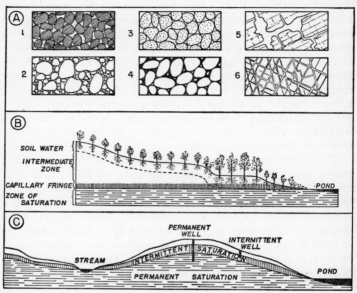

Fig. 51 :

(A) *Rock-structures and their effects on porosity.* 1. *Large well-sorted grains. The air spaces are large, and the rock will hold much water.* 2. *Ill-sorted sediment. The pore-spaces are mainly filled with smaller particles.* 3. *Large grains, themselves of porous material, give optimum water-holding capacity.* 4. *In this well-cemented rock, the pore-spaces are largely filled in with cement. Water capacity poor.* 5. *An unporous rock penetrated with solution-fissures (e.g. a massive limestone) will hold much water.* 6. *Similarly, a compact igneous rock shattered with joints and fractures will both hold water and allow it to pass through.*

(B) *Water-zones in the soil and sub-soil.*

(C) *The water-table in homogeneous porous rocks.*

water to pass through it. Rocks which prevent the passage of water are styled *Impermeable*; those which permit it *Permeable*. A rock may however allow water to pass through it though having no porosity. Granite is intrinsically quite unporous, for the rock material is compact and solid. But in nature granite formations are generally fractured by numerous joints and faults along which water can pass freely. A rock without true porosity, but which contains cavities and fissures may both allow water to pass through it and may itself contain large amounts. Such rocks are termed *Pervious*. Many compact limestones are of this type.

Clearly all these properties are of importance in relation to ground-water. Totally impermeable strata prevent the infiltration of rainwater, but such rocks only outcrop over restricted areas, and where permeable or pervious strata occur water can sink in and move through the underground formations for long distances, to accumulate in favourable structures and build up extensive water-reservoirs. But why, it may be asked, does such water not drain away downwards ? The answer is that as depth increases all rocks become more dense, because the increasing pressure crushes the grains together in porous rocks, and seals the joints and fissures in fractured formations. Thus in depth all rocks become impermeable. Above the limiting depth, however, the extent and thickness of water-holding formations (or " aquifers " as they are often called) in any region depends on the character of the underlying rocks and their arrangement, and the structures into which the formations have been thrown by faults and folds.

Let us start with a simple case : a region where the surface formation is porous, and rainfall sufficient to keep the ground well watered (Fig. 51 B). Generally it will be found that the upper few feet of soil, sub-soil, and perhaps even bedrock, are not in fact full of water. This is because evaporation from the soil surface is always drawing water out, while underground flow, set up by the differences in level over the uneven ground-surface, leads the water down from the higher areas towards the lower and the various outlet-points. The upper soil, save in low, waterlogged areas, will probably be moist only. This is the zone of soil-water, tapped by plants. Water is always slowly moving through it, the net movement varying according to whether supply or withdrawal from above is in excess. In heavy rain water moves downward ; in dry spells upwards.

Some way down, however, the upper level of permanent saturation will be met. This is called the *Water-Table*. The water-
table normally follows approximately the contour of the ground-
surface, rising under hills, and falling under hollows, the slopes
being maintained by the quantity of water flowing and its rate of
movement (Fig. 51 C). These in turn are governed by the water-
head pressure, and the permeability of the rock. In fine-grained
rocks a gradient as steep as 1 in 20 may be maintained, but in
more open-grained rocks, where the water flows more easily,
gradients would be much lower. The level of the water-table
at any one place is not, however, constant. Its position varies
in accordance with the rate of water-supply from above, so that in
heavy and prolonged rains it rises as large supplies of water move
down to it through the soil, while in dry periods it falls since
water flows away continuously down the underground water-
slopes, more water is drawn up to the surface and evaporated,
and no new water arrives to replace these losses. Ordinarily
there are fairly fixed upper and lower limits to water-table movement in any locality, and " permanent " wells have to be sunk
to below the minimum summer position. In abnormal droughts,
however, such wells dug with insufficient " overlap " into the
saturation zone may dry out altogether as the water-table falls
below their floors (Fig. 51 C).

But it is usually only on the higher ground that the water-
table is some distance below the surface. In humid climates it
approaches the surface in the hollows and valleys, and in regions
of disturbed structure it may " outcrop " on slopes to give
lines of springs and seepages where the underground water-flow
emerges at the surface. In Britain the water-table is but little
below the ground-surface in most river-valleys, and water seeps
out along river-banks and beds to contribute to the river flow.
It is this seepage, as we mentioned, that provides the steady flow
of rivers, and in dry spells, the only flow. Should a valley-floor
lie above the low summer water-table position, stream-flow in it
may be intermittent, the winter streams ceasing to flow in dry
summer weather. The " winterbournes " of the Chalk country
of southern England are examples.

Variations in underground rock-structure, however, generally create complications in the disposition of the water-table when large areas are considered. Small local water-concentrations may occur lying high above the true water-table if a saucer-shaped bed of impermeable material like clay occurs within porous strata. These are called "perched" water-tables (Fig.

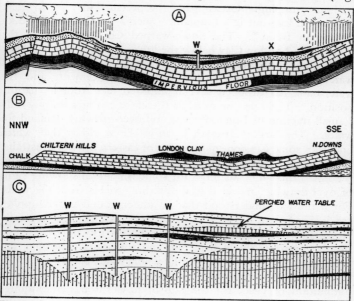

Fig. 52 :

(A) *Conditions of an artesian basin.*

(B) *The artesian basin underlying London.*

(C) *The sandy formation, with included lenses of clay, illustrates on a small scale how perched water-tables are formed. Note the cones of exhaustion around the deep wells into the permanent water-table.*

52 C). On the other hand a widespread impermeable surface formation may overlie water-bearing strata which are disposed in a broad synclinal basin, the porous beds outcropping round the edges. In such a case rainwater falling on the porous outcrops will move down the dipping beds towards the centre of the basin where a great hidden water-reservoir may be formed

" sealed down ", as it were, below the impermeable beds (Fig.
52 A). If the intake areas lie at higher level than the ground in
the centre of the basin, the sealed-in water may be under considerable pressure, and in a well sunk through the cap-rock on the
lower ground to tap the aquifer water will rise to the surface
without pumping. Occasionally the pressure may be so great
that it will leap out in a fountain. Such a structure is called an
" Artesian Basin ". The down-warped Chalk underlying the
impervious London Clay below the lower Thames Valley is such
a basin, but so many wells have been sunk into it that the rate of
water-withdrawal exceeds the rate of replacement, and the
water-table has dropped several hundred feet from its natural
position. The 1,000 or so wells therefore can now supply only
a small fraction of London's vast and ever-growing demand for
water. The largest artesian basin in the world is that which
underlies some 640,000 square miles of eastern interior Australia.
Invaluable in that arid country for supplying watering points
for stock, this huge basin has for some time been showing signs
of over-drawing, reflected in diminishing yields from the wells.
For it must be understood that no underground water-supplies
are inexhaustible. The rate of water-replacement is generally
rather slow, and if too much is drawn off too fast the whole
supply is progressively depleted, and the water-table may fall
continuously. Even although the whole water-body may not be
affected, over-drawing from single wells will equally result in a
diminution of yield, for the rate of flow through the aquifer
towards the well may not be fast enough to make good the
withdrawals. A " cone of exhaustion " forms around the well,
and a period of rest may be necessary to allow the water-flow
to catch up before the well will yield again (Fig. 52 C). For wells
to maintain a good and reliable yield, therefore, they must tap a
suitable water-bearing formation of good capacity which con-
nects freely with an " intake area " sufficiently large to maintain
the supply against the withdrawals. Wells sunk with inadequate
knowledge of the underground structure may tap only small
local " pockets " of water which soon give out, or a thin aquifer
in which the water-flow is too slow to keep pace with the withdrawals. In areas of crystalline rock, or fissured limestone,

well-sinking is a particularly chancy business. The rock itself
being non-porous, the well may hit a large fissure with abundant
feeders, or a small isolated fissure soon exhausted, while an
unlucky boring may easily hit no water at all.

Often, however, a water-bearing formation will lie between
two impermeable sealing beds which restrict the flow of the

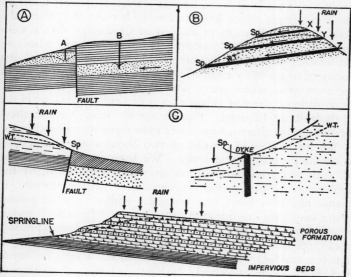

Fig. 53 :

(A) *Effect of a fault upon the water-table.*
(B) *Alternating pervious and impervious beds causing a succession of spring-lines.*
(C) *Springs created by a fault (on left) and an igneous dyke (on right). Below, springline at the foot of an escarpment (line-shading indicates impervious beds).*

underground water, and if severe faulting or folding has occurred
the whole underground reservoir may be divided up into separate
compartments. Fig. 53 A illustrates such a case. Here a well
sunk at A would afford little return; one at B would be much
more satisfactory. Variable structure below ground also plays
a large part in determining the points or lines along which water
emerges naturally as seepages or springs. In Fig. 53B the

impermeable beds X, Y, Z will bring water out to the surface at a series of "spring-lines". Again faults, or igneous dykes, by placing an impermeable bed against the fractured ends of pervious strata will often cause a ponding up of water below ground and the emergence of local springs (Fig. 53C). In scarpland country, by contrast, such as is found in the English midlands or the Paris basin, lines of seepage frequently occur on the scarp slopes where less pervious beds outcrop. Along the foot of the Chalk scarp to the east of Cambridge such a well-marked "spring-line" occurs. In earlier days, when all settlements depended entirely on local water-supplies, the locations of springs virtually determined the settlement locations in many areas where water was not plentiful on the surface. Such spring control of village sites is particularly obvious in the chalk-lands of England. Equally springs emerging in valley-heads form the ultimate sources of a great many streams and rivers.

We may here add a word or two about some complexities concerning underground water. We have so far implied that all such water has been stored up, and is maintained, by the infiltration (or percolation downwards) of surface rainfall. It seems probable, however, that some bodies of underground water may have originated in other ways. "Juvenile" water, released from the earth's interior during the formation of primary rocks, probably contributes a good deal to the supplies in some igneous regions, while so-called "Connate" water, i.e. water included in sedimentary rocks during their original formation on sea-floors or in lakes, may still be present in some areas. The salty water found at great depths in some older sedimentary rocks in the interior of the United States is thought to be of this origin. Again, in coastal areas occasionally we find places where sea-water has apparently seeped into land formations. Apart from these extraneous sources, we have also to recognise that in some underground waters the supplies, though of atmospheric origin, may have been built up at some earlier period of greater rainfall. The underground waters in some of the great desert areas are probably in part of such origin. They are thus not being completely maintained, and any withdrawals from them may not be made good. The water that can be found deep in the stony beds of the great dry " fossil " rivers of the French Sahara is probably of this character, as may be the deeper underground water that exists under much if not all of the totally desiccated Libyan Desert and " outcrops " in the deeper hollows to nourish the oases. Although there is no definite evidence to support the view, it seems possible that these oases draw their supplies from underground reservoirs which, although vast, are not now being adequately nourished, and so are destined to dwindle away unless some new climatic change sets in. There are many other problems of great interest connected with underground water; the rate at which it moves, for instance, which experiments indicate may sometimes be almost incredibly slow (so that water emerging in springs today may well, if it has travelled long distances, have fallen as rain before the Great Ice Age); or the curious pulsations that affect some ground-waters, causing well levels to fluctuate sometimes in regular cycles, and the phenomena known as " ebbing and flowing springs ". But such matters take us too far afield. We must now proceed to the last, and the most obvious category of land-waters—those that lie on the surface.

We commonly think of lakes and rivers as very different things, and so in one sense they are; but both are elements in the surface-drainage of lands, and represent that fraction of the total rainfall that the rocks cannot hold, and that evades the demands of evaporation. For permanent lakes and streams to exist at all therefore presumes a situation in which precipitation exceeds evaporation. Although in the same category of water and often physically linked, it will however be convenient to say a little about lakes alone first, before ending this chapter appropriately with the streams which carry the surplus land waters back to the ocean whence they came.

For any lake, pond, or marsh to exist the first requirement is obviously an enclosed hollow in which water can collect. The second requirement is that water should flow into the hollow at least as fast as it is withdrawn from it. Given these conditions, the floor of the hollow need not be watertight, and in fact it seldom is. The supply of water is not of course confined to rain actually falling direct into the hollow; according to the conformation of the surrounding land the rainfall of quite an extensive catchment area may all be converged into the one basin, and not only surface streams, but underground flow may contribute. Most large lakes are, at least relative to the surrounding land, at low elevations, or if they stand high, are in situations where the local water-table is intersected by their beds. Thus they receive considerable water-intake by direct seepages and spring-flow from underground reservoirs. It will be clear that this condition is almost essential for the creation of a large lake, for it is unlikely that such a body could have an entirely watertight floor, and if its floor lay above the water-table water would continuously drain out by leakage, and the surface inflow would have to be very great and continuous to offset this loss as well as that of evaporation. Where the land drops into an enclosed hollow with its floor *below* the water-table level, however, a lake or pond will automatically form, even if the floor is quite pervious. One can thus get small open water-pools in hollows even in the middle of sand-dunes. Higher-level lakes can occur with their beds above the water-table, but unless inflow of water into them is exceptionally rapid their floors must be fairly watertight if they are to persist. Lakelets and ponds standing on high waterless limestone plateaux are thus generally found on examination to lie in hollows on an outcrop of some other impermeable rock, or if on the limestone itself to have a " seal " of clay on their floors. Not uncommonly such shallow upland pools, overlying pervious strata, have drained away through cattle walking in them and breaking through the watertight clay floor. The " dew-ponds " high up on our chalk downs hold their water because they have clay floors of this type.

Percolation out through the floor is clearly one way in which an enclosed hollow can lose water, but assuming little is so lost the water will normally rise either until the surrounding rim is overtopped, and any further intake drains away as an outfall stream, or until the higher evaporation-rate from the enlarging surface balances the rate of inflow. The former condition is typical of humid climates, the latter of arid regions. Lakes in arid regions often have no outlet, and their levels tend to fluctuate markedly with changes in the rate of water-supply balanced by the great and constant evaporation-loss.   Clearly such lakes have the greatest chance of being permanent if their basins are deep. If they are extensive and shallow, as many are, they generally experience gross fluctuations of size, and may for periods dry out entirely.   Lake Chad in the French Sudan typifies such lakes, its outline changing almost every year. Lake Eyre, in central Australia, is a lake by courtesy only.   Normally it is almost or completely dry, and its bed is thickly encrusted with salt.[1]   Old lake-beaches, and expanses of lake-floor muds, are evidence of former extensive lakes in many arid regions which existed in periods of wetter climate.   Some of the biggest, the long-vanished Lakes Bonneville and Lahontan, existed in the Pleistocene period in the Great Basin of the western U.S.A., where the Great Salk Lake presents a shrunken relic today.

In humid climates, with a high water-table, abundant inflow, and limited evaporation, the level of a lake's surface, and consequently its size, are determined by the level of the spill-over point, and hence size and level normally vary little through the year. In the long-term view, however, all lakes, even the largest, are doomed to extinction, and that for two reasons.   Slowly, but continuously, the inflow streams bring in sediment which accumulates on their floors to fill in the original hollow, while concurrently the drainage stream slowly saws down the level of the outfall point.   Combined filling-in and draining-away thus steadily proceed.   Small lakes have been obliterated in Britain by these means even during the historic period, but the processes go on too slowly to affect appreciably the earth's larger lakes.   A process which can markedly alter lake outlines, however, and help materially to clog them and fill them up, is the growth of reeds and other aquatic vegetation around their edges.   The outlines of the shallow Norfolk Broads have altered greatly from this cause in quite short time-intervals, and in Tropical Africa the growth of papyrus grass and other vegetation plays a dominant part in controlling silting, blocking water-channels, and diverting the directions of water-movement in sluggish rivers and shallow marshy lakes and swamps.

[1] At the present time (Sept. 1950) L. Eyre is reported to be filling up with water, for the first time in many years.

As regards their size, depth, and topographic features lakes vary enormously from bodies like the Caspian Sea and the American Great Lakes down to tiny ponds. The most convenient way of classifying them is by their mode of origin. We may note briefly some of the main types.

Most of the earth's large lakes occupy basins created in part at least by tectonic deformation of the surface. Sinking of slices or blocks of country between great fault-systems permitted the formation of the long deep lakes of East Africa (some of whose floors descend below sea-level), which are true rift valley lakes. The Dead Sea, with its floor 2,600 feet below the level of the Mediterranean, is another example, as is Lake Baikal, one of the world's deepest lakes. The Great Lakes of North America occupy structural basins of a different type—relatively shallow down-warpings. There are vast shallow tectonic basins in interior Africa and central Asia which would hold huge lakes were the climate wet enough to nourish them.

Other lakes occupy hollows created by erosion. River erosion, by its very nature, cannot cut deep hollows without outlet, but passing over outcrops of soluble rock river waters can dissolve out wide shallow hollows that fill with water. The lakes of the lower Shannon in western Ireland are probably of such origin. Wind and moving ice, can, however, carve out enclosed hollows, as we saw earlier. Since wind-erosion is only effective in arid conditions, the hollows it scours out seldom fill with water, but ice-scoured rock-basins are a well-recognised type of lake in glaciated regions. We noted some examples in Chap. X.

More common than lakes created by erosion, however, are those produced by deposition, or by erosion and deposition combined. Small " ox-bow " lakes are often formed, as we saw in Chap. VI, when a meandering river cuts off meander elbows. Shingle bars or sand-spits built by the sea may cut off shallow depressions and create fringing coastal lagoons like the " étangs " along the edge of the Rhone delta. Then lakes of a variety of types, shapes, and degrees of permanence, may be formed by the blocking of pre-existing valleys by such events as landslides, the outward building of screes, or lava-flows. Even the upward growth of peat can block surface drainage on moor-land country and create small pools. Most lakes formed by such blockages are small and of limited life, but drainage-blocking by deposition of boulder-clay and morainic material from large ice-sheets and glaciers has been responsible for the majority of the earth's existing lakes. Among the many other ways in which lakes can be formed we need note only two. Open volcanic craters which have become extinct generally fill with water to create distinctive lakes (*vide* Chap. IV), while of similar form, though very different origin, are a few small lakes which occupy hollows created by large meteorites hitting the earth.

Of interest to the hydrologist are the changing patterns of temperature distribution in lakes throughout the year, and various curious physical effects bound up with the freezing of the surface waters, but over these we cannot linger. It is worth noting, however, that large lakes exercise quite an appreciable ameliorating effect on the climate of their shores, as does the sea. Another point of similarity is that lake waters are sometimes subject to swinging oscillations called " seiches ", in effect like the tide, though due to quite different causes. We must now, however, proceed to rivers.

We dealt with the landscape-sculpturing operations of rivers early in this book, but something must be added on their patterns of flow, for no river maintains a truly constant flow throughout the year. Reviewing the earth we find every sort of variety from rivers of nearly-constant flow to those which, although having a defined bed, only flow at all perhaps a week or two in the year—or even once every few years. The variations are of course based in climate, and reflect more or less faithfully the changing balance of water-supply. Since in most regions there is a marked seasonal variation in the precipitation-evaporation balance, rivers generally show a fairly consistent annual " flow-regime " in response, having high water phases and low-water phases at fixed periods. In detail, however, the regimes vary a good deal, both in the pattern and timing of the flow-variations, and in the range of difference between maximum and minimum flow conditions. In general the longest rivers, and particularly those whose tributaries drain regions of differing climate, show the most complex flow-patterns.

As we should expect, rivers in Equatorial regions show a fairly steady flow reflecting the steady rains, but often with higher waters following the minor rainfall peaks. In the Tropical rain-regimes rivers generally follow the rainfall pattern by alternating between long low-water periods in winter (during which they may dry out completely) and high single floods when the summer rains arrive. Some, however, like the Niger, show complex flow conditions. In its upper reaches this river is lowest in Spring and rises to a peak flow in August and September with the heavy summer rain. The river, however, flows away inland towards the desert at first, and most of its flood-waters are lost by evaporation in the swamps round Timbuctu. Onward downstream only a small portion of the original water proceeds, and a bare trickle would reach the sea, many months after the headwater flood period, were there no other supplies. But lower west-bank tributaries bring in supplementary Autumn floods in the lower reaches, so that in fact, despite its length, the river floods at much the same time all the way down, although in the middle reaches its waters are scanty. Most carefully studied of all rivers, because of its vital importance to irrigation in Egypt, the Nile reveals a somewhat simpler picture. It has two main feeding-grounds. The White Nile, draining from the Equatorial lakes, brings down a fair amount of water all the year round, with maximum flow in late summer. Running north into the dry country of the Sudan, with a gradient which flattens out to become very gentle, the White Nile, however, loses most of its water by evaporation in the great " Sudd " swamps. A diminished trickle proceeds, reaching Egypt to maintain a minimum flow in winter. The other main feeders, the Sobat, Blue Nile, and Atbara, are virtually dry in winter, but with the heavy summer rains on the Abyssinian mountains they rise rapidly and bring down enormous quantities of silt-laden water to create the annual Nile flood. At Khartoum, the confluence of the Blue Nile (the main feeder), the flood reaches its peak in Aug.-Sept., and so great is the flow of water that the White Nile waters are ponded back. Moving on, the peak flood reaches

Wadi Halfa in early September, and Lower Egypt a few weeks later. So many barrages have been built, however, that the natural flow-conditions of the Nile have been somewhat modified, and new major schemes being planned, such as building a barrage at the Lake Tana outfall in Abyssinia, canalising the clogged section of the White Nile, and increasing the size of Lake Albert by a large dam, will alter it still more. The object is to trap more of the Blue Nile flood-water and hold it back for use in the winter low-water period, and also to increase the White Nile flow over the same critical months. Below Khartoum the Nile receives no tributaries, and loses water steadily both by evaporation and by irrigation-withdrawals. Today, save at the flood-peak, little water reaches the sea at all, and in the future none may do so. All will have been diverted on to the riverside lands to grow crops to feed Egypt's teeming millions.

In temperate and colder lands the factor of spring and summer snow-melt comes in to complicate the picture. In the continental interiors, with intensely cold but relatively dry winters, winter is the low-water season, and most rivers are frozen. Flow is greater in summer with the summer rainfall, but commonly great floods occur in spring with the melting of the snows and break-up of the ice. The Mississippi has high waters in spring; most western European rivers are highest in winter and spring; but the Danube has its peak flow in early summer. Rivers fed by melt-waters from glaciers are generally at maximum flow in summer. Our British rivers, in harmony with our more equable climate and even distribution of rainfall, maintain a fairly even flow throughout the year, though there is a general diminution of volume in summer because of the increased evaporation loss. Being relatively short, they do not experience the great " travelling floods " that characterise some of the earth's largest rivers, and flood periods, which occur irregularly but generally in winter with the incidence of abnormally heavy and prolonged rains, affect regional areas, and all the streams in them almost simultaneously. We seldom get enough snow, or a sufficiently rapid melt, for this factor to cause serious flooding.

We may end with a word about floods in general. A flood

occurs when water is supplied to a river-basin so fast that the river's normal channel cannot contain the resulting flow. The water overtops the banks, and may spread widely over low-lying land, causing widespread devastation. Liability to severe flooding is thus based in climatic conditions which give large and sudden accretions of water, whether by rains or snow-melt. Rivers in cold lands, which freeze in winter, often flood extensively in spring when the ice melts, for floating blocks of ice frequently jam in narrow passages and block the flow. Topographic factors also affect a river's liability to flood, steep slopes (which accelerate runoff) and a tributary pattern which concentrates the augmented flow of wide areas into one trunk river, being obviously favourable factors. But one factor is so important as to demand special attention, and that is vegetation cover. Flooding results essentially from quick or " flash " runoff, too much water getting into the main channel too quickly. If means can be found to hold back the water, and release it gradually, no flood need occur however much water is present : and vegetation, as we saw earlier, is the most effective of all agencies for checking swift and excessive runoff. Flood-control measures can aim at many things ; at keeping the river-channel as open and clear as possible ; at strengthening and heightening levees in the flood-plain ; and at building dams to check the violent flow and storage reservoirs to hold back for slow release some of the surplus waters. But experience in many parts of the world, best utilised to date in America, has shown that the maintenance of a good cover of vegetation over the collecting-grounds is the best of all preventatives of disastrous flooding. The centuries of deforestation in China caused by overcrowding of the land and the constant search for fuel have certainly contributed greatly to the virulence of the dreaded floods of the Yellow River. Equally certainly deforestation, thoughtless land-clearing, and badly-conceived cultivation methods in, for example, the United States, have in more modern days created dangerous flooding habits in rivers which lacked them when in a natural state, and have linked flooding to soil erosion and other disasters that have resulted from an incautious disturbance of nature's balanced situations. We will look further at this theme in the final chapter.   To summarise the last two chapters, Fig. 54 expresses in diagrammatic form the cyclic and never-ending movements of the earth's surface water.

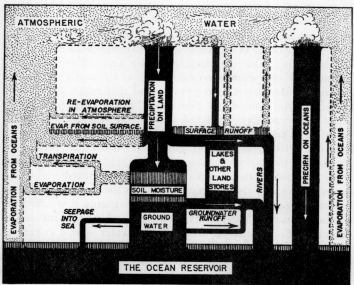

Fig. 54. *Schematic diagram of the Hydrological Cycle*

CHAPTER XIV

THE WATER RESERVOIR: THE OCEAN

HAVING followed the travels of water in its journeyings about the face of the earth, we now turn to the great reservoir from which the circulation is maintained. We noted at the beginning of this book that more than two-thirds of the earth's surface is covered by the waters of the ocean, and that land only exists at all because the continents " float high " in the crust. When we examine the relative levels of continental surfaces and ocean floors more closely, this statement takes on a new force, for we find that not only is the land *area* much smaller that that of the waters, but the exposed *volume* of land is relatively insignificant. Some 23 million cubic miles of crust are exposed above the ocean surface, but the volume of water in the ocean basins is no less than 324 million cubic miles. This means that were the continents planed off flat, and their rocks used to fill in the deeper oceanic hollows until all was smooth, water would cover the whole globe to the rather astonishing depth of nearly two miles. Compared with this vast volume of water held, as it were, " in reserve ", the quantity out in circulation is but trifling. Precipitation of all the water in the atmosphere would raise the ocean level no more than an inch of two. A much greater rise would result from the return of all water located on or within the lands and of this a substantial fraction would come from the snows and ice of the Polar regions. The water held there in cold storage would, if returned, raise the ocean surface the world over by no less than 150 to 190 feet. Even this figure, however, pales beside the present average ocean depth of about $2\frac{1}{2}$ miles. It is tempting to speculate on where all this water came from, and whether the total amount is fixed or changing, but such enquiries are beyond the scope of this book. We must confine attention to the waters as they are, but first we may pick up a thread left loose in earlier chapters and glance at the forms and features of the basins they occupy,

which after all make up the bulk of the earth's surface.
It is natural to think that the change from continent to ocean
basin occurs where land meets water at the visible coastline, but
examination of the form of the submerged crust as revealed by
soundings shows that this is far from the case. Generally the
continental land-masses are surrounded by a belt of quite shallow
water, the land sloping gently outwards at gradients of as little as
1 in 500 for quite a long distance before plunging down to the
ocean depths. This fringing platform of shallow water is called
the " Continental Shelf ". It varies greatly in width in different
areas. Off N.W. Europe, for instance it is very broad. Our
islands stand on it, and the North Sea and Channel represent
parts of it very shallowly submerged. It is also widely developed
off northern Australia and through parts of the E. Indies. By
contrast, down the entire Pacific coast of the two Americas it is
narrow or virtually absent. In general, the Continental Shelf
is believed to represent marginal strips of the Continental blocks
which have been left just below the water-level by the last major
vertical movements, but we will return later to further ideas
about its mode of origin.

Whether wide or narrow, the shelf normally terminates at its
outer edge with a marked change of slope. The depth at which
this occurs varies from 60 to some 300 fathoms, but is often
around 100 fathoms. Beyond, the bottom slopes away much
more steeply, average gradients being 1 in 15 to 1 in 30, and these
steep slopes, which seem to represent the real edge of the
continental masses, are often maintained down to depths of 1,000
to 1,500 fathoms (6,000 to 9,000 feet). Clearly the pattern of
land and water as we see it on atlas maps is quite misleading as
a guide to the structural pattern of ocean-basins and continental
blocks. Changes of ocean-level of even a few hundred feet
would link many continents to islands, and we have abundant
evidence that movements of this order have occurred in quite
recent geological times—Britain, for instance, was linked to
the Continent for much of the Great Ice Age, and the first
colonists of our islands almost certainly walked across from
Europe dryshod. The ancestors of the American Indians, too,
are believed to have migrated across from Asia along the line of

the present Behring Straits during a period of low ocean-level, while a rise of water cut off Australia quite late in geological time, and isolated its remarkable indigenous fauna. Many of the *seas* which fringe the continents are parts of the oceanic water which lie on continental areas but shallowly submerged.

Below the " continental slopes " extend the true deep ocean floors. It used to be thought that these were almost featureless, but modern techniques of echo-sounding are revealing a surprising ruggedness over some areas, with evidence of widespread volcanic activity. Neglecting this, however, the deep ocean floors are remarkably uniform in depth. Over 60% of the whole ocean floor lies at depths of between 2,000 and 3,000 fathoms, forming the " abyssal plain ". Here and there this is broken by great hollows called " deeps ". These are generally of elongate shape, forming trenches rather than holes. The majority lie in the Pacific, where they are located mainly around the margins, and especially on the outer sides of the lines of arcuate islands on the Asiatic side. These deeps are presumed to be downfolds in the ocean floor created by the same pressures that thrust up the lines of folded mountains that emerge as the islands. In the Atlantic, however, the fewer deeps mostly lie further out, save for the great trench off Puerto Rico which is of the arcuate Pacific type, and in which has been obtained the deepest sounding yet recorded in the Atlantic—4,812 fathoms. This figure, however, is easily exceeded by some in the Pacific deeps, where soundings of nearly 6,000 fathoms have recently been obtained.

Apart from the deeps, the ocean floors show some other features of interest. Down the centre of the Atlantic, for instance, there runs a long and continuous " rise " which divides the whole ocean into eastern and western basins. From its crest rise the isolated volcanic islands of the Azores, Ascension and Tristan da Cunha. The crest of this rise follows the alignment of the two oceanic coasts with remarkable fidelity, and enthusiasts for continental drift have seen in it the residual " scar " left by the ancient splitting and drifting apart of Eurafrica and the Americas (*see* Fig. 10, page 41). Certainly geophysical soundings indicate that it is built at least in part of " sial " material, like the continents.   Some transverse ridges also occur on the floor of the Atlantic, and north-west of our islands it is separated from the Arctic basin by the Wyville-Thomson Ridge, on which stand the Faroe islands and Iceland.

The Pacific basin shows various contrasts.   Around it there is little development of continental shelf, and its shores are typically composed of steeply-plunging ridges of longitudinal folded mountains, in contrast to the broken " fracture " type of coasts that predominate round the Atlantic.   There is no central rise, although recent research has revealed various broad " swells " in the floor, while the strings of islands that festoon the Asiatic side, themselves the crests of folded mountains with many volcanoes, often stand on curved plateaux-like foundations. [1]

The untold thousands of islands that dot the seas and oceans are of various types, and originated in many different ways.   Many fringing the continents are but detached parts of the neighbouring land, and would be united to it by small changes of sea-level. The arcuate mountainous island-strings around the edges of the Pacific we have already mentioned.   Islands standing alone far out in the deep oceans are, however, mainly either volcanic peaks, like all the " high " islands of the open Pacific, or coral constructions.   These latter are so distinctive that we must give them greater attention.

The marine organisms called corals thrive particularly in the warmer seas within 30° or so of the Equator.   By extracting lime from the sea-water they build hard stony structures welded into great masses, and so prolific are they that these constructions, started on the sea-floor, readily reach the surface and form reefs and islands.   These are of three main types : fringing reefs built around small islands, like the volcanic peaks of the Pacific ; great " barrier-reefs " skirting larger land-masses, of which that bordering the coast of Queensland for over a thousand miles is by far the largest ; and atolls which are the true " coral islands ", and are generally of horseshoe or ring shape with an open-water lagoon in the middle.   Coral reefs and islands abound in the central and eastern Pacific, and in the Indian ocean. In the Atlantic they are plentiful in the Caribbean and off the coast of Brazil, but the only mid-ocean ones are in the Bermudas.

[1] The progress of oceanic investigation in recent years has been revealing many new features on the floor of the Pacific, including numerous conical hills ("sea-mounts"), and great linear fractures and cliffs (1961).

They are unknown, however, in the eastern parts of the oceans, probably because (for reasons connected with the oceanic circulation) the waters there are colder. Corals cannot live above water, and their upward growth generally ceases at low-tide level, so that coral islands always remain low, and many stay as reefs. On some, however, pieces broken off by waves get piled up to form land several feet above high-tide level, and some reefs have been elevated by earth-movements. On the other hand, corals cannot live on the sea-floor at depths of much more than 30 fathoms, and herein lies the problem of coral-reefs, for many of them rise from depths much greater.

The mode of formation of ordinary shallow-water fringing reefs is quite easy to understand. Corals colonise the sea-floor, and gradually raise a platform towards the surface. Their growth is most active a short distance out from land, because they do not like the turbid water inshore, and as the platform rises to the surface, further growth is concentrated on its outer side where the water is cleaner and contains more oxygen and foodstuffs. Outward growth is checked, however, when the sea-floor corals reach a water-depth of some 30 fathoms. The reef therefore tends to stabilise at this stage as a flat-topped structure separated from the land by a channel or lagoon which may later be enlarged by solution of the dead coral on the inner, inactive, side of the reef.

So far, so good ; but the large barrier reefs, and the mid-ocean atolls, rise from depths at which no reef-building corals can live. On what sort of foundations, then, can these structures rest ?

There have been two main theories. That proposed by Charles Darwin and Dana involved slow subsidence of the ocean floor. The deep-ocean atolls, they suggested, must have started as ordinary fringing reefs around small islands. When subsidence of the ocean floor set in, these islands would gradually sink and disappear, but the coral would grow upward to keep pace with the sinking, and the stronger growth on the outer side would enlarge the original reefs into wide ring-shaped atolls (Fig. 55). Barrier reefs like that off the Queensland coast, which in places lies 80 miles offshore, and rises from great depths, they explained in similar fashion.

The alternative theory proposed by Sir John Murray and others avoided the need for subsidence by suggesting that barrier-reefs grew outwards into deep water through waves building a platform of torn-off blocks of reef coral in advance of the main reef on to which the living corals could advance, the lagoon behind being gradually enlarged by solution. Deep-ocean

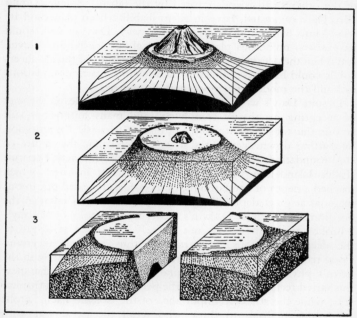

Fig. 55. *Darwin's theory of coral reefs. Three stages in the subsidence of an island to transform an original fringing reef into an open atoll.*

atolls, however, they could only explain by postulating numerous pre-existing shoals and shallow platforms on which the corals could build. No very satisfactory suggestion as to why such numerous shoals should exist was forthcoming, however, until in 1915 Daly, an American geologist, pointed out that in the Great Ice Age the tropical seas must have been considerably chilled, while the level of the ocean-surface over the whole earth must have been lowered between 200 and 300 feet (30 to 50 fathoms) to provide the vast quantities of water locked up in the great ice-sheets. Corals would probably have died off in the marginal seas around the Tropics, and there the emergent pre-existing reefs would probably have been rapidly cut away by waves into banks and platforms at the new ocean level. Many of the other small islands created by the fall of sea-level would also, Daly suggested, have in all probability been planed-off by waves into banks and shoals. In this way, Daly argued, could have arisen numerous platforms all at about the required level, and when the oceans rose again with the melting of the ice-sheets corals could have re-established themselves on these foundations to build the modern deep-ocean atolls and reefs.

Despite Daly's work, there remain some difficulties in the way of accepting his theory completely, and many authorities still favour the subsidence theory. Attempts to settle the question by putting down deep bores so as to determine the nature of atoll foundations have been inconclusive. Both that at Funafuti (Ellice Islands) in 1904, and those at Bikini in 1947 (which reached a depth of 426 fathoms, or 2556 feet) revealed calcareous material at great depths, but whether this was reef coral in the position of growth (as Darwin's theory would imply) or Murray's " broken fragments ", was not clear. The mode of origin of the deep-ocean atolls, in particular, thus remains uncertain. Coral reefs are, however, of more than theoretical interest in the earth's physical geography. Coral can grow so fast that new uncharted reefs often appear, to the peril of navigation in tropical seas, while the strategic importance of the isolated Pacific atolls needs no emphasis to those who recall the naval war with Japan.

Brief mention of two further topics relating to the ocean basins must suffice before we turn to their waters. Returning to the Continental Shelf we mentioned earlier that it appears to be in essentials " continental " in structure, but other factors than direct submergence may have played a part in its creation. It may be, in part, a great bench cut into the edges of the land-areas by the attack of sea-waves, and it may be in part built of the material resulting from such wave-cutting. Broad wave-cut benches do certainly exist around many sections of coast, as around the Faroes and Iceland, and along the Norwegian coast such an erosional bench has in many places been uplifted clear of the waters. We need much more information before we can be sure how the Continental Shelf originated, but of very direct relevance to the problem are the remarkable " submarine canyons " which trench across it off many coasts. Large numbers of these mysterious features have been traced by modern methods of detailed underwater survey off the coasts of the United States; there are some off western Europe; and recently comparable features have been discovered off South Australia, in the Indonesian area, off the coasts of India and various parts of Africa, and elsewhere. Their distribution indeed appears to be world-wide, although no large canyon has yet been found off a desert coast. Some of these " canyons " have the pattern of ordinary river-valleys, and continue the line of rivers like the Hudson, the Congo, and the Adour (W. France) out across the sea-floor. It is tempting to consider them as true river-valleys, formed at some earlier period of lower sea-level and later "drowned." The difficulty is that the change of sea-level required so to explain them runs into several thousands of feet, and few have been hardy enough to claim changes of level of such magnitude in *recent* geological time. It is possible, however, that in some cases the valley-sides have been built up by sedimentation around some strong bottom current, rather than that the channels have been carved out. Also not all the channels continue the lines of land-valleys. Many of these off the New England coast only commence well out to sea, and trench the continental edge (here a steep, scarp-like slope) in great gorges apparently almost cliff-sided. Many suggestions have been made as to how these remarkable features could have been formed, which invoke faulting, erosion by submarine currents, the sapping-back of big springs emerging below sea-level, and the effect of concentrated gravity-flows of water heavily charged with mud.[1] We know too little yet about the world distribution of these features, about their detailed forms, alignments, and slopes, or about the materials into which they are cut, for any final views to be offered. They remind us

[1] This " turbidity current " theory has become increasingly favoured as an explanation (1959).

how little we really yet know about the two-thirds of the earth's surface that is hidden from our direct inspection below the ocean waters.

One process that goes on there does, however, demand a few words. The sea-floors, and to a lesser degree those of the oceans, are par excellence the regions of rock-building. Here, blanketed by deep water, the earth's crust is protected from the ravages of atmospheric attack, and the material worn off the "high-spots" of the earth and regions of greater natural activity here comes to rest. Slow sedimentation is thus the dominant process, as particles slowly filter down through the still waters to settle layer upon layer. The supply of material is, however, very variable. The greater part of it is derived from wear and tear of the lands, and so enters the ocean around its coasts, whether brought in by rivers and glaciers, or carved away by the sea itself. Because of the agitation of the shallow coastal waters this land-derived material is sorted out in large measure before it comes to rest. The larger pebbles and stones, moved only by strong waves and currents, remain close inshore, there to accumulate as shingle beds. Sand can be moved by gentler currents and thus gets swept further out, but as the water-depth increases the disturbance of the bottom-waters rapidly dies away, and all the sand therefore comes to rest in fairly shallow waters. Finer silts and muds get carried further out, to settle in the deeper waters on the continental slopes, but practically all the land waste settles in waters of less than 1,500 fathoms in depth, save for the small quantities carried far out by melting icebergs, and the dust dropped over the whole ocean surface by the wind[1]. In the deep oceans far from land, the material settling to the floor is mainly produced by the ocean itself, and consists of the skeletons, shells, and other hard limey or siliceous parts of dying marine organisms. Slowly accumulating, these build soft deposits called "oozes".

[1] Recent oceanographical research has revealed puzzling complexities in the more detailed distribution of sea-floor deposits. Patches of coarse gravel and cobbles have been found out near the edge of the Continental Shelf, and the pattern of sand and mud deposition appears to be most irregular. A leading authority has indeed stated "The actual picture . . . (that emerges) . . . is that of irregularly distributed sediment zones which show little relation either to depths of water or distance from the shore". (F. P. Shepard; Submarine Geology, 1948).

Various types are known, distinguished by the predominant types of shells composing them, but in the deepest areas of all the tiny shells appear to dissolve again before they reach the bottom, and the material accumulating is typically " red clay ", a mineral deposit composed largely of volcanic dust. This accumulates so slowly that samples brought up have revealed the teeth of sharks of species now extinct lying still unburied on its surface.

Organic deposits of marine shells are not, however, confined to the deep ocean. Material of this type accumulates also on the sea-floors nearer land at all depths, and if, for any reason, little land-waste reaches any part of even a shallow sea-floor, the accumulating material may be composed largely of shells. Such deposits, consolidated and cemented together, are represented on land by the great range of marine limestones, rocks which, when thick and pure often (as we have seen) give rise to very distinctive scenery. Sedimentation on the sea-floor, and the modes of origin of rocks, are matters of interest to the geologist rather than the geographer, but clearly some general idea of the subject is of value to an understanding of the nature and disposition of land-rocks today. Even from the above brief sketch it will not be difficult for the reader to envisage how the sediment now being laid down on sea-floors changes by gradual transition from almost pure limestone in one area, to sand in another, and then to mud, and that between the regions of " pure " deposition there are vast tracts where mixed sediments are forming, half-mud and half-sand, or sand with a strong limey admixture. Changes in water-depth, temperature, and supplies of material, may alter the character of the sedimentation as time goes on, and replace the sand accumulating in an area with overlying layers of mud. Visualising all this, and reflecting on the long history of fluctuation between land and sea, changing climatic conditions, and slow evolution of organic life, the observant reader will have little difficulty in understanding the meaning of the varied sequence of rocks revealed in quarries, or why a bed that is limestone in one area gradually changes into a shale if traced far enough across country. But for details on these matters, he must refer to works on geology. We can only add here that modern investigation of sea-floor sediments is revealing many interesting things.

For instance, the Swedish " Albatross " expedition which returned in 1948 brought home many long cores of ocean and sea-floor sediment which have revealed direct connections between these dim zones below the waters and events on the surface. Some from the Caribbean show alternating layers of shells belonging to organisms liking respectively warm and cooler water, suggesting that these layers accumulated during the inter-glacial and glacial phases respectively of the Ice Age. Again from the Mediterranean come cores containing whole sequences of layers of volcanic dust, each layer representing a major phase of activity of the Mediterranean volcanoes. By counting backwards Professor Pettersson, who led the expedition, believes he has iden-tified the actual layer laid down by the great outbreak of Vesuvius in A.D. 79 which overwhelmed Pompeii and Herculaneum.

Turning to the oceanic waters, we note first their most obvious feature—their saltiness. Water is an almost universal solvent, and as met in nature it is seldom if ever chemically pure. Even rainwater contains small quantities of impurities washed down out of the atmosphere, and all river and spring waters contain mineral matter dissolved from the ground over or through which they have moved. The reader will recall that about one-third of all the rock-waste removed from lands by rivers is held in solution. The ocean, lying in contact with the earth's solid crust for millions upon millions of years, has naturally accumu-lated an enormous content of soluble salts. Almost every known chemical element can be found in sea-water, though most of them only in minute quantities. There is, for instance, enough dissol-ved gold in a cubic mile of sea-water to make its possessor happy, could any economic means be found of extracting it. The common salt which forms the bulk of the dissolved matter has, however, been extracted by simple evaporation around tropical coasts for thousands of years ; iodine extracted by seaweeds is widely used to enrich the land ; we ourselves consume a wide variety of sea-water minerals every time we eat fish ; and during the war, when short of magnesium, we evolved a successful process of extracting this key metal from sea-water which supplied the bulk of our requirements. Could we invent similar practicable means of extraction, a high fraction of all our mineral requirements could be met from the ocean.

The bulk of dissolved matter held in the ocean is, however, made up of common salt (sodium chloride) and a few other salts. In the water, these salts divide up into their constituent "ions", so that we can most properly express the constitution of "sea-salt" as :

Chlorine	55.2%
Sodium	30.4%
Sulphate	7.7%
Magnesium	3.7%
Calcium	1.2%
Potassium	1.1%

The remaining 0.7% contains all the other elements ; but although the proportions are so small, many of those distinguishable only as "traces" are of key importance to marine life, especially the so-called nutrient salts like various phosphates, nitrates, and nitrites. The proportions of the different salts remain remarkably constant throughout the whole ocean, a fact which emphasises the perpetual movement and mixing to which its waters are subjected ; but the degree of concentration of the salt-solution varies appreciably in different areas. This is called the "salinity", and is expressed as parts of solid matter per 1,000 parts of sea-water. The average value is 35°/oo, but where there is little evaporation and a large influx of fresh water from rain, rivers, or melting ice, the solution is diluted and salinity values are lower. In the Baltic Sea, for instance, the water is comparatively fresh, salinity here being only about 7°/oo. By contrast in the Red Sea, where surface evaporation is strong and few rivers enter, salinity rises to over 40°/oo. In totally enclosed "seas" where evaporation is intense, naturally the salt concentration is much greater. In the Dead Sea figures reach nearly 240°/oo, the water being so dense that it is almost impossible to sink in it. In the lakes of deserts we have the extreme of such concentration, many such "lakes" normally containing no water at all. Each flood that enters them persists only a short time before all the water evaporates to add a further layer to the accumulating bed of dry salt covering the floor. Parts of the vast spread of "Lake" Eyre in Australia, normally quite dry, are covered with a solid cake of salt some eighteen inches thick. In the open ocean, because of free mixing and the enormous volume of water, the range of salinity is naturally much less, but we find areas in the trade wind zones, where evaporation is high and rainfall low, in which salinity is over 36°/oo, while around the Arctic and Antarctic with low evaporation and melting ice the values drop below 34°/oo. There are also variations of salinity with depth.

A point of interest about sea-salt is how it attained its present constitution. Common sense would suggest that it must have accumulated mainly from dissolved matter washed in by rivers, but the proportions of different salts contained in average river-waters are very different from those in the ocean. The most abundant solutes in river-water are carbonates, and chlorine is only present in small quantities. Probably much of the chlorine in the ocean has been contributed by volcanic emissions, while the low lime-content finds its explanation in the continuous extraction of lime by marine organisms to build shells and skeletons, which in time go back into the earth as new rocks built on the sea-floors. We have thus in the oceans not only a great repository of chemicals, but a sort of chemical factory, taking in, altering, and yielding up. Even so, it is calculated that enough solid matter is held permanently in the ocean to form a bed of salt 150 feet thick over the entire earth.

Apart from variations in salinity, the oceanic waters also vary from place to place in temperature. This we would expect, from the variable distribution of heating over the earth's surface. The pattern is most complex, and there are annual variations to take into account, while modern research has also revealed complicated patterns of temperature distribution in depth. These variations are all closely tied up with the general oceanic circulation; for the ocean waters respond to the differential heating over the earth and throughout the year in somewhat the same manner as does the atmosphere, although the circulation is complicated by surface currents set up by the frictional drag of winds, and density differences occasioned by varying salinity as well as by varying temperature. We can here only note some of the main points about this circulation.

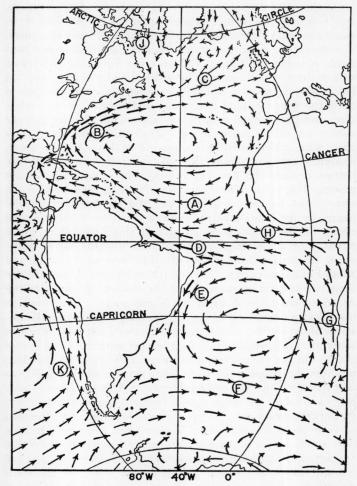

Fig. 56. *Surface currents in the Atlantic.   A. North Equatorial Current ; B. Gulf Stream ; C. North Atlantic Drift ; D. South Equatorial current ; E. Brazil Current ; F. West Wind Drift ; G. Benguella Current ; H. Equatorial Counter Current ; J. Labrador Current ; K. Humboldt Current.*

On the surface in the Tropics the water is heated, expands, and becomes less dense. Evaporation tends to increase its salinity and make it more dense, but the former effect is dominant. In consequence the surface waters swell up, and tend to flow outwards towards the Poles. Colder water from below rises to replace them, only in turn to be warmed and to move out. In Polar seas, again two competing processes go on; cooling chills the water making it contract and become denser, while snow and rain, limited evaporation, and melting ice decrease the salinity and make it less dense. Again, however, the former effect wins, and thus there is a general tendency for the water, becoming cold and heavy, to sink and creep back along the bottom towards the Tropics, replacing the warm surface water moving Poleward. However, this simple circulation is much complicated by the variable shapes and depths of the ocean basins, by the rotation of the earth, and, on the surface, by the effects of the atmospheric circulation (Fig. 56). The Trade winds, blowing in from N.E. and S.E. towards the Equator, swing the surface drifts westwards, thus creating the North and South Equatorial currents (A) and (D) in Fig. 56. In the Atlantic these two streams on running into the shallowing waters off the American coast are diverted north and south. The northern one piles up in the Gulf of Mexico to emerge flowing north-eastwards along the N. American coast as that great flow of warm water, the Gulf Stream (B). As it reaches northward this stream swings out and the prevailing eastward drift of air helps to drag it across the Atlantic (C) to impinge on our islands, and give north-west Europe the remarkably warm offshore waters which help us to escape the worst rigours of the " continental winter ". Part of this stream flows on past Norway into the Arctic (helping to keep the Norwegian ports ice-free), but southern branches turn south and join with a southward-directed flow off the Spanish and Moroccan coasts which completes a sort of gigantic clockwise " wheel " of the surface waters in the north Atlantic.

In the southern Atlantic a comparable surface circulation takes place, the South Equatorial Current (D) being deflected by the coast of Brazil (E) and carrying warm water south until it is swung east by meeting the great " West Wind Drift " (F), a surface flow of water that circles round the world in the open oceans south of 40° under the drive of the westerly winds. The circulation here is completed by a north-bound current moving up the west coast of southern Africa (G). This, an offshoot of the West Wind Drift, is composed of cool water, but as it runs north it tends to swing away from the shore and colder water comes up from below to replace it. A similar condition obtains off the Moroccan coast, and it is this cold water inshore that helps to give these localities their peculiar cool and misty, though desert, climates. Completing the surface circulation of the Atlantic there is a reverse flow of water eastward between the two Equatorial Currents (the Equatorial Counter-Current H) which is apparently maintained by the water-slope across the ocean set up by the westward drive of the two Equatorial currents.

In the Pacific a similar great double circulation is maintained, a clockwise wheel in the northern basin, an anti-clockwise in the southern, with an equatorial counter-current between. In the Indian Ocean a regular anticlockwise wheel persists south of the Equator, but in the restricted waters to the north the circulation reverses its direction seasonally under the influence of the changing monsoon.

Many secondary surface currents add to this great circulation. Thus a consistent drift of cold Arctic water runs south along the Labrador coast (Fig. 56, J), bringing icebergs down to add perils to the north Atlantic shipping lanes. It is the chilling of warm damp air blowing off the Gulf Stream as it crosses this cold water that creates the dreaded fogs off Newfoundland. A general drift runs clockwise round the Greenland coasts, and there are various slow drifts in the Arctic basin. Nothing in the northern hemisphere, however, can compare with the great West Wind Drift of the southern ocean which circles the whole earth, for in the north the crowded continents break up any widespread movements.

These surface currents and flows vary much in speed, character, and degree of definition, but their general pattern has been familiar to navigators for centuries. What has only recently been revealed is that the ocean also has a most complex circulation in the vertical sense, below the surface waters, and our knowledge of its details is still very incomplete.

It is clear, however, that the variations of temperature induced by solar heating only directly affect a shallow surface skin of water, and that the resultant circulation set up in the Tropical oceans does not penetrate deeply. Below it there is a sharp " discontinuity " separating off the deeper waters, which remain very cold over the whole earth. It has indeed been suggested that we have here a sort of " mirror reflection " of the division of the atmosphere between active turbulent troposphere, and tranquil, uniform stratosphere, but the parallel is in no sense exact. Samples of water brought up from varying depths differ in density, salinity, temperature, and oxygen content, suggesting that various distinct " layers " exist in the deeper oceanic waters, and the data indicate that vast slow movements go on in these superimposed water masses. By tracing back such water-masses from their present characteristics to their presumed sources of origin (for every water-mass must at some time have been at the surface), oceanographers are beginning to get some idea of how this vast slow circulation works.

To illustrate it, we may glance briefly at the south Atlantic (Fig. 57A). In the Antarctic region there is relatively little precipitation, and the surface waters, being very cold, remain dense. Around 50°S., as they spread slowly outward they meet warmer, and hence lighter, water moving east in the West Wind Drift. A sharp dividing line separates the two, called the " Antarctic Convergence ", and here the cold Antarctic water sinks down below the lighter sub-Antarctic water to continue moving north at intermediate depths. Around 40°S. occurs another meeting-line of surface waters, the " Sub-Tropical Convergence ", where the still warmer sub-tropical waters meet the sub-Antarctic. Again there is down-sinking, and a sub-surface spread northwards of cooler water at intermediate depths. Similar convergences and down-sinkings occur in northern latitudes, but are less well-marked owing to the constriction of the oceans. Where *divergences* of surface water occur, water wells up from below, and is generally cold in comparison with local surface waters. Such conditions obtain in the "upwelling" areas we noted off Morocco and S.W. Africa, which are matched in comparable latitudes off California and Chile. Some upwelling also occurs between the North and South Equatorial Currents as they drift apart, bringing up cool water off the coasts of Guinea and Colombia.

The result of all this is a sort of " interdigitation " of layers

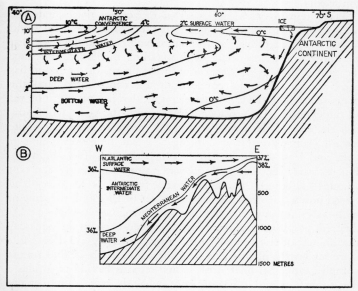

Fig. 57 :
  (A) Distribution of temperature and water movements in vertical section, South Atlantic.
  (B) Currents and salinity distribution at the Straits of Gibraltar.

of warmer and colder water in the vertical structure of the great oceans. In the tropical Atlantic, for instance, cold bottom-water from the Antarctic creeps north across the Equator below cold water creeping south from the high Arctic, while there are various disctinctive zones of intermediate-depth water leading up to the surface circulation. Dense saline waters from some enclosed seas like the Mediterranean also spill over into the oceans to

flow out as distinctive water-layers ; in the case of the Mediterranean the bottom outflow being replaced by an inward surface
flow of less dense water (Fig. 57 B). The deeper circulation
of the oceans is clearly very slow, but quite sharp dividing-lines
between the different water-masses persist for surprising distances
and times, and the resulting water-structures are of great
complexity.

There remain two other types of movement that agitate the
oceanic waters to which we must give some mention : tides and
waves. The rhythmic rise and fall of water round the coast that
we know as the tide occurs with unfailing regularity, and since
the earliest days its connection with the phases of the moon has
been known. But the connections are complicated, and the
phenomena themselves are exceedingly diverse and are not yet
all understood. Any reader familiar with the coast will know
that the size of the tidal rise and fall varies in a regular cyclic
fashion, being greatest at " springs " when the moon is full, or
new, and least at the " neaps " which occur halfway between.
But each day the time of high water alters by a fairly constant
amount—although the amount varies from place to place—and
traced down, for instance, the east coast of England, the time of
high-water on any one day shows a progressive change. At
different points around the coast, however, even on the same day
the amount of rise and fall of the water varies a good deal, while
if we review the phenomena over the whole earth we find a most
complex range of differences—some regions having two tides a
day, some four, and some only one ; while the range of movement
of the water-surface varies from almost nil to 40 or more feet. In
the Atlantic twice-daily tides of roughly equal magnitude are the
rule, but on the coast of California one of the twice-daily tides is
much larger than the other. At Tahiti, out in the open Pacific,
not only is the tidal range only about a foot, but high water
occurs steadily at the same time each day, around noon and
midnight. In enclosed seas like the Mediterranean the tidal
range is very small, but the Bay of Fundy has the largest tidal
range known.

We cannot in this short book do more than hint at all the
variations in tidal phenomena, nor can we attempt to describe the

complex modern theories of their mechanisms, which need mathematical demonstration. It must suffice to say that the basic cause of all true tides is gravitational attraction between earth and moon, and earth and sun, the lunar attraction being considerably the more powerful because the moon, despite its small size, is so much nearer the earth than is the sun. The differences between spring and neap tides find their explanation in the alternating conjunction and opposition of the lunar and solar tide-producing forces. The actual rise of the water-surface is in the form of a kind of gigantic wave, into which water flows from either side as it advances, but instead of the simple " progressive " waves of earlier theory, modern views envisage a number of separate " oscillatory " waves set up and maintained in different parts of the various ocean basins ; movements similar to those you can create in a basin of water by holding it in the two hands, tilting it back and forth rapidly, and then holding it level, but twisting it round to give the resultant swinging oscillation a rotary movement. (This sounds complicated, but is quite easy to do). Movements of this sort, some swinging about a point, some about a line, seem to occur in profusion over the ocean basins, and the actual water-movements that we observe result from their various interactions. Clearly the whole subject is one of some complexity, and indeed the details are not yet worked out for most of the earth. Around coasts, however, from long records of the past sequences of changes, it is not difficult to forecast the tidal movements with high precision, and such forecasts are published for the use of mariners in tide-tables.

Apart from their primary nature, tides have various important secondary effects, especially in the shallow and restricted waters around coasts. Many ports are only accessible to large vessels at high water, but apart from the up-and-down movement of the water surface, tides produce horizontal movements, or currents, and in restricted channels these can seriously impede navigation in small craft. In narrowing estuaries the tidal rise sometimes produces the peculiar phenomenon of a " bore ", a rapidly-advancing steep-fronted wall of water that may move forward with the speed of a racehorse. In Britain the bore in the Severn estuary is the best-known, but a similar phenomenon occurs in the lower Trent.   Much bigger bores occur in other parts of the world, the largest known being on the Tsien-tang-kiang in China.   Where bores occur they, like tide-races, are phenomena which affect small-ship navigation in no small measure.   But tidal currents are also important agents in physiographical change, for they can move large quantities of sand and silt about the sea-floor, and help either to silt up estuaries or, more usefully, to keep them scoured out.

Finally we come to waves, the most obvious and universal type of movement that disturbs the oceanic waters, but one which is confined effectively to a relatively shallow zone near the surface, for waves are, in the main, the product of wind, and so, ultimately, of solar energy.   Wind-formed waves start as gentle ripples created by the drag of air moving over the water-surface, and grow by the pressure exerted by the wind on their windward slopes.   The movement in a wave is oscillatory.   Water particles travel round in circles, but the water as a whole does not advance. This is obvious if you watch ripples or small waves around a piece of floating wood in a pond.   In small ripples the wood simply bobs up and down, but as larger waves pass under it, it moves round in a vertical circle—forwards on the wave crest, downwards on its lee slope, backwards in the trough, and up again on the advancing slope.   (Actually there is a slight forward advance, as the water-particles do not quite return to their original positions.)   With a rising wind waves grow, at first rapidly, then more slowly, until they reach a maximum size determined by the wind strength.   When waves attain a height of about one-seventh of their wave-length (the distance from crest to crest, or trough to trough), the crests become sharp and begin to break, so that the longer the wave-length the larger waves can grow without breaking.   The largest waves measured in the open ocean have been about 80 feet in height.   When the wind drops, the wave-motion does not immediately cease, but the waves become rounder and more regular, travelling away from the centre of disturbance as ocean " swell ".   As swell, they may travel thousands of miles before dying out, and in the open ocean a long swell may measure a thousand feet from crest to crest.   The constant rollers that thunder on the beaches of oceanic islands are the product of such swells, often originating as storm-waves hundreds of miles away, and intersecting sets coming from different directions can give most complicated wave-patterns approaching a beach.

The water-movement in waves is not entirely confined to the surface. In deep water, particles below the surface move in similar orbits as the waves pass overhead, but the size of the orbits decreases rapidly downwards. At a depth equal to the wave-length, the movement is only 1/500th of that on the surface, so that it is only in relatively shallow marginal areas of the ocean that waves appreciably disturb the bottom waters. In such shallow waters the movement of water particles below the surface becomes elliptical, and often there is a greater movement one way than the other, so that wave disturbance can raise and move bottom sediment effectively on the shallower sea-floors. In this way waves assist currents to disperse and move about the material entering the sea from the land ; but waves themselves create much of this material by gnawing into the land edges. This aspect of wave-action we will follow up in the next chapter, but one final point may be added. Newspaper reports often record disasters caused by " tidal waves " striking unprotected coasts. In fact, such waves have nothing to do with the tide. They are generally caused by a submarine earthquake or volcanic outburst, or sometimes by abnormally violent storms like typhoons. Often of great size and arriving without warning, they can create tremendous devastation and have on occasion carried large ships inland and left them high and dry, but happily such catastrophic waves are not of very frequent occurrence.

CHAPTER XV

THE PHYSIOGRAPHY OF COASTS

HAVING surveyed in turn lands and waters, we end at the zone of their meeting. But any reader who wishes to pursue the study of physiography in the field (which is of course where it should be studied) could not do better than start on the coast, for nowhere else in so restricted a space will he find so wide a range of interesting features and so many clearly observable interacting processes. Here are demonstrated the contrasting effects of land and water on the phenomena of weather. The build of the land, and the nature of its constituent rocks, are conveniently laid open for inspection in natural cliff sections. Rock-building can be seen in operation in silting estuaries and salt-marshes : rock-destruction is demonstrated in endless variety in the effects of marine erosion. Streams trickling down the beach from pools left by the falling tide offer miniature working examples of complete river-systems, meandering, eroding, transporting, and building deltas. Waves can be watched moving shingle and sand about, building up or combing down the beach, and constructing spits and bars. Even desert processes can be studied in the rippling of drying sand by the wind, and the building of dunes. The sea-coast offers an almost endless wealth of object-lessons to the student of physiography. It is for him a ready-made demonstration laboratory.

In the opening chapters of this book we touched on the instability of the earth's crust when viewed on the geological time-scale, and glanced at the evidence pointing to frequent and widespread past changes of level and hence alterations in the relations of land and water. With any significant movement of the crust clearly new coasts must come into existence. Hence all existing coasts must be relatively young in the geological sense, having originated with the last important variations in level of land and sea. Equally clearly the initial character of any coast must have been determined by the nature of the movements that created it—that is whether pre-existing land was submerged to give the new coast, or pre-existing sea-floor exposed—and by the nature of the land-surface against which the water came to rest.   Had the sea been totally inactive since, all coasts would still display those original characteristics substantially unmodified, and many do in fact clearly reflect their mode of origin in their general character.   The majority, however, have undergone a good deal of modification, so that it is sometimes difficult to decide how they were created, and most of the modification is the work of the sea.

Although locally the sea occasionally creates new land, by piling up sand and shingle along the coast, its dominant action is destructive.   It eats away at the land all round the waterline, the rate of cutting varying with the power of the marine processes and the degree of resistance offered by the land.   The erosive powers of the sea reside of course in the waves, tides, and currents that agitate its waters.   Were the waters still they would affect the land edge hardly at all, and seas would serve simply as dumping-grounds for the land wastes washed in by rivers. These would accumulate round the river-mouths as gigantic deltas, only wind-borne material reaching the deeper sea-floors. One important result of the continual movement of the ocean waters is thus to disperse the land-wastes, so that deltas only grow where the coastal waters are little disturbed.   But the main results are to cut back the edge of the land and in the process to create a great variety of distinctive erosional forms.

In this erosive action waves play the leading role.   As we saw, the common sea waves are generated on the surface by the wind, the disturbance decreasing rapidly downwards.   Hence the main wave-attack on the land occurs along the plane where sea-surface meets the shore.   Tides affect marine erosion mainly by moving the water-surface up and down, so extending the range of attack from a line to a zone which reaches from rather above high-water mark to some way below low-water mark. Within this restricted zone it is as though a gigantic saw were cutting horizontally into the land all round.   Tides themselves play little part in the direct attack on hard-rock coasts, but the currents they set up are of importance in moving away the

resultant debris, as are other types of currents.   It is largely such
currents that move the sand and silt around the coasts, to accumulate it in sheltered locations.   Only in confined waters and
estuaries, however, do currents normally achieve sufficient
velocity to become important agencies of direct erosion.   In
that waves reign supreme.

Wave erosion works in a variety of ways.   When waves beat
against a cliff they subject it to repeated heavy blows like those of
a battering ram, which can in time smash up the most solid rock.
On a shelving shore, they curl over and break, so that tons of
water repeatedly crash down on the edge of the land.   The
pressures exerted in either case can be tremendous.   Atlantic
breakers have been observed to exert pressures of over 3 tons per
square foot on harbour works, and breaking over promenades
quite moderate waves will twist and tear away strong iron railings,
and break up concrete and masonry walls.   The power of big
storm waves is awe-inspiring.   The solid 2-yard cubes of rein-
forced concrete often used in protective works can get thrown
about bodily like skittles.   Thomas Stevenson in his work on
" Harbours " (1886) describes how, at Wick in 1872, a vast
monolithic mass of concrete weighing, with its foundations,
some 1350 tons, was torn clean away by storm waves and lifted
unbroken over its foundations into the harbour.   Nor is the
effect limited to the water-line.   When waves strike cliffs, the
water is often thrown violently upwards and may do damage
high above.   In the northern Shetlands walls nearly 200 feet
above sea-level have been broken down by waves.   The actual
erosion accomplished by all this expenditure of energy—which,
be it noted, although most spectacular in time of storm continues
in a quieter way all the year round—is, however, achieved only
in part by the direct blows inflicted by the water.   Much disrup-
tion is done by water being forced violently under great pressure
into cracks in the rock, and probably more by the alternating
compression and dilation of air in rock crevices.   When a large
wave curls over and smashes into a cliff much air is trapped under
its falling crest and thrust violently into joints and other cavities.
All this helps to split up and shatter rock faces, while loosened
blocks are plucked away and burst out by the air compression

and suction. Finally further destruction is caused by the bombardment of cliffs, rocks and beaches by the broken fragments of rock and shingle hurled against them, even as a river uses such material to wear down its bed. The residues of all this destruction are progressively broken up and ground down by wave battering and rolling to give the vast masses of shingle and sand that line our coasts. This material represents the ground-down residues of land long since destroyed.

The effects of wave erosion, and the way in which distinctive features are developed by it, can best be studied on a cliffed coast. Here, if erosion and land-retreat are proceeding fast, the cliff is likely to be steep and cut into at its base, where lie accumulated fallen blocks in process of removal. Seaward, at low tide, can be seen extending a flattish rock platform dipping gently outward. Sometimes it is bare, sometimes partly or wholly hidden under a veneer of shingle and sand. This platform has been cut by the waves, and left behind in the retreat of the cliffs. At high tide waves cross it to dash against the cliff base and undercut it until further masses of rock fall, to be broken up and removed. While water-covered, the rock-platform itself also undergoes some erosion by the grinding of sand and gravel across it, but the rate at which it is worn down is relatively slow since the energy of wave motion decreases rapidly below the surface. The shingle and sand resulting from the wave erosion in part drift seawards into deeper water, in part move away along the coast laterally. As time goes on, therefore a distinctive " profile of erosion " is created and extended as is illustrated in Fig. 58. In this figure, it is imagined that originally the sea came to rest against the land at A. By wave-cutting, a " nick " was quickly formed, and extended inward, with a narrow erosion-platform left behind, across which much of the eroded material travelled to build up an outer bank (profile B-B'). Continuation of the process extended the profile to C-C', and now D-D'. As the rock-bench widened, the rate of cliff-retreat would slow down, for the waves would be checked as they crossed the widening expanse of shallowing water. Consequently in the later stages of development we generally find the erosion-platform veneered with shingle and sand, and a more stable beach

at the cliff-foot. Eventually a condition of near-equilibrium
may be attained, further retreat of the cliff depending on progressive scouring away to a greater depth of the rock-platform to
permit the necessary powerful waves to run in to the cliff-base.
Thus the whole profile, in time, may move landward very slowly
as a unit.

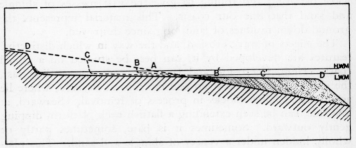

Fig. 58. Evolution of the shore profile.

The actual forms of cliffs developed by wave-erosion depend
on a variety of factors. Normally, with land rising in height
inland, cliffs will grow higher as erosion proceeds, but should
the cliff be cut back right through a ridge, further retreat down the
falling slope will cause the cliffs to diminish in height (Fig. 59 A).
The actual profile developed will depend on the material and
structure of the cliff, and the relative speed of sea advance.
Rapid erosion generally gives steep and even overhanging cliffs
in strong rocks, but if marine advance is slow, rainwash and
weathering may wear back the cliff-face sufficiently fast to give
only a moderate slope (Fig. 59 B). Much too depends on the
structure, especially the arrangement of bedding and joint-planes.
With horizontal bedding and vertical joints vertical and
stepped profiles are typical. Beds dipping inland generally
resist erosion well, and the profile may even be undercut,
but with beds dipping seawards, as overhangs develop great
slices of cliff may slide away, to leave a gentler slope
(Fig. 59 C).

In detail, the wave attack is concentrated along joints and
bedding planes, and sometimes joints get opened up and enlarged

into caves. Occasionally such caves are extended long distances
into the cliff-base, and waves, surging in, compress the air and
get themselves hurled upwards. In this way openings may get
drilled through to the surface, and "blowholes" created
through which water spouts up as waves drive into the cavern.
From this it is but a step to the enlargment and union of such

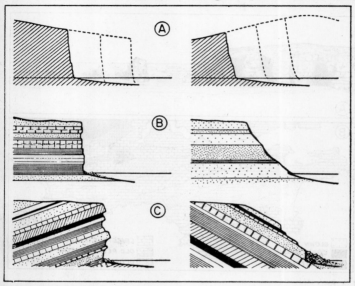

Fig. 59. *Cliff profiles* :
   (*A*) *Increasing cliffs* (*to left*), *decreasing cliffs* (*to right*).
   (*B*) *Vertical cliffs cut in horizontal strata which resist erosion* (*left*) ; *with the
      same structure, weak rocks give a gentler cliff profile* (*right*).
   (*C*) *Cliffs cut in strata dipping away from* (*left*) *and towards* (*right*), *the sea*.

caverns, the creation of "natural arches", and the falling-in
of the roofs to leave blocks of cliff isolated with deep channels
behind them. In this way evolve isolated marine "stacks",
like the famous Old Man of Hoy in the Orkneys. The Needles,
at the western end of the Isle of Wight, are another well-known
example of detached stacks created by cliff recession. Whenever
stacks are seen, extensive retreat of the land under marine erosion

is demonstrated for the stacks were clearly part of the mainland in the past. In later stages of evolution, large stacks may get cut down to small islets and reefs lying offshore (Fig. 60 A). Naturally variable structures in the cliffs affect the pattern of cliff recession, for patches of weaker rocks are eaten away most rapidly, while harder formations stand out as headlands. Thus considered in plan, the progressive erosion by marine

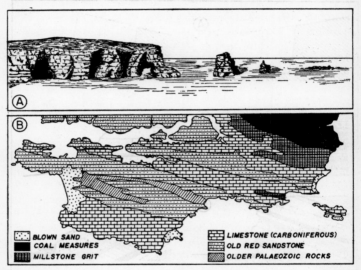

BLOWN SAND
COAL MEASURES
MILLSTONE GRIT
LIMESTONE (CARBONIFEROUS)
OLD RED SANDSTONE
OLDER PALAEOZOIC ROCKS

Fig. 60 :
  (*A*) *Marine cliffs showing caves, pierced rock arch, isolated stacks, and residual rocks.*
  (*B*) *Structure and coastal outline of South Pembrokeshire.*

attack may lead to the evolution of intricate coastal patterns of bays and headlands in areas of variable structure.   Fig. 60B shows the relations of geological structure and coastal outline in southern Pembrokeshire.

High and steep cliffs are usually common in regions where mountainous country of tough crystalline rocks faces exposed and stormy sees, and some of our grandest British cliffs lie in the remote Outer Hebrides, exposed to the full fury of the

Atlantic gales[1]. Our western coasts are indeed mostly well-cliffed. But where erosion is rapid, high and steep cliffs can be formed even in relatively soft rocks, as witness the great chalk cliffs of south-eastern England. The rate of retreat of cliffs under wave attack depends, indeed, mainly on the resistance of the rock, save in unusually sheltered locations. Despite strong wave attack, the cliffs of Cornwall retreat but slowly. In the softer rocks of eastern England, however, erosion is in places alarmingly rapid. Along the soft boulder-clay cliffs of East Yorkshire between Flamborough Head and Spurn Point the coast has retreated about $3\frac{1}{2}$ miles since Roman times, at an average rate of 7 feet a year, and the village of Kilnsea disappeared entirely in the middle 18th century. Comparable destruction proceeds along the boulder-clay and sand cliffs of East Anglia south of Sheringham, where recession at rates of from 12 to 20 feet a year is not uncommon. Many villages, safely inland in the Middle Ages, have completely disappeared, and every year cliff-edge properties in such villages as Overstrand and Mundesley are more and more eaten away. So close is the sea to every part of our small islands, and so valuable every inch of the land, that such losses are serious, and in 1906-1907 a Royal Commission investigated the whole situation. The best of human efforts to hold off the sea are, however, of limited avail, and in the distant geological future large tracts of our islands will undoubtedly be carved away unless renewed uplift gives them a new lease of life, as it has so often in the past.

We can now turn from cliffed coasts, and those where erosion is proceeding fast, to cases where a condition of greater stability temporarily obtains, and the sea may even be building new land. The material carved away by wave erosion in the long run mostly works outward to settle in deeper water, but a good deal of it moves temporarily around the coast, and in favourable conditions it may there accumulate. Again, in some conditions material may be moved up off the sea-floor back again towards the land. Various types of currents play a great part in these complex move-

---

[1] Some of the Hebridean cliffs, however, face sheltered waters, and others plunge straight down into deep water. Tectonic factors have probably played a large part in their evolution.

ments of the lighter materials, but in the case of shingle, and along the actual shoreline, waves are again the main operative agency.

Moving in towards land, waves in deep water advance at a rate proportional to their wave length, but as the water shallows a drag is set up which progressively checks their speed. The waves thus " close up " on one another, but if the sea-floor is of variable form, and the water therefore of varying depth, the surface pattern of the waves is also altered. Approaching a coast of irregular outline, waves thus get bent or " refracted ", being checked more rapidly in crossing the shallower water off the headlands than in the deeper water off the bays (Fig. 61 A). The effects of this are twofold. Erosional attack is concentrated on the headlands, which thus get cut back the most rapidly, and normally develop cliffs, while the bays are relatively sheltered ; but in addition the oblique wave-approach on either side of the headlands tends to drive the debris of their erosion into the bays. In this way bay-head beaches are built up, and so arises the well-known alternation of steep cliffed headlands dropping sheer into the sea, and sheltered coves with wide beaches.

In the long run, since erosion proceeds faster on the headlands, unless marked differences of structure intervene to preserve and create irregularities the whole coast will slowly evolve towards a simpler and straighter pattern, so that the " mature " stage of the evolution of a coast in profile (Fig. 58) will often coincide with a straightish outline in plan. With such changes however the movement of beach-material does not cease. On the contrary, it tends to become more extensive and systematic. Approaching any straightish section of coast head on, waves will merely roll shingle up and down the beach, but in fact very few waves do run in exactly " square " despite the " refraction " which tends to pull them round parallel with the beach (Fig. 61 B). Generally they retain a slight sideways component on striking, and thus tend to drive the beach material consistently one way. The direction of movement will change with a change in direction of approach of the waves, but on most beaches there is one direction of shingle-movement that is " dominant ". This is the main factor behind the building out of the long shingle spits that are so distinctive a feature of many stretches of coast, but to understand their formation we must examine the work of waves on beach material more closely.

On approaching a shelving beach not only are waves progressively checked and refracted, but in addition the shape of the

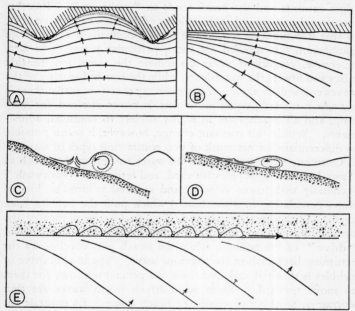

Fig. 61 :

(A) *Wave refraction on an indented coast.*
(B) *Wave refraction on a straight beach.*
(C) *Mechanism of a short, destructive, wave.*
(D) *Mechanism of a long, constructive, wave.*
(E) *Movement of a beach pebble in beach-drift, or longshore drift*

(C. *and* D. *after* W. V. Lewis).

waves changes, the crests becoming steeper and higher, the troughs flatter, until at some critical depth of water (which varies with the size of the waves) the crests hollow out, curl over, and " break ". (The detailed explanation of this phenomenon is quite complicated). By this time, however, the agitation of the water on the bottom as each wave passes has become sufficient to lift sand and small pebbles by a sort of pumping action, and as each wave passes over these are jerked forward and then drawn more gently back again.   The forward jerk, on a gently-sloping beach, appears to be the more effective, so that bottom-material edges inwards and the beach tends to " make up ".   But this increases the slope, and so the efficacy of the backward movement, so that if conditions remain the same, eventually a " profile of equilibrium " is reached for those particular waves.   In fact, of course, conditions never do remain the same, for the tide raises and lowers the water-level, while the size and spacing of the waves continually alters.   All we can say therefore is that there is a *tendency* towards equilibrium that is never attained for very long, and all beaches are in reality subject to continual adjustments.   Within this constant change, however, it seems possible to differentiate the net work of two contrasting types of wave.

Once any wave has broken, its water rushes up the beach as " swash ", rolling pebbles forward, and returns as " backwash " (generally with lower velocity, and reduced volume by loss of water percolating into the beach) which pulls the pebbles back again.   With short steep waves (Fig. 61 C), the plunge of the breaker is nearly vertical, so that there is relatively little inward " drive " of the pebbles, while the swash gets checked by the returning backwash of the previous wave.   The inward drive of pebbles is thus reduced, and there is a general tendency for them to move seaward.   Short wind-driven storm waves are thus *destructive*, working to comb the beach down.   By contrast the slow lazy " ground-swell " type of waves are generally *constructive* and build the beach up.   In them the orbital motion is flatter, and gives a greater forward impulse to the shingle, while the longer interval enables the swash to work without interference.   More of the backwash is also lost by percolation into the shingle (Fig. 61 D).

On beaches where destructive waves predominate we therefore tend to get a net removal of material seawards, and this clearly assists erosion of the land, for a good belt of shingle is the best protection against marine erosion, forming a sort of cushion on which waves can expend their energy harmlessly.   Where constructive waves predominate, by contrast, beaches make up. The relative frequency of the two types of wave thus appears to be an important factor behind liability to coastal erosion. But shingle does not only move up and down the beach. As we noted, there is nearly always a tendency for it to migrate laterally along the beach, due to waves running in at an angle. The movement is shown in Fig. 61 (E). Individual pebbles are rolled up and down the beach in a series of loops, each time returning to a position laterally displaced from their starting-points. As the tide carries the belt of wave-action up and down over the beach the whole surface is thus worked over, and the result is a net slow migration of the surface shingle one way. The direction will change, of course, with varying angles of wave incidence, but over the year there is in most regions a consistent net one-way movement. This is called the " Longshore Drift ". It goes on both landward and seaward of the breaker line, and the direction seems to be determined by the angle of approach of the *dominant* waves, i.e. those which produce the greatest effects. These need not be the most frequent waves. Observations indicate that they normally come in from the direction of the longest " fetch " of open water, across which the waves can grow to the largest size. In E. England this direction is from the north-east, and waves coming in from this direction generally strike the coast at such an angle as to give a southward component of movement. On the exceptional north Norfolk coast the component is westward, the direction of longshore drift changing near Sheringham. Along the south coast the dominant waves come up from the south-west, and cause a general easterly drift of material, exceptions being generally explicable by a change in direction of the coastline (Fig. 62 A).

Longshore drift is of great importance, for it is often the main factor controlling the supply of shingle to beaches. Where coast erosion is troublesome local authorities commonly build groynes across the beach to hold up and accumulate moving shingle, and where such exist the direction of movement is obvious, for you can see the shingle consistently piled up against one side of each groyne. The object is to create a protective shingle " cushion " to absorb the wave battering and prevent it reaching soft ground and promenades. Unfortunately, however, such action may " starve " a locality further down the coast by cutting off its shingle supply, and in areas hitherto stable beaches may disappear and severe erosion, hitherto unknown, may be started. Beach drifting is, however, often checked by natural obstacles, such as bold headlands which may divert the stream of

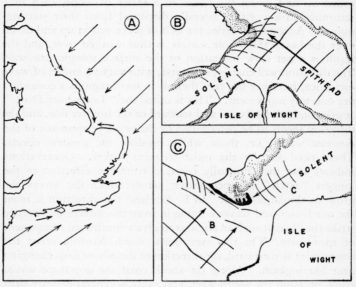

Fig. 62 :
(A) *Dominant wave directions and longshore drift on the south and east coasts of England.*
(B) *Calshot Spit* ⎫ *Shingle in solid*
(C) *Hurst Castle Spit* ⎭ *black*

shingle seawards, or the mouths of swift-flowing rivers, but where the shingle drift is powerful enough, it may build out a spit and divert the river-mouth. Longshore drift, in conjunction with constructive waves and favourable currents, is the factor responsible for most distinctive coastal shingle features. We may glance at a few.

Calshot Spit, and Hurst Castle Spit, on the shores of the Solent, offer instructive examples.   At Calshot, (Fig. 62B), located at a sharp angle in the shore, the main longshore drift of material is up the Solent from the south west, and the drift tends to continue north-eastward at the angle and to build out a spit in this direction. A limit is set to the extension of the spit however by deepening water, and the occasional powerful waves coming up Spithead from the S.E. pile the shingle up into a steep embankment and twist its head round towards the north.

Hurst Castle Spit, at the mouth of the Solent, (Fig. 62C) again stands at an angle in the coast, and similar factors are involved, though the conditions are a little more complex.   Beach-drift is from the north-west (waves A, Fig. 62C), and the spit builds out south of east continuing the same direction, and being piled up by big waves running in from the south-west.   Some distance out, however, the spit bends to run east, and later turns sharply to run west of north.   These changes seem to be at critical points of balance between different sets of beach-building waves, the first (B, Fig. 62C) twisting to approach from the south, the second set (C, Fig. 62C) running in from the E.N.E.   Hurst Spit also exhibits a series of short " lateral " spurs all parallel to the present distal portion, but truncated by the main ridge.   These seem to represent the ends of earlier spits cut off by rolling back of the main ridge under general coastal recession.

Behind these spits, in the sheltered waters, sedimentation of sand and mud has been active, and salt-water plants like Spartina grass (*Spartina Townsendii*) by colonising the mud are helping to convert it into saltings.   Much bigger stretches of salt-marsh, however, are to be found on the north coast of Norfolk, where the present flat sandy shore is separated from the old cliff-line behind by a belt a mile or more wide of mud-flats, salt-marshes and reclaimed land, fringed at the outer edge by various types of protective shingle bars and spits some of which carry extensive dune-systems.   The evolution of this fascinating stretch of coast cannot be treated in detail here, but we may note Scolt Head Island and Blakeney Point (Fig 63A and B) as two of the major shingle structures, the latter a true spit, the former possibly originating as an off-shore bar.   Both have a long main shingle

ridge founded on sand-flats and carrying numerous recurved
lateral ridges marking stages in their growth. Both appear to
have grown westward, although at Scolt older ridges landward
of the island reveal an earlier *eastward* drift of shingle. Behind

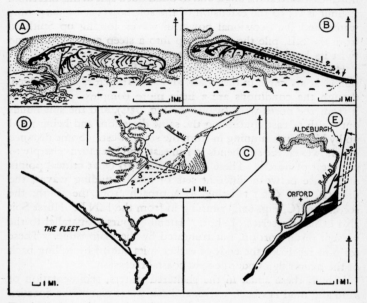

Fig. 63 :

    (*A*) *Scolt Head Island, and*
    (*B*) *Blakeney Point, Norfolk coast.*
    (*C*) *Dungeness.*
    (*D*) *Chesil Beach.*
    (*E*) *Orford Ness.*
    Shingle in solid black, save in (C) where it is dotted. In (B), (C), and (E), the
    numbered broken lines show successive stages in the growth of the features.

each, wide stretches of sheltered mud-flats are drained by a
myriad natural creeks, and every stage of marsh-growth from
bare low-level sand, through successive higher levels of mud
accumulation and vegetation cover can be traced up to the grassy
" high saltings " only covered at Spring tides. Successive

associations of halophytic (salt-water) vegetation colonise these saltings, and do much to help the natural growth by trapping mud brought in by the tide and binding the surface. At the landward edge, wide tracts have been reclaimed by " inning " with water-excluding dykes, and draining and pumping out the water, in the same way by which much of Holland was in earlier days reclaimed from the sea. Large tracts of reclaimed mud-flats occur round the shores of the Wash, while areas of natural marsh occur at places along the Welsh coast, around Bridgwater, and in Poole Harbour (where again parts have been reclaimed). Some of the best natural salt-marshes, however, fringe the shallow Essex estuaries, where mud sedimentation, creek development, and all types of marsh vegetation can be found in profusion.

Among other types of shingle construction around our coasts only two or three outstanding examples can be mentioned. Dungeness (Fig. 63 C) is a great triangular " foreland " more than 100 square miles in area, the outer part being a maze of bare shingle ridges, the inner reclaimed marshes. With the Darss Foreland of northern Germany it ranks as one of the finest structures of this type in the world. Outstanding as a spit that has diverted the original mouth of a river many miles is Orford Ness (Fig. 63 E). The River Alde originally flowed out at Aldeburgh but by progressive growth southwards the great shingle bank has diverted its mouth ten miles. Finally Chesil Beach (Fig. 63 D) is probably the most famous shingle formation in Britain. Sixteen miles long, it consists of one great shingle ridge linking Portland Island with the mainland, and enclosing a narrow belt of water called the Fleet. The shingle is uniformly graded, increasing steadily in size to the Portland end, concurrent with a steady increase in the breadth and height of the ridge. Clearly built by wave action (it faces the dominant S.W. waves), the mechanism of its formation has not yet been satisfactorily solved, and the perfect grading of the pebbles remains a puzzle. The " Coorong " on the coast of South Australia is an even bigger feature of this type, and outstanding examples of shingle and sand spits enclosing large lagoons somewhat nearer home are to be seen in the great " Nehrungen " of the eastern Baltic.

However, our British shingle features can compare in variety, if not in size, with any in the world.

A final group of coastal features we cannot entirely neglect are dunes. Wherever large expanses of bare sand are exposed at low tide, and onshore winds occur with sufficient frequency to carry the sand landward over low ground, dunes are likely to grow. Coastal dunes, however, seldom if ever show the severe simplicity and regularity of form of those in the great deserts for moisture tends to bind the sand, irregular topography and vegetation set up complex eddy systems in the wind, and animals and man disturb the sand surfaces. Vegetation, especially Marram Grass (*Psamma arenaria*) is an important factor in the growth of most coastal dunes. Marram thrives best where sand is continually piled on top of it, growing up with the dune, and by extending its enormously long root systems binding the whole mass together. If the sand supply dwindles, the marram becomes less lively, and fires, or the activities of men or rabbits, may open up bare patches on the surface. The wind then often cuts out great " blowout " hollows in old dunes, and sand may be driven inland over valuable fields. Landward transgression of sand dunes has been a distinct menace along many stretches of coast in the past, and the Culbin Sands dunes on the Moray Firth in the late 17th century overwhelmed and buried a valuable estate. To check sand driving and dune movement the favourite device is to plant the surface artificially with Marram grass, and when that takes hold, to plant pine trees and other quick-growing conifers. Belts of coniferous forest hold the dunes in place at many points around our coasts, but the greatest nearby area so treated is that of the Landes on the coast south of Bordeaux in western France where over 2½ million acres of valuable forest now cover what was once one of the most useless and troublesome dune areas in Europe.

We may end with a few words on some broader considerations about coasts. The overall character of every coast, as we noted at the beginning of this chapter, must have originally been decided by the sort of movement that created it, and the nature of the land-surface brought against the sea. Coasts have been classified in both these respects. Taking the mode of origin first, we can distinguish coasts of *depression*, or *submergence*, from coasts of *elevation*, or *emergence*. The former type of movement, whether due to sinking of the land or rise of the sea, will "drown" the pre-existing land surface. The lower sections of river-valleys will thus be converted into estuaries, and the divides between them into promontories, outlying hills becoming islands. The flatter the coast, the greater will be the marine encroachment. With a movement of elevation, however, a strip of former sea-

Fig. 64. A Norwegian fjord (Geirangerfjord), a valley over-deepened by glacier action into which the sea has entered. Compare the form of the valley with that in Fig. 38.

floor will be exposed to fringe the new coastline, and (since the sea-floor is generally less dissected than is the land) the coast would normally begin its career with much less indentation. We earlier examined the effects of such movements upon the evolution of rivers. We can now note how the coast itself would most likely evolve in each case.

With *submerged* coasts created by the drowning of lowlands cut in soft rocks, long shallow estuaries would form in the lower river-valleys, but in them sedimentation would be rapid, as the sluggish rivers, marine currents, and tidal drifts would pile into the estuaries both land-waste and material carved away from the soft-rock promontories. Estuaries would thus silt up and become marshy ; headlands and islands would be fairly rapidly carved away ; and the coast would evolve towards a simpler outline. Spits, beaches, and other constructional features would probably be built in abundance in the earlier stages. The coasts of Essex and Suffolk illustrate such conditions, evolution having gone further in Suffolk than in Essex.

If a hard-rock mountainous region is submerged, the original coastal pattern is likely to be equally complex but much more durable. Promontories will be higher and bolder and will resist erosion strongly, though being slowly cut into great cliffs. The drowned valleys will indent the coast as long deep inlets, only slowly filling up. A fringe of rocky islands might well persist along such a coast. Norway and western Scotland illustrate coasts of this type, the deep " fiord " inlets having been overdeepened by the gouging of land glaciers (Fig. 64). South-western Ireland affords an illustration of such a coast not modified by ice, the inlets here being of the shallower " ria " type, i.e. drowned river-cut valleys. Here the coast cuts across the structural grain of the country, i.e. the coast is " Discordant ". The sort of pattern that results from submergence of a zone of folded mountains that run parallel to the coast is well illustrated in Dalmatia, where the drowned outer ridges form strings of elongated islands running parallel with the coast, into which break patterns of rectilinear inlets. Such a coast is termed " Concordant " (Fig. 65).

Extensive *elevation*, apart from leaving evidence in raised beaches, will most commonly add a belt of flattish coastal plain around a country, fringed at the inner edge by the old cliffs. Such a plain, up to 100 miles wide, extends down the Atlantic coast of the United States southwards from New York. The rivers crossing this plain drop in falls and rapids over the old cliffs which comprise the well-known " Fall Line ", the limit of river navigation, and the site of much water-power development. Offshore the water is likely to be shallow, and (for reasons not well understood), extensive offshore bars commonly develop

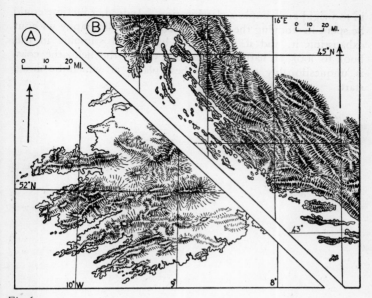

Fig. 65:

(*A*) *Discordant coast ; S.W. Ireland.*
(*B*) *Concordant coast ; Dalmatia.*

under such conditions, to create marshy lagoons behind them. These marshes may later be slowly destroyed if the bars are driven inward.

Many coasts, however, do not fit either of the above major "genetic" categories. Some originate by fault-movements, others against upthrust mountain-chains. In tropical seas coral-reef coasts, and mangrove swamps, provide distinctive types. In Britain, as we noted in the opening chapters, we have a variety of old beaches elevated above the present sea-level at heights up to 100 feet, but also submerged forest-floors on the foreshore, and in general our coasts reveal features more consistent with an origin by submergence. Broad generalised classifications are useful, but the back-history of many coasts is probably long and complex, and the reality of nature is not always caught in too rigid and simple a classification. Indeed, a lifetime could be spent in studying the variety of coastal physiography without exhausting it, and if any reader has found stimulus in this book to look at nature with a new eye in the field, the coast is unquestionably one of the best places at which he could start.

CHAPTER XVI

PHYSICAL GEOGRAPHY AND HUMAN AFFAIRS

To conclude this book we may take a brief look at the wider significance of our subject, and its relations to human affairs. The material problems that beset mankind are of two main types. Those which preoccupy our attention are in the main related to the inability of peoples to live harmoniously together; but behind these social, economic, and political issues, are much deeper and more permanent problems based in our relations with the earth. All living creatures must adapt themselves and their activities to the earth's conditions; all must achieve a successful working relationship with it to survive and prosper. Too often, engrossed with our tangled human affairs, we forget that these simple rules apply to man just as to any other creature. We like to think that our civilisation has freed us from the bonds of nature. In reality it has increased the number and complexity of our relations with the earth, without in the least reducing our fundamental dependence on it. Man is indeed unique among the earth's creatures in his ability to escape the direct control of physical environment, and he has unique powers to modify the earth's natural conditions. But these powers do not make him independent of the earth, and they are becoming increasingly dangerous to him. They have the potentiality for our complete ruin unless used with discretion and above all with full knowledge of their effects.

The world's population today numbers over 2,700 millions. It has doubled in size in the last hundred years, and it continues to increase so fast that fears are being expressed about the capacity of the earth to support it in the near future. No empty fertile lands remain to accommodate the continual increase, and exploitation of the earth in consequence becomes ever more intense. Inevitably much attention is continuously given to the problems of improving the earth's productivity, and eyes are turning increasingly toward the comparatively empty regions from which hostile natural conditions have so far effectively excluded human settlement. The stimulus for their exploitation ever intensifies, and the advance of scientific knowledge and technological discovery continually places in men's hands more effective means of attacking their problems and difficulties. Deliberate alteration of the earth's features and conditions is, of course, no new thing in human history. In Holland and elsewhere land was being reclaimed from the sea hundreds of years ago, and men were combating the desert with irrigation before the dawn of recorded history. But all previous efforts at improving the habitability of the earth are likely to be dwarfed by the vast projects we may expect to see undertaken in the future. Already we are familiar with irrigation schemes and the control of rivers on a scale that would have amazed our grandfathers. It has been found possible, although as yet only in a very small way and in the most favourable conditions, to create rain artificially by scattering " dry ice " upon rain-ripe clouds. If report is true, atomic power has already been used to assist in the diversion of great rivers in the U.S.S.R. Such developments are clearly but a foretaste of what is likely to come under the combined stimulus of increasing population pressure and continued scientific advance ; and as they involve physical situations, they impinge very directly upon Physical Geography, and our subject is intimately bound up with their solution.

The Geographer viewing these trends will be wise to look carefully at what has already happened as a result of man's interference with the earth, so that future action may be guided to avoid past mistakes. As we have seen, the earth is not an inert and haphazard collection of materials that can be altered piecemeal without danger. Land, water and air are all active, and all interact on one another through a host of connected processes. The physical environment of any region is somewhat like a highly complex machine, and a machine which is often rather delicately balanced. Unthinking alteration of one part of it will inevitably affect others, and may set in motion a sequence of changes having unforeseen consequences which may spread far beyond the immediate locality. Man has been producing such changes in the face of the earth for thousands of years through his practices of agriculture and animal husbandry, and the effects, until recently little heeded or even suspected, have in many areas been wholly disastrous. In considering the contribution a knowledge of Physical Geography can make to human welfare we may thus usefully glance at the effects, often quite unintentional, of man's interference with nature in the past.

The outstanding theme in this context is, of course, soil erosion. This term appears frequently nowadays in the popular press, but there is still widespread ignorance of what it really is, and what it implies. We have not been able to deal with soils in any detail in this book, but they are an element of supreme importance in the physical environment, for they support all land vegetation, and it is upon land vegetation that we depend for almost all our food. Beyond that, however, soils play a vital part in the natural balance of water-movement, and are linked with a host of physiographic processes. They knit together the inorganic elements of water, rock-minerals and air with the whole world of life. To afford a background to the meaning of soil erosion, we must therefore say a word or two about soils themselves.

Soils are built mainly from the weathered residues produced by the natural decay of the exposed rocks of the earth's crust. They form a sort of flesh over the underlying rocky skeleton of the ground. But the flesh is of very variable thickness. For soils to exist at all the rate of creation of rock wastes must exceed the rate at which they are transported away by the agencies of denudation. This means that true soils are normally absent on really steep mountainous ground, are thin in hilly country, and only become thick and fertile on the gentler slopes and plains. But soils are much more than mere aggregates of rock waste. An infinite variety of living organisms inhabits them, and the vegetation that grows on them continuously adds to their upper layers organic matter which becomes incorporated into the body of the soil and altered by chemical and bacteriological processes into the dark nitrogenous material called " humus ". This humus is vital to soil fertility. It holds the mineral particles together, gives soils their open " crumby " texture, and provides many essential plant foods, especially nitrogen. Being supplied from the top, it is concentrated in the upper few inches of the soil, which is normally the richest and most fertile part. But apart from humus content, mature soils show other changes in colour, texture, and chemical reaction downward from the surface which give them a characteristic " profile ", ranging from the dark humus-rich " A " horizons of the topsoil down through less rich and less highly evolved " B " horizons underneath to raw sub-soil which grades into the parent bedrock at the base. The soil profile, however, is not a thing which develops quickly. It is the product of slow changes and processes proceeding over hundreds of years, so that we can classify soils according to their degree of maturity as well as by their variations in depth and inherent character. The processes which create the soil profile, and produce the distinctive differences between soils, involve the upward and downward movements of water through the soil and many complex chemical reactions, all of which are controlled in large measure by conditions of climate, so that the older soils grow, the more distinctive become their profiles, and the more in harmony with the locally-prevailing climatic conditions. Young soils reflect clearly the influence of variable local geology and parent material, but where soils are fully mature, these original differences may be largely obscured by new characteristics imposed by climatic factors, and on the world scale we find that the major pattern of soil types conforms closely to the pattern of climate. The vegetation that grows on soils is itself mainly governed by climatic conditions, while in turn it helps to produce the soil character. Given time enough topography, soils, vegetation, and climate evolve into a nicely balanced harmony ; but that harmony is only attained by ages of slow evolution. This is not to imply that soils fully mature undergo no further changes. Material is constantly being removed from their surfaces, for if it were not, the general lowering of lands by denudation could not proceed ; but in the natural state where mature soils exist the rate of removal of material from their surfaces is exceedingly slow, and is balanced by the rate of weathering at their base. The thickness of the total soil cover is therefore not diminished, and its characteristic profile is maintained.

" Soil erosion " occurs when this delicate balance of conditions and processes is upset by some change that results in *accelerated* removal of material from the surface. The processes which create new soil and maintain the whole profile are then unable to keep pace, and the soil is progressively stripped away and destroyed. The top horizons, the richest in plant foods, are naturally the first to be lost, so that even slight soil erosion results in decreased fertility ; but if the process continues the intermediate and lower horizons may in turn be removed, and eventually the sub-soil itself may be cut away and nothing left but the emergent bare bedrock. Such accelerated erosion can cut away in a few years soils which have taken thousands of years to grow, and although it can be initiated naturally—as for instance by climatic change—most of the soil erosion that has attacked the earth like a scourge in the last few hundred years has resulted directly or indirectly from the actions of man. Few regions settled by man have escaped it entirely, and over wide areas it has destroyed the productivity and value of the land, humanly speaking, for ever. The story has varied in different countries, but is well illustrated from the United States, where soil erosion was first recognised as a national menace and where the most energetic remedial measures have been undertaken.

In the United States a survey held in 1935 revealed that of the *total* land area only a third or so showed little or no soil erosion. " Moderate " erosion (involving the loss of 25 to 75% of the topsoil) had affected no less that 41% of the country, and " severe " erosion, implying virtually total loss of the original topsoil, together with some sub-soil, had ruined some 12% of the whole area. Dr. H. H. Bennett, a leading authority, said in 1939 :

" In the short life of this country (the U.S.A.) we have essentially destroyed 282,000,000 acres of land. . . . Erosion is destructively active on 775,000,000 additional acres. About 100,000,000 acres of cropland, much of it representing the best cropland we have, is finished in this country. We cannot restore it. It takes nature from 300 to 1,000 years to bring back a single inch of topsoil, and we sometimes lose that much topsoil as the result of a single rain. . . ."

(Quoted from W. VOGT, *Road to Survival*)

In the space of two centuries, it thus appears that man has seriously damaged perhaps two-thirds of the total agriculturally-useful land in the entire United States. How has this come about ?

The primary cause has undoubtedly been reckless and thoughtless clearing away of the original vegetation, and its replacement by systems of cultivation ill-adapted to the conditions, which exhausted the soil and gave it no adequate protection. The mere removal of the natural vegetation, as in logging operations, was often enough. We noted in Chap. XIII some of the multiple influences of vegetation upon the disposal of rainwaters, and we stressed in particular its functions of checking surface runoff and facilitating the percolation of rainwater into the ground. With its removal soils that had grown under its protection for thousands of years were subjected to the lash of rain and the scour of surface water-flow which on sloping ground washed them away by millions of tons into the streams and rivers in a matter of a few years. Various different processes and stages have been recognised in the destruction. The mere beat of raindrops can have staggering effects on sloping ground. Each drop splashes a multitude of tiny particles into the air which mostly fall back to earth a little downhill. Repeated millions of times this process alone can move tons of soil off a field surface. Even more insidious, however, is the so-called " sheet-erosion " carried out by the flow of thin films of water over the ground surface. Often unnoticed in its operation, this process will gradually remove all the fine silt particles from a field surface, leaving it hard and caked with coarse sand and stones. Many farmers have been unaware of its occurrence until they noticed wheat standing with its roots exposed to the air, or were forced to investigate the cause of persistently declining yields. Nowadays a close watch is kept on field drains and local streams, for these will often indicate that sheet-erosion is going on by the discoloration of their waters with fine topsoil mud. The most extreme stage of soil erosion, however, is that called " gully erosion ", which can develop with horrifying rapidity where folds in the ground or even accidental wheelruts concentrate the runoff into little streamlets. Insignificant in appearance in their early stages, such channels can extend and deepen in soft soil at an alarming rate if neglected. In the hilly lands of the southeastern U.S.A. rain-gullies fifty feet deep and cut right down to bedrock now scar fields which were producing bountiful crops a few decades back, and in the areas worst affected whole districts have been converted into something like the " badlands " mentioned in Chap. V.

Accelerated water-erosion is not the only culprit, though it is the dominant factor in moist climates. In drier areas the wind has ruined vast tracts of country that were fertile within living memory. Often the initial cause was again injudicious clearing of the land, but ill-conceived attempts to conserve soil moisture by breaking the surface into a dust-mulch, and the overgrazing of thinly vegetated sub-arid country, have also contributed to the destruction. Over-grazing has predominated in the drier cattle lands of the western U.S.A., and has had disastrous effects in South Africa and Australia. The herbage is rapidly eaten away, the soil is pounded into dust by the trampling of the animals' feet, and the wind does the rest. Fine dust settling on the decks of ships hundreds of miles out from the coasts of Australia and South Africa reflects the constant depletion of fertile soils by the wind, while in the famed " Dust Bowl " of the Dakotas and Kansas in the 1930's a succession of drought years witnessed the conversion of tens of thousands of acres of farmland into useless sandy desert through the blowing away of the finer soil particles. Soil dust from the prairie provinces darkened the skies in Chicago, and much found a resting-place out in the Atlantic.

The extent of soil-erosion over the earth today is frightening. Estimates vary, but probably there are few areas of longestablished cultivation and settlement that have not suffered in some degree, although it is in the more recently-developed continents where " get-rich-quick " methods of extensive agriculture have all too often been the rule that the destruction has been most rapid and spectacular. Even in the areas of ancient civilisation, however, the effects are plain to see. The often claimed " extension of the Sahara ", for which evidence has been advanced in the apparent contrast between the sterility of southern Tunisia today and the accounts we read of it when it was a Roman province, is probably in large part due to destruction of vegetation by man and his animals. The gleaming white limestone hills of the Mediterranean countries of southern Europe were probably in large part covered with soil and trees in prehistoric times. The forests have been progressively destroyed for timber and fuel, and by the unrestricted grazing of goats, while the soils they held to the slopes have been washed down to the sea. The numerous deltas around the Mediterranean are the product not only of its small tidal range. Soil erosion has contributed much of the material, and according to some authorities has been responsible for much of the prevalence of malaria by choking the stream beds and building marshes in which the anopheles mosquito can breed. In Britain we have suffered relatively little, largely because our climate is mild and equable. Seldom do our soils dry out sufficiently for wind erosion to attack them, and seldom do we experience truly torrential rainfall after periods of drought. Moreover, our lands are for the most part tilled with care and skill on a fairly intensive pattern, and the countryside is cut up by hedges and ditches into a chequerboard of tiny plots which offer little opportunity for the development of widespread rain-erosion. Yet even in Britain soil-erosion is not unknown. In a recent storm in the north-east soil was washed off some fields in quantity sufficient to cover minor roads to a depth of several feet, and in any dry Spring you can watch the fine peat soils blowing away in clouds off the open Fenland fields. No country is immune, and only the most rigorous care and well-ordered land use can preserve cultivated soils from serious loss.

The preventive and remedial measures that have been developed to combat soil erosion are of great interest, but we can touch on them only briefly. With wind erosion the only cure is to prevent over-grazing, to encourage plant-growth (in serious cases grass and bushes have been deliberately replanted over wide areas), and to plant belts of trees to act as wind-breaks, as has been done on a huge scale in the dry steppe country north of the Black Sea by the U.S.S.R. If water is the culprit, ground-surface runoff must be checked. Ploughing with the contours instead of up and down the slopes is an excellent deterrent for this checks surface runoff, and gives the water more chance to soak in. In graver cases various types of slope-terracing have been developed in the U.S.A., while crop-patterns and rotations are designed to cut down to a minimum the amount of soil left bare. Gully erosion is treated by building check-dams across the gullies and by planting their sides with grass and bushes, but in bad cases it has often been found that the only effective remedy is to replant a forest cover, and while this is growing to protect the ground with a layer of scattered brushwood and twigs. To such laborious and costly expedients have farmers and Governments in many parts of the world been forced by the damage done through thoughtless and short-sighted inter-ference with the balanced situations of nature. Given an elementary knowledge of physiography the results could often have been foreseen and avoided, and the remedies are simple enough in their technical principles. In practice, of course, infinitely complex social, economic, and political problems are bound up with their application, and similar difficulties often prevent the proper use of land even when soil erosion is known to be in full swing. The technical aspects of preventing and combating soil erosion are indeed often the simplest parts of the problem, but without a proper understanding of the physio-graphic principles involved any remedial or preventive action is wasted labour.

A second field in which the Physical Geographer will find much on which to ponder is the relation of his subject with the whole question of water-supply and the control of natural waters. In the broader sense much of soil-erosion falls under this head, and one of the most vicious effects of soil-erosion is that it creates artificial deserts through washing away the soil which retains water in the ground. But we can pick out innumerable other aspects of man's relations with water which illustrate our theme. In the past, such practical matters as obtaining water-supplies for towns and villages, the improvement of rivers for navigation, the diversion of river-waters for irrigation, and the control of flooding, were all too often conceived as entirely separate issues, and handled by quite separate and independent authorities.

Such, unfortunately, is too often the case even today. Inevitably such procedure results in much waste of labour and all sorts of unforeseen and undesirable consequences resulting from local tampering with but one portion of the whole hydrological cycle without adequate understanding of the intimate connections and systems of balance running through the whole. We may pick out a few illustrative points.

One of the features of advancing civilisation and particularly of the urban communities of the western world has been an enormously increased use of water for everyday domestic and manufacturing purposes. Water-supply has always been a factor of great importance in deciding the location of man's settlements, but the growth of villages into towns, and towns into cities, has in many areas altered all the old relationships. Large cities like Birmingham and Manchester long ago outran their local supplies, and have had to bring water in by pipe-line and aqueduct from the hills of the Lake District and Wales. London faces a chronic problem of water-supply, and continually has to seek new resources further afield. London's daily consumption of water is now about 350 million gallons; but it is far outstripped by New York, which consumes no less than 1,000 million gallons a day. Most large cities have faced at one time or another crises in water-supply, and some have never satisfactorily solved them. But in the attempt all sorts of complications have been caused by overdrawing on old-established sources, and breaking up the natural patterns of water-movement.

In speaking of underground water we earlier noted that in a single well sunk into water-bearing strata overpumping will often create a " cone of exhaustion " round the well, which will yield no more water until pumping is stopped and the cone can fill in. If water must be obtained, there is a strong temptation to sink new wells, but with heavy withdrawals each in turn may suffer the same fate, and the whole water-table may be lowered through inability of the natural intake to keep pace with the withdrawals. We noted earlier how excessive well-sinking has caused a great and permanent drop in the level of the artesian water-table below London. Such changes may force development of alternative sources of supply, often involving great expense, but they may have more serious consequences. One that is quite likely to occur is contamination of the waters pumped up, for with the draining out of strata normally full of water, channels may be opened up by which foul surface water can seep into the wells and get mixed with the drinking supply. In extreme cases the natural relationships of underground waters may be upset, and in regions near the coast it is not unknown for over-pumping of ground-water to permit sea-water to percolate into the land, while the very ground-surface may sink through the drying out of underground strata. A notorious example occurred in the Santa Clara valley of California, where an artesian basin was opened up early in the century for irrigation. The cultivation prospered, wells multiplied, and no attention was paid to water conservation in the hills from which the artesian basin was fed. The water table inevitably began to fall. It fell about 5 feet a year from 1915 to 1933, in which year it fell no less than 21 feet. The artesian springs all failed, the average pumping-lift by 1934 had increased to 165 feet, and eventually in that year the pumps began to suck up sea-water that had filtered in from San Francisco Bay. When the seriousness of the situation was at length realised it was too late for effective remedy, for it was found that the valley-floor had sunk by several feet, and the original capacity of the underground water-reservoirs had thereby been greatly reduced. Nothing man can do will now replace the abundant artesian water that once flowed in the valley.

Mention of irrigation invites a word on some other troubles that have arisen from injudicious and over-enthusiastic development. Apart from using up underground water stores which may never be fully replaced, the artificial diversion of water in large quantities over the ground in hot climates naturally changes the character of the natural movements of soil-water. This has often led to water-logging and sour soils, or even worse, to a slow but progressive alteration in the chemical balance of the soil which in some cases has rendered it in time quite sterile. We noted in discussing deserts that the high evaporation tends to produce saline concentrations in the upper layers of the soil and rocks, and occasionally builds thick saline incrustations. Incautious irrigation has frequently produced similar conditions, the water continually evaporating away and leaving its dissolved salts behind, until originally fertile soils became quite useless. Ambitious current schemes for bringing large tracts of sub-desert country under cultivation in North Africa will have this difficulty to contend with no less than those of actual water-supply and conservation.

In all hot and semi-arid countries, like south and east Africa, conservation of water is a major problem in further development. It is no use bringing water in from long distances by aqueduct and constructing vast surface reservoirs, if most of the water is going to be lost by evaporation. To check ground-surface evaporation, unfortunately, the only effective means is to encourage vegetation-growth, but this itself needs moist soils. Losses from surface storage-reservoirs, however, can be reduced by covering the water-surface in some way. Experiments have been tried in laying over the water-surface some types of harmless floating chemicals, or even a film of mineral oil. These check the evaporation, and if the water is drained off from below, do not affect its value for many purposes. Recent research in Palestine has suggested that flake nylon may form an effective and less unpleasant substitute. The use of natural sands as storage-containers for water is also being developed, and in the whole field of water-supply in the drier lands there are innumerable problems in which a knowledge of physiographical principles can suggest valuable expedients, and avoid undesirable complications.

In the field of water-control and utilisation, however, the regulation of river-flow and the exploitation of river-waters offer outstanding examples of the need for a wide understanding of physiographic processes and relationships. The more turbulent and variable rivers of the earth are a great trial to the peoples using the rich alluvial soils of their valleys, for all too often disastrous floods alternate with periods of low water in which water-supplies are endangered and navigation is made impossible. In many rivers also man's misuse of the land has considerably worsened the natural conditions of flow. " Improvement " of such rivers generally implies regularisation of their flow-level throughout the year. This involves a careful study of the causes of the flooding and flow fluctuations, and the selection of the best means to offset them. The climatic factors are still virtually outside human control, so that the most usual measures concentrate on checking the *sudden* flow-off of storm-waters and enlarging the channels by which they can escape. Cleaning out of the river bed, shortening it by cutting through meanders, and building dykes in the flood-plain to prevent widespread inundation, are all obvious commonsense measures ; but more important are the creation of means to hold back the excess of water which causes flooding and to release it gradually during low-water periods. The construction of dams and emergency reservoirs can be of great assistance, but as we mentioned earlier the most effective measure of all has been shown by experience to be the maintenance of a good vegetation cover to absorb as much of the rainfall as possible and prevent the " flash " runoff which produces sudden floods. In this field the problems of river-control overlap those of soil erosion, and if experience in tackling the many aspects of applied hydrology has taught any lesson it is this : that river-basins should be treated as complete units. All too often in the past divided control and conflicting interests have nullified the effects of expensive and well-intentioned schemes conceived in too narrow a framework. Authorities controlling the headwater sections of rivers have been interested only in power-development ; those downstream only in irrigation ; those at the outfall only in flood control. Too often the upstream authorities have taken an attitude akin to that expressed in the song " We don't care where the water goes, if it doesn't get into the wine ", while those at the mouth have wasted money on vast schemes of dyking and reservoir construction which proved of little effect in the absence of co-operation and proper regulation higher up. The Tennessee Valley Authority, although its actual works were not always well-conceived (some reservoirs designed to store flood-waters were filled to the brim with silt in a few years), gave an invaluable lead in pointing out the vital need for unified control of all aspects of river-regularisation. The much-discussed Missouri

Valley Authority is a more ambitious project on the same lines ; but logically one authority should control all works connected with water over the catchment area of the entire Mississippi system, from soil conservation and forest management on the watersheds to harbour works at the mouth.   The same principle should clearly be applied to all rivers, however large, such as the Danube, the Yangtse, or the Nile.   Unfortunately divided political control renders this idea an unrealisable dream for many of the earth's great rivers ; but it will have to come if we are to manage the earth to the best advantage.   It has been well said that " River-control should begin at the watersheds ".   This text might well be adopted by those responsible for current projects of development in East Africa, where political boundaries seldom bear any relation to the natural hydrological divisions of the land.

Further examples of problems incidental to man's continually-changing relations with the earth, and of the difficulties he can create for himself by haphazard and ill-informed interference with nature, could be multiplied indefinitely.   Problems of harbour maintenance and the control of coastal erosion, of land reclamation from the sea, and of the fixation of moving sand-dunes, all offer fascinating fields of study ; and there are many others.   Of these, as of the instances mentioned, we can however only say that in working to check nature, or change her conditions, success is more likely to be achieved by guiding natural processes to produce the desired result than by riding roughshod over nature.   Many physical situations are delicately balanced, and it is sometimes possible, by applying slight guidance at a critical point, to cause far-reaching changes to man's benefit.   It is, unfortunately, equally easy by intervening at the wrong point or in the wrong way, to set in train sweeping changes that may be wholly disastrous, as in the case of soil erosion.   These lessons deserve careful study by all who may be concerned with planning or directing operations designed to modify natural conditions in the future ; for it is perhaps not too much to say that man now has it in his power to render the earth uninhabit-able, even as he has the power to increase his wealth and well-being to an unprecedented degree.   The extent to which he will ultimately be able to exploit and modify the natural earth remains a matter of speculation. Already we have had an imaginative short story which conceives a future Great Power controlling the high lands of central Asia trying to drown out its rival in North America by melting the Polar ice, only to be itself vanquished by an even great inundation set in motion by the western Power which triumphantly moves its headquarters to a vastly enlarged and virgin Greenland rising isostatically from the waters when relieved of its load of ice.[1] Such a vision recalls the fantasies of H. G. Wells, but some of the wonders that gifted writer built into his futurist stories are already sober fact. Though he may operate in less spectacular ways, man of the future will most certainly try to alter the earth nearer to his heart's desire.[2] Science must try to ensure that his experiments will be based on knowledge rather than on hope.

[1] Gerald Heard (H. F. Heard): *The President of the United States, Detective.*
[2] Mention may be made, in this reprint, of the proposed scheme just published (Oct. 1959) by a Russian engineer to build a dam across the Behring Straits, with the object of modifying the oceanic circulation in high latitudes, drawing more of the warm Gulf Stream waters into the Arctic Ocean, and so ameliorating the climate of the whole area.

BIBLIOGRAPHY

MANY excellent general textbooks, and whole libraries of many specialised books and monographs, exist on the topics covered in this volume. Any short selection of recommendations must necessarily be somewhat arbitrary. In the following list, I have tried to include a limited number of non-technical introductory works, together with one or two more advanced works of reference in each section. The latter are marked with an asterisk.

CHAPTERS I TO VIII

The material dealt with is covered in most general textbooks on Physical Geography and Physical Geology. Short general introductions include:

Trueman, A. E.	*An Introduction to Geology.*
Seward, A. C.	*Geology for Everyman* (Camb. Univ. Press, 1943).
Read, H. H.	*Geology, an introduction to earth history* (Home Univ. Lib. 1949)
Raistrick, A.	*Teach Yourself Geology* (E.U.P. 1943).
Monkhouse, F. J.	*Principles of Physical Geography* (Lond. Univ. Press, 1954).
Dury, G. H.	*The Face of the Earth* (Penguin Books, 1959).

Larger works include:

Lake, P.	*Physical Geography* (Camb. Univ. Press. 2nd Edn. 1949).
Holmes, A.	**Principles of Physical Geology* (Nelson 1944).
Wooldridge, W. S., Morgan, R. S.	**The Physical Basis of Geography* (Longman's, Green, 1937).

On particular topics:

Tyrrell, G. W.	*Volcanoes* (Home Univ. Lib. 1931).

Jeffreys, H.   *Earthquakes and Mountains*
                                (Methuen 1935).
Umbgrove, J. H. F.   *The Pulse of the Earth* (M. Nijhoff
                                (The Hague) 2nd Edn. 1947).
                                (a standard advanced work on
                                the structure of the earth).

Two valuable short books cover the physical features of
Britain:
Trueman, A. E.   *The Scenery of England and Wales*
                                (V. Gollancz 1938, Penguin
                                1949).
Stamp, L. D.   *Britain's Structure and Scenery*
                                (New Naturalist Series, Col-
                                lins 1946).
The series of 18 pamphlets   *British Regional Geology* (Geologi-
                                cal Survey Office, H.M.S.O.)
                                afford standard material on
                                the geology of the whole
                                country.

Chapter IX

There is no comprehensive work on deserts in English.   *See*
Bagnold, R. A.   *Libyan Sands* (Travel Book Club
                                1935).
Gautier, L.   *The Sahara*, English translation
                                (Columbia Univ. Press, 1935).
Bagnold, R. A.   *The Physics of blown sand and
                                desert dunes* (Methuen 1941)
                                is a standard advanced work.

Chapter X

Good accounts will be found in the general textbooks.

Flint, R. F.   *Glacial and Pleistocene Geology*
                                (J. Wiley, New York, 1957) is
                                a recent standard work.

Cotton, C. A.   *Climatic Accidents* (New Zealand: Whitcombe and Tombs, 1942).

Chapters XI and XII

First of all, the reader is urged to read:

Stewart, G. R.   *Storm* (Sun Dial Press, New York, 1943). A novel, but of great value and absorbing interest.

The principles of meteorology are set out in many excellent short works:

Brunt, D.   *Weather Study* (Nelson 1942; 1956).

Kimble, G. H. T.   *The Weather* (Penguin Books, 1949).

Hare, F. K.   *The Restless Atmosphere*, (Hutchinson's, London 3rd Edn., 1958).

On climate:

Kendrew, W. G.   *Climatology* (Oxford Univ. Press, 3rd Edn., 1949).

ibid.   *The Climates of the Continents* (O.U.P., 4th Edn., 1954).

Austin Miller, A.   *Climatology* (Methuen, 4th Edn., 1946).

Gordon Manley   *Climate and the British scene* (New Naturalist Series, Collins, 1952).

Chapter XIII

An excellent general treatment of the earth's waters is:

P. H. Kuenen   *Realms of Water* (Cleaver-Hulme Press, London, 1955).

(Ed.) Meinzer, O. R.	*Hydrology. Vol. IX, Physics of the Earth* (McGraw Hill, 1942).
Foster, E. E.	*Rainfall and Runoff* (Macmillan, N. Y., 1949).
Wisler, C. O. Brater, E. F.	*Hydrology* (J. Wiley: Chapman and Hall, 1949).
Fox, C. S.	*Water* (Technical Press, 1951).
ibid	*The Geology of Water Supplies* (Technical Press, 1949) is a general treatment of this field.

Two French works are classics:

Collet, L. W.	*Les Lacs* (G. Doin, Paris, 1925).
Pardé, M.	*Fleuves et Rivieres* (Armand Colin, Paris, 1933).

CHAPTER XIV

Ommaney, F. D.	*The Ocean* (Home Univ. Lib. 1949).
Coleman, J. S.	*The Sea and its Mysteries* (G. Bell, 1950).
Carson, Rachael	*The Sea around us* (Staples, 1952).
Sverdrup, H. V.	*Oceanography for meteorologists* (Allen and Unwin, 1945).
	Admiralty Manual of Tides (H.M.S.O.).
	Oceanography. Bulletin No. 85, National Research Council, *Physics of the Earth, Vol. V*, National Research Council, Washington D.C., 1932.
Shepard, F. P.	*Submarine Geology* (Harpers, New York, 1948).
Guilcher, A.	*Coastal and Submarine Morphology* (tr. B. W. Sparks, R. H. W. Kneese, Methuen, London, 1958).

CHAPTER XV

General accounts are given in the text-books earlier listed.

Johnson, D. W.   *Shore Processes and Shoreline Devel-
                                  opment* (J. Wiley, New York,
                                  1919).

Steers, J. A.   *The Sea Coast* (New Naturalist
                                  Series, Collins, 1953).
                                  The Coastline of England and Wales
                                  (Camb. Univ. Press, 1948).

CHAPTER XVI

Among the vast literature on the themes mentioned, the
following selection will afford much of interest and value:

Sherlock, R. L.   *Man's Influence on the Earth* (Home
                                  Univ. Lib., 1931).

Brade-Birks, S. G.   *Good Soil* (E.U.P. "Teach Your-
                                  self Farming" Series, 1944).

Kellogg, C. E.   *The Soils that Support Us* (Mac-
                                  millan, N.Y., 1941).

Jacks, G. V., Whyte, R. O.   *The Rape of the Earth* (Faber and
                                  Faber, 1939).

Bromfield, Louis   *Pleasant Valley* (Cassell, 1946).

Vogt, W.   *Road to Survival* (V. Gollancz,
                                  1949).

Graham, E. H.   *Natural Principles of Land Use*
                                  (Oxford Univ. Press, 1944).

U.S. Dept. of Agriculture Year-   *Soils and Men* (1938).
    books.   *Climate and Man* (1941).

Thomas, W. L. (Ed.)   *Man's Role in Changing the Face of
                                  the Earth* (Univ. of Chicago
                                  Press, 1956).

INDEX